● — LOCALITIES OF
FRANC JOUBIN'S
TECHNICAL ACTIVITIES

NOT FOR
GOLD ALONE

NOT FOR GOLD ALONE

The Memoirs of a Prospector

By FRANC R. JOUBIN
and D. McCormack Smyth

Deljay Publications

Deljay Publications
500 Avenue Road, #105
Toronto, Ontario, M4V 2J6

Canadian Cataloguing in Publication Data

Joubin, Franc R. (Franc Renault), 1911-
   Not for gold alone

Includes index.
ISBN

1. Joubin, Franc R. (Franc Renault), 1911-
2. Prospectors – Canada – Biography.*
3. Geologists – Canada – Biography.   4. Prospecting.
I. Smyth, D. McCormack (Delmar McCormack),
1922-   II. Title.

TN140.J68A3 1989   622'.092'4   C89-093782-6

Cover and Book Design: V. John Lee
Literary Consultant: Jack McClelland

Printed and Bound in Canada by
T.H. Best Printing Company Limited

In memory of my late wife Mary Toine,
who endured for over forty years
my seemingly endless will-o'-the-wisp career
with wonder and love,
*   yet understanding.*

Apart from the pleasure of re-prospecting along memory trails with McCormack Smyth during occasional periods over a span of several years, he provided the constant encouragement for this book to be written and happily shared the labour. We were effectively supported by a bevy of interested ladies, including Wanita Smyth, Joanna P. Stewart, Helen Quirk, and Daphne Shandley at the typewriters. During the same period, Charlotte A. Wolf, Secretary of my professional office, relieved me of much of the burden there for the pursuit of this effort. To all of these I owe my thanks.

Prologue

Like many people around the world, I greatly enjoy Robert Service's poems about the Yukon Gold Rush of the late 1890s. Lines from Service's writings are etched permanently in my memory.

> There's gold, and it's haunting and haunting
> It's luring me on as of old;
> Yet it isn't the gold that I'm wanting
> So much as just finding the gold.

> I wanted the gold, and I got it,
> Came out with a fortune last fall,
> Yet somehow life's not what I thought it,
> And somehow the gold isn't all.

When I first read those lines I wondered if a day would ever come when I would meet a prospector such as Service sought to describe. Then one day it happened. I met Franc Joubin.

In the spring of 1968 I had gone to a meeting of the Board of the Elliot Lake Centre for Continuing Education, to which I had just been appointed. Having a few free minutes after I had checked into the Centre, I decided to go for a brief walk before the meeting. As I went out, I met a fellow board member who suggested that we walk together. I knew who he was – Franc Joubin, the man who had discovered Canada's largest uranium deposits, bringing wealth to many people, including mining promoter Joe Hirshhorn. Hirshhorn's riches had enabled him to develop his renowned art collection, now in a museum on The Mall in Washington, D.C. That museum in the United States' capital was created to house that collection. It stands as a silent monument to Dr. Joubin's skill as a prospector and geologist as much as a widely acclaimed monument to Hirshhorn's shrewdness in collecting art.

What I did not know then was that after his great success in the discovery and development of the Elliot Lake uranium deposits, Franc Joubin had become involved in the Technical Assistance Program of the United Nations. Despite the dangers, he had at that time already made several mineral discoveries as significant as his dramatic successes in Canada, which had led reporters to call him "The King of Uranium Prospectors."

Walking along with Franc Joubin in Elliot Lake, I noticed his strong sinewy hands and his vigorous gait. He obviously had worked hard for many years and enjoyed being out of doors. My conversation with him helped me to realize why our mutual friend, prominent federal Liberal Bob Winters, had told me that Dr. Joubin was not only a world-renowned geologist-prospector, but a man of remarkable insights – a perceptive philosopher.

I became convinced that others should share in his recollections. I suggested that he write his memoirs; he pleaded that he was too busy; I persisted.

Finally the day came when we sat down with a recording machine and began. It became increasingly clear to me that his is an authentic Canadian "Horatio Alger" story. Alger, one of the most popular American authors of the late nineteenth century, wrote "rags-to-riches" stories of poor boys who made good. Franc Joubin's story is the record of how he, an honest, cheerful, persistent, hard-working boy, overcame adversities to finally achieve outstanding personal success. In so doing, the discoveries he has directed have been recognized as adding some $30 billion to Canada's national mineral wealth. His work in the United Nations Technical Assistance Program has produced similar results in a number of overseas countries. By any measure his achievements have been amazing.

This book is the record of some of the memorable events in the remarkable career of this remarkable man. Each chapter reveals insights into his thoughts and into the secrets of his career.

If, as you read, you are ready and eager (as any good prospector must be), the secrets the book contains will become clear to you. Were they identified directly you would be deprived of the joy of discovery. That would be contrary to the whole spirit of this book. Such joy has always been at the centre of Franc Joubin's life.

You may wonder from time to time if this book is fiction. It isn't. It is the professional memoirs of just one man who, in his long life, has demonstrated that prospecting is a romantic adventure which often can be, as it has been in his case, enormously helpful to human beings in many lands.

D. McCormack Smyth

9 December 1988

Finale, Almost

It was 8:16 P.M. on July 25, 1977, and I was in Fresno, California. After a most enjoyable family reunion with the Renaults, relatives on my mother's side, in a California redwood forest resort, I was to board a plane to Canada the following morning. I had checked into an airport hotel and was undoing my necktie in my room when there was a gentle knock on the door. The maid, I thought, and I opened the door. It was no maid!

Two men, in their mid-thirties perhaps, confronted me. Side by side, blocking the doorway, they motioned me back into my room. One was tall with blond curly hair, much larger than I in height and weight. The second had a gun, a big revolver. It seemed too big. Perhaps, I thought, it is only a plastic toy. Since I have never used firearms I could not be certain. He pushed the gun into my chest – it didn't feel like plastic – and pressed me backwards down a short corridor past the bathroom door and into the main section of the room. There we stopped, facing each other. The other man left the hall door slightly open, presumably for a fast getaway.

"You know what we're here for. Your money – all of it – fast!" barked the man with the gun, jerking it for emphasis. I pulled my wallet from my jacket, which I had thrown on the bed, and opening it, I took out all the money I had in the wallet, maybe fifteen or sixteen American twenty-dollar bills. Making a mental calculation of what I'd need for taxis to the airport and to my home on arrival in Toronto, I picked off two of them. All the rest I tossed onto the edge of the counter where luggage is placed. Looking at the men I said, "I'm a long way from home. I'll need these to get back," and returned the two twenties to my wallet.

Out of the corner of my eye I saw the tall blond man take a step forward. Good! I thought, he is going to pick up the money and they will leave. Instead, he struck me on the head, just over my temple, with the side of his hand.

My head spun. I was dazed. His chop to my head broke my glasses and they in turn cut my nose. I felt blood on my face. My wrestler's reflexes of forty years earlier took over. I gave him no time to step back. With my right arm I had a strangle hold on him. I gripped him around his throat with my forearm, cutting off his wind.

We were both upright, trying to keep our balance while tussling around. He was struggling to escape, but I had him disadvantaged – he couldn't breathe. As we scuffled, my saner mental reflexes suddenly surfaced. With shock I asked myself, Why am I doing this? Later I realized that my mental reflexes were about three seconds behind my physical reflexes. In desperation, not knowing what else to do, I continued choking him. How am I going to get out of this mess? I wondered. If I make enough noise, perhaps help will come. After all, this is a hotel!

At one end of the luggage counter there was a large table lamp. I hooked its cord with my foot and the lamp thudded to the floor. To my dismay, the thick carpet muffled the sound.

How long the scuffling continued I don't know; it felt to me like a minute or two, though probably it was only twenty seconds or even less. But finally we bumped into the man with the gun. He probably realized that using his gun would attract unwanted attention and had been standing to one side. As we bumped into him I saw his gun hand fly upward. Instinctively, I let go of the first assailant, who by this time was groggy, and caught the gunman by the wrist of his gun hand. My first assailant, to my relief, staggered towards the entrance door, and I grappled with the gunman. Twisting his wrist I tried to force him to release the gun.

The gunman panicked, pulled the trigger, and the bullet passed within inches of my head. Deafened and blinded by the noise and flash of the shot, I hung on grimly. Sensing that the gunman was dragging me toward the door, I realized that he wanted to get away. Bumping him with my hip I spun him around. Again he pulled the trigger: another blinding flash and he and his companion, who had been standing at the door, scrambled through it and ran down the hall. I quickly closed my door and locked it.

A glance around the room revealed that the money I had tossed on the counter was still there. That detail amused me at the time. Not much profit for them in that effort! I thought as I hunted for the telephone. To my surprise, the operator came on the line im- mediately. "Two men have just tried to rob me," I said to her, "a tall blond fellow with an orange shirt and a smaller swarthy-complexioned guy in blue jeans and a blue shirt. They tried to shoot me!''

I was puzzled that guests in nearby rooms were not bombarding the switchboard with calls or hammering on my door with concern. It was about eight o'clock in the evening, and many rooms were occupied. Surely someone must have heard the shots and sensed what was going on.

Limply I sat down on the bed. I felt as if I were sitting in a tub of water. Looking down, I saw blood trickling over the edge of my left shoe and soaking my trouser leg.

There was a banging on my door. Remembering that I had locked it, I hobbled to open it to the group gathered in the hall – a uniformed policeman or security man and two or three plain-clothes policemen. Well behind them was the hotel manager. In short order, two paramedics appeared with their gear and began to tend to me. They put a tourniquet on to reduce the flow of blood, gave me an anti-tetanus shot, hooked me up to an intravenous saline solution system, and monitored my blood pressure carefully. I was soon on a stretcher and in the corridor being peered at curiously by other guests. "Bastards,'" I murmured to myself, pulling the sheet over my head. "No T.V. thrills for you from me!"

The shrieking ambulance sped to nearby St. Agnes Hospital, apparently straight across the desert plains! We seemed to bounce all over. Once at the hospital, I was wheeled into X-ray and then into surgery where a soft-spoken surgeon, an older man, arrived to examine my X-ray pictures. "Well," he said to me, "if you had to stop a bullet, you certainly couldn't have handled it more beautifully!" He explained that the bullet had entered at the back, below the hip, and come out just above my knee on the inside.

The doctor mopped around the exit wound in my leg, and probed the skin and flesh where the bullet had entered and where it had exited. "No," he said " I don't think any surgery is necessary. Not at present anyway. It should heal up all right by itself. But we must watch your blood pressure carefully. Do you want plasma or more saline?"

"You mean blood, or more of this?" I asked, indicating the intravenous drip to which I was still attached. "Do I have a choice?"

"Oh yes," replied the doctor. "You have the body and stamina and the heart. You can take saline only."

"Okay, I'll just take saline, then," I replied. I had confidence in this man and his practical approach in dealing with my wound.

"I'm going to give you a sedative," he said, "You'll sleep. I'll be back in the morning. Don't worry. You are a very, very, lucky man."

My Bodyguard

Before I fell asleep, a stranger entered my private hospital room. "I'm the chief of detectives here." he said. "We've got to get a message to your family. Can we have your address?"

"No! My wife has a heart condition," I said immediately. "She must not be troubled."

"But your family must be reached. You're not in a stable condition at all," said the chief of detectives, whose name I later discovered, was McIntyre. "It will be a lot harder for us if anything happens to you and we have not notified your next-of-kin. You are not yet in stable condition. Do you know what that means?"

I did know, of course, but I still replied, "No. I won't give you an address. Let's talk about it in the morning."

"All right," he said, "but remember, I must have a name in the morning." With that I fell asleep and slept well.

I awoke in an entirely new world. I was still hooked to the saline drip and various monitors, but I had been moved during the night and was now in a large bright room. On a chair opposite the bed sat a character right out of Hollywood. He had a wispy white beard and a large silver star pinned to the chest of his checked shirt. He was wearing jeans and a revolver in a holster. I even recall a faded cowboy hat beside him. When he saw me looking at him in wonder, he got up. He was the right height, over six feet. Beaming down at me he said, "Ya seem to be in pretty good shape!" He even had the right drawl.

"Yes, I feel pretty good," I replied.

"That's fine, just fine," he said. "I'm yer bodyguard. Don't you worry. I've been sitting here quite a while, just watchin' yuh. We're goin' to get along just fine. The television and newspapers are full of yer story. You've got to see a morning paper; you've got to see a morning paper. I'm goin' ta get ya a paper." And with that he disappeared.

It seemed strange to me that while someone had decided I needed a bodyguard, he had now casually sauntered off to pick up a newspaper! But nothing should surprise me, I thought, Fresno is the backyard to Hollywood.

While I was alone, McIntyre arrived. "Where's the bodyguard?" he asked.

"Gone to get a newspaper," I replied. The detective muttered something derogatory and then turned to me, asking once again for my wife's address.

"No address!" I replied, determined that they wouldn't trouble Mary. "Look," I said to McIntyre, "*I'll* send a telegram." He found this acceptable and produced a telegraph form. I wrote out a message which said simply, "Regret return delayed by a few days because of illness in the family. Love Franc."

After thirty-nine years of marriage my Mary could read me like a book. Right away she knew that something had happened to me. She got on the telephone and tried to reach my Renault relatives in California and New Mexico to learn what had happened. She could reach no one – most of them were still at the resort in the mountains. But at least, she concluded, I was alive.

McIntyre told me that my hotel room had been thoroughly examined and that all my possessions – and my money – had been brought to the hospital. "We're puzzled as to why these people didn't take the money," he added. "Do you know why they didn't take it?"

"Perhaps I didn't give them enough time," I replied.

After McIntyre had gone, my bedside telephone rang. The caller asked, "Is that the Canadian? Are you the guy who beat up the muggers? Well, I'm a former deputy mayor of this town, and I've cousins who live in Winnipeg. Would you know them? America needs more people like you, my friend!" I thanked him and hung up, after assuring him that I had never met his cousins. Isn't that nice, I thought. People way down here in California are taking an interest in me.

That was before the flood of calls began. To my utter amazement, people who had heard of my encounter with the muggers on television or radio, or read about it in the morning newspaper, were being connected right through to me, by-passing the hospital switchboard. As the calls continued I phoned the receptionist in desperation. "For heaven's sake," I said, "please, no more telephone calls to my room unless I okay them!"

At some point during that busy morning my bodyguard returned with a copy of the newspaper. "There's yer picture," he said, pointing to a photograph of a sheet-covered hump on a stretcher. The accompanying story bore the striking headline: AGED CANADIAN SLUGS MUGGERS.

The F.B.I. Enters My Life

After lunch the telephone rang again. I swore, but picked up the phone. "There's a gentleman here to see you," said the hospital receptionist. "I think he has something to do with insurance."

"Impossible!" I replied. "If anyone has given you that story he's a fake." I was on the point of hanging up when a whispering voice came through the receiver. "Joubin, it's all right. It's me, McIntyre. Can I come up? I have someone with me."

In a few minutes McIntyre arrived in my hospital room accompanied by a burly fellow who pulled a notebook and pencil from his pocket. "You're from the press!" I accused.

"No, no, not at all" he replied, and flipped out an identification card for me read. In faint blue capitals about half an inch high, I saw on the card the letters, "F.B.I."

"We've been through your papers and passports," said the stranger. "You have a Canadian passport and a United Nations *laissez-passer*. You've been travelling widely in Central America and in Colombia only a few months ago and in Burma a year earlier. What's your business? In your passport is a special visa with reference to the International Atomic Energy Agency in Vienna, Austria. What do you do?"

"I work for the United Nations preparing projects for mineral search; prospecting for metals: copper, lead, zinc – things like that," I explained.

"Yes, but what about the atomic business?" he asked.

I was clearly puzzled, and McIntyre spoke up. "In your passport there is reference to the United Nations. We've phoned the headquarters in New York. Someone there told us you were mixed up with atomic and nuclear things, uranium, you know."

The F.B.I. man resumed his questioning and I tried to explain to him. "Right," he said, "I'll run a few checks. Maybe I'll be back. Maybe I won't." McIntyre and the agent left.

An hour or so later, McIntrye phoned me to tell me I was in the clear. "But we can't understand why that pair didn't take the money. We've been kicking around all sorts of ideas here in the office, including the possibility that you might be involved in the drug traffic. Fresno's a clearing house, you know. It's a back door for the Central American trade. We have incidents like yours almost every week in this town. Guns fired, people hurt. We can't understand why these fellows didn't take your money. That's one thing they don't usually ignore!"

I Return Home

Four days later I was on my way home. I arrived on two canes. Mary greeted me at our apartment door. "Illness in the family!" she said in her gentle way. But she was reassured to see me standing upright and talking intelligently. I told her the story. Typically, she had little to say, not even a mild reprimand like, "Why did you start fighting, Franc?" But I could read it on her face.

The experience prompted in me a rare mood of reflection upon my past. The first recollection that came to mind was of a rare relaxed evening shared with Val (later Sir Valentine) Duncan of Rio Tinto in London about 1960. It was after the acknowledged success of creating the Elliot Lake mining empire, in which effort Duncan himself had been a leader, and this was one of the very few occasions when Duncan philosophized in my presence.

Looking at me he had said, "Franc, I am sure you have found, as I have, that only the most dedicated and highly motivated individuals achieve lasting success and survive where others fail. They are few in number. That unusual drive, powered by visions that many others are blind to, leads such individuals to challenge, sometimes successfully, the accepted view – or conventional wisdom – be it artistic style, a religious doctrine, or a scientific theory. I think of this as 'a Sacred Fire,' and I view those that have it as highly privileged. I regard you as one of that few."

As I reflected on the course my life had taken, I saw that I had met many challenges with some success, all seemingly under the influence of some mystical balance or equilibrium. How else could I explain my good fortune and my survival after so many adversities and several brushes with death?

When I was only seven years of age, my brother Gerald not yet six, our father died of war wounds, leaving our mother destitute. We were sent to orphanages, although fortunately we were subsequently re-united with our mother. By the time I was eleven I was almost always working when I wasn't in school, and I've been working ever since.

By constantly searching for employment and working hard when I found it I earned my way through high school, college, and university, and became a prospector and geologist. Before I embarked on my prospecting career I had already survived my first brush with death, a fall down an elevator shaft on a construction site. Later I escaped death from a rock slide in an abandoned mine. Then there were encounters with a large, enraged bear, tsetse flies, and venomous snakes. I survived the crash of an aircraft in a stone quarry in Mexico, and most recently, of course, I had fought off the Fresno muggers.

My work with the United Nations Technical Assistance Program, beginning in the 1960s, was the third and, in various ways, the most satisfying and successful phase in my long career as a prospector and geologist. The first phase had been in the mid-1930s when I had prospected and worked as a geologist with colleagues of the Pioneer Company in various areas of British Columbia and the Yukon Territory. That had been a life full of challenges. The second phase began when Mary and I and our infant daughter Marion came to eastern Canada. I enjoyed professional and financial success far beyond anything I had ever dreamed possible during this time, through my participation in the discovery of several mine-making ore-bodies in both eastern and western Canada, but the discovery of the uranium deposits which led to the development of Elliot Lake marked the highlight of this phase of my career.

Now I am in the fourth phase of my technical career, in the less physically demanding role of "technical guru" to younger professionals.

I have been privileged to live two long and enjoyable lives concurrently. The most satisfying and precious has been that shared with my family and friends. My professional life, on the other hand, has seemed an endless chain of dramatic adventures in many countries, and more often than not I have been focal to "where the action was."

As I reflected on the many events in which I have participated – particularly in my professional life – it seemed to me that I have some stories which merit telling. I hope you will agree.

II

The Chemistry of Character

I Arrive and am Labelled

I was born and given the name Francis Guy Renault Joubin in San Francisco, California in mid-November, 1911. The registry office recorded my birth as having occurred on November fifteenth but my mother insisted I was born on the sixteenth. Questioning her on this point years later brought the answer, "Oh, that was your father, celebrating your arrival with drinking friends. He was confused when he arrived at the registry office."

My father Auguste Joseph Joubin was born at Chantenay, a modest French community near Nantes, in Britanny, sometime in the late 1870s or early 1880s. Like many Bretons, he was an independent and self-motivated individual. Several generations of his male ancestors had been bakers and chefs, and he continued in that tradition. Before he met my mother he had completed his apprenticeship and embarked on a career as a pastry chef.

My mother Marthe Jeanne Renault had grown up in Falaise, France, where she was born on May 16, 1884. When she and Auguste Joubin met in a French seaport town where her family was on holiday, they seem to have fallen deeply in love. Following anguished consideration on Marthe's part – she was always a worrier – and possibly after writing to and hearing from her brother who was already in California, she and Auguste agreed to elope. This enabled her to escape the strict traditions in which she had been reared.

Marthe and Auguste were married in Bordeaux, France, in September 1909. While Marthe took her husband's name, her high regard for the Renault family name continued. Indeed, both my brother (who was born in 1913), and I were given the middle name of Renault. As we grew up, first in the United States and later in Canada, our mother told us stories of the Renault family, their ancestors and relatives in far-away France. In our home my mother always spoke in French to my father, my brother, and me. She had been taught English, Italian, and Spanish, but she had been born and raised a Frenchwoman and she felt that her family should be French as well.

The Renaults – My Mother's Family

The Renaults had their own romantic history. They had had connections with the town of Falaise in Normandy since at least the beginning of the nineteenth century when, the story goes, a woman of considerable wealth, fleeing Paris and the political turmoil of the day for her country estate in Falaise, heard a baby crying beside the road. Directing her coachman to stop, she found a baby boy whom she subsequently adopted. This story may have been merely a romantic explanation for the arrival of a "love-child" of her own, but, in any event, the boy was given her surname "Renault" and in due course inherited her estate. With the arrival of the next generation of Renaults, he became the grandfather of Arthur E. Renault, my mother's father.

One branch of the family tree became butchers and blacksmiths. I remember being especially impressed that during the Napoleonic Wars, while some of the Renault men served in the Emperor's armies, the women kept the family's blacksmith shop operating. This part of the family was particularly enterprising, and their skills grew to include the building of wagons and carriages. One member of this branch was Louis Renault, the famous pioneering French automobilist who lived from 1877 to 1944. He may have been a cousin of Arthur Renault, my grandfather.

Photographs of my mother as a young woman reveal a petite, elegant brunette with dark flashing eyes and an expressive face and hands. Her five-foot height and physical frailty were due, in part, to a well-concealed deformity which had resulted from a childhood illness. Her poor health necessitated that my mother be educated at home, which, luckily, the family was wealthy enough to permit. Brought up in the strict traditions of the Catholic Church, she was not, however, narrow-minded in her interpretation of religion. Still, I remember that she carefully preserved a number of religious books given to her, perhaps by her family, when she had first shared in the Holy Eucharist.

Marthe's older brother, Marc Renault, had married an older and wealthy French lady from Burgundy named Claudine Payen, who had inherited considerable money from a previous marriage. Marc and his wife had sought freedom and new life in San Francisco, California, where there was much re-building and employment following the great earthquake and fire of 1906. It was they who encouraged my mother and father to come to America.

We Emigrate to Canada

California was booming when Auguste and Marthe Joubin arrived there. My father quickly found employment in a pastry shop, and my mother's intellect, linguistic ability, and charm enabled her to gain employment as an aide to the socially and politically prominent Crocker family. The Crockers occasionally entertained American presidents, either at their mansions in San Francisco or resorts at Lake Tahoe.

My parents rented an attic apartment in a handsome house on Summit Avenue, at the top of a hill with a beautiful view of the city of San Francisco. There I was born within a year or so of my parents' arrival in California, and my brother Gerald Renault arrived a little more than a year later.

I was less than three years old in August 1914 when the First World War broke out in Europe. Many patriotic or adventuresome men, my father among them, rushed to enlist. But the United States would not enter the war until 1917, so my father and his small family were soon on their way to Victoria, British Columbia, where, within a week of our arrival, Auguste Joubin had enlisted in the Canadian army. Auguste was still a French citizen, and before he had met my mother, he had completed his required service in the French military. When an official directive from the French authorities arrived ordering him to report for military service in the French army, he was already on active service with the Canadians.

My Father Goes to War

Life became exceedingly difficult for my mother when her husband went to war. Auguste Joubin had always acted intuitively, but once he had decided on a course of action, he followed it with patience and persistence. These characteristics typical of natives of Britanny, my mother later told me, gave him (and, to a degree, both my brother and me), a "*tête de Breton*" of unshakeable determination or, as it was sometimes described, sheer stubbornness.

Given such headstrong determination it was, perhaps, not surprising when my father decided to go to the defence of his motherland, domestic considerations did not deter him. Perhaps he assumed that since my mother had already demonstrated her confidence in him by eloping, such innate confidence would sustain her until he returned from the war. But the reality was that my mother was left alone without sufficient means in a strange new country with two infant children.

We moved into a small cottage on the edge of the Chinese district of the very British town of Victoria, on Vancouver Island. And there my dear mother was left almost penniless while my father went off to war. She couldn't turn for help to her brother, Marc, as he had by now largely squandered his wife's money. Her sense of guilt concerning her elopement prevented her from turning to her parents in France. My mother's anxiety about the future, combined with her frailness and her intense nature, soon resulted in a nervous collapse which required hospitalization. A community welfare agency took charge of my brother and me, not yet of school age. It was arranged that we would go to an orphanage. Since we had a French name we were sent to a Catholic orphanage north of Victoria, at Tzauhalem, on Vancouver Island.

My Life in Two Orphanages

Gerald and I had never been separated from our mother before; we were desolated. Besides, life in a Canadian orphanage early in the twentieth century was wretched. We soon felt that perhaps we had nothing to lose and something to gain by running away from Tzauhalem to rejoin our mother.

So one fine day Gerald (who I called Tibby) and I boldly set off along the gravel road in search of our mother and a happier home. Soon we were picked up by the driver of an old farm truck. We must have looked an awful sight because he took us to see a doctor who found that we had impetigo, a highly infectious skin disease. Some years later I learned that the report this doctor made had resulted in a comprehensive inspection of the orphanage at Tzauhalem. Other cases of impetigo were found and it was revealed that an attempt had been made to conceal the dreadful conditions there from the public.

After my impetigo was cleared up by a spell in the quarantine section of a hospital in Victoria, I was re-united with my brother at a non-sectarian orphanage on Hillside Avenue in the same city. There were also occasional tearful reunions with our mother. Looking back, I realize the year or so we spent in that orphanage was one of the happiest periods of my childhood. The spacious grounds and forest surrounding the orphanage filled me with joy and stimulated my interest in outdoor life and the world of nature.

While my brother and I shared the rigours (and, at Hillside Avenue, the joys) of orphanage life, our mother's health gradually improved. In due course she was able to care for herself, and we, by then of school age, were returned to her.

Reunion with Our Mother and Father

My father, in the meantime, had suffered serious shrapnel wounds at the front in France. He was hospitalized over there, and then, owing to the seriousness of his wounds, transferred to a hospital in Cardiff, Wales. When his general condition had improved sufficiently, he was invalided home and discharged as medically unfit early in 1917. He was, however, still in need of medical care, and became a permanent resident of military convalescent hospitals in British Columbia, at which, as his health appeared to improve, he served as a baker and pastry chef.

My memory of my father after his return from the war is of a man who came home once or twice a week with a small bag of his freshly baked shortbread cookies. Sometimes he was happy and singing. Sometimes he was not. My mother clearly understood the severity of his wounds, and so, despite her own uncertain health, she gradually assumed full responsibility for the upbringing of her two vigorous boys.

My mother worked hard to instill high standards of conduct in us. In particular, emphasis was put on the need for us always to do our best, to do what was right, and tell the truth whatever the cost. Time and again she would say to me, "Fon-fon (her nickname for me), you must always try to be the best, the very best. And you can be. Don't ever let me hear you say 'I did better than someone else.' Be the best!" Whenever my brother or I strayed from the high standards she set for us, she did not hesitate to demonstrate her disapproval.

Gerald and I didn't have our hair cut before we were of school age. My mother seemed to delight in our long wavy locks, which served a practical purpose for her. When we did things she didn't approve of, she would occasionally seize us by our long hair and shake our heads. If the offence called for more force we would be held by the hair while being spanked. This did not happen often, but I certainly remember those times when it did!

The first time it happened to me was when my brother was given a handsome doll. The opening and closing of the doll's eyes absolutely fascinated me. I became determined to figure out the answer to the mysteries of how this magic happened. So one day, hiding behind the corner of the cottage, I took a rock, broke open the doll's head and examined the exposed mechanism. Of course, my mother soon found the broken toy, and confronted me with the evidence. I denied responsibility. She grasped me by the hair and gave me a tanning I have never forgotten. That was lie number one.

I was often told by my mother never to take the dangerous shortcut along the railroad tracks which ran between the school and our home. The repetition of this warning seemed only to stimulate my interest in the shortcut. A fence of barbed wire made access to the tracks difficult, adding to the excitement of the challenge.

One afternoon, with several of my chums, I climbed over the barricades and strolled along the prohibited railroad tracks looking for "treasure." In those days cigarette packages often included little cards with pictures of baseball and other heroes. Metal bottle caps and other trinkets were eagerly picked up along the tracks. We soon lost all sense of time and it was almost dusk when I reached home. My mother had become deeply alarmed by the lateness.

"Where have you been? What have you been doing, Fon-fon?" she asked with mixed relief and anger.

I realized I had a problem. I had to tell the truth or else devise a very good story. I chose the latter course. With calculated calm I replied, "I stayed to help my teacher."

"Doing what?" was the next question.

Impulsively, but with germinal flair and desperation, I replied "Miss Smith, my teacher, took me downtown to help her buy a new hat."

My mother questioned me no further. Taking a firm grasp of my hair, she grabbed me, put me over her knees and gave me another tanning. And that was lie number two. It was also the last lie that I ever told my mother. I was beginning to learn from the discipline as well as the love my mother gave me. In the spring of 1918, I learned about life from my father's death.

My Father's Death

It had been hoped that my father might be restored to full health through supervised convalescence. But this proved to be a vain hope. His health deteriorated due to his war wounds and on May 28, 1918, he died.

The death of my father and the funeral which followed are a jumble of memories to me. There were many flowers. As the cortège made its way to the cemetery my mother cried inconsolably in the back seat of the open car. At the cemetery there were more flowers and a few of my father's mourning friends gathered about the grave. As my father disappeared into the earth I was filled with questions: Why was this happening? Why was my father put in a box and put in the ground?

The questions continued to puzzle me after my mother moved us into a house on Fisgard Street, then on the edge of Victoria. Our new neighbours were Chinese. I was fascinated by their commercial garden and I watched them cultivating their vegetables. Then they built a chicken house, and before long I saw many lovely newborn chicks. Then I noticed some of the baby chicks begin to stumble and fall: they lay very still. Soon there were so many dead chicks they seemed to cover the ground. I watched this sequence of events with concern. Mysteries were involved which I could not understand.

Several weeks later I saw small green sprouts appearing from the ground were the baby chicks had been buried. These little sprouts developed into beautiful white flowers with orange centres. The colours reminded me of the tiny chicks with their fluffy bodies and orange beaks. These flowers fascinated me. Several days later I watched them being cut and tied into beautiful bouquets for the marketplace. I was now certain that I had the explanation for my father's disappearance into the earth surrounded by flowers. I secretly concluded that I now understood the mystery of death.

Soon afterwards I told my mother, with a measure of pride, of my understanding of life and death. She cried and turning to me said, "Yes, Fon-fon, that is the way it happens."

The death of my father brought my mother not only deep sorrow but desperation. Since she was not a Canadian she was not immediately eligible for a Canadian war widow's pension. Because of my father's voluntary enlistment with the Canadian forces, without the knowledge of the French military authorities, the French government denied responsibility toward his widow. She was in a terrible financial state. But somehow, thanks to her extraordinary commitment to and hopes for her sons, our devotion to her, and the care of several compassionate friends and institutions, the family held together.

Unconsciously I was learning fundamental principles and practices which became an enduring foundation for my life. While my parents were never able to provide me with many of the normal material comforts, nevertheless they did provide me with a rich inheritance of ideals and internal discipline. My early upbringing and environment taught me thrift and fostered within me a growing understanding of the role of money in human life. As I grew up I came to realize that an individual without sufficient money suffers, but that many individuals suffer even more because of too much money. And so, while I knew that I had to earn money to survive, I never aspired to wealth. I learned that in order to survive I had to work, and that work is the primary means whereby individuals should expect to achieve their goals. This became increasingly clear to me after my father died.

A boy's sense of security – or lack of it – is often dramatically influenced by the death of his father. In my case, my father's death stimulated in me both a determination to survive and a sense of pride in doing so. This meant extra effort had to be expended to excel in whatever task I was engaged. While my mother was my primary source of inspiration as a youth, I had inherited patience and persistence from my father.

One of the remarkable characteristics of many young children is their ability to recover quickly, at least on the conscious level, from tragedies in their immediate family. There are various logical explanations for this. One of them is the expanding range of interests, the optimism and curiosity of young people. This was certainly true in my case.

At Home in Victoria

On the other side of our new home on Fisgard Street lived a whaling captain. Sometimes he came to the door of our house with a large piece of whale meat which my mother used to make into a delicious meal. I was enthralled by the captain's exciting stories of whales and the sea, and we often got so engrossed in these tales that we lost track of time and the captain's wife had to come to fetch him for a late dinner.

Living in a port city also kindled my interest in a much larger world. The Victoria harbour with its ships and sailors was a focal point of continuous activity and change, and Gerald and I often spent hours here gazing out to sea observing the bustling maritime traffic.

As children we occasionally received gifts and cards from relatives across the sea in France. Our mother impressed on us the need to thank each person who sent us a letter or present of any type. She instructed us carefully in the preparation of such thank-you notes and in this way contributed not only to our sense of courtesy but also to our ability to write in French as well as English.

As a child in Europe, my mother had been taught to be respectful of her elders. As a mature woman she understood the value of such respect and was determined that her sons should acquire her natural manners, politeness, consideration for others, and her softness of speech. Her use of the French language to speak to us, even though there were no other French-speaking persons living nearby, proved to be of great future value to us. While we rarely replied to her in French, her natural use of it gave us an excellent phonetic foundation and a comprehensive French vocabulary. As a result it was relatively easy for me later in life to become literate and fluent not only in French but in Spanish.

My mother drilled us in other matters as well. She urged us to be precise in what we wrote, said, and did. This emphasis on courtesy and precision, in thought, speech, and action proved to be a rich endowment in our lives.

My Foster Parents and My First Mineral Discovery

Following the death of my father, the task of raising two active boys with no financial resources or male support soon took its toll on my mother. She had another nervous breakdown and had to spend several weeks in hospital. Friends prevailed upon her to consider making arrangements for her boys to be adopted. I was placed with a wealthy English gentleman and his second wife, a vivacious young French woman, who lived in one of the most exclusive suburbs of Victoria.

My foster mother was determined that I would be the best-dressed and best-mannered boy in Victoria, and I soon had a fine array of clothes. Jim, their Chinese cook and valet to the master of the household, kept my shoes sparkling. He became my best friend and confidant. But the stress of keeping my clothes spotless and my shoes shined bewildered me. Also there were no other children living nearby. I thought perhaps people in that neighbourhood were too rich to have children!

My foster mother gave a small train one day. I quickly decided to build a "line" for it and my planned railroad grade was gradually ploughed through the middle of the path beside the house. During the course of these excavations, I had to dig under a thick root of a tree. Scraping away, I miraculously came upon a treasure! It was a metal disc, over an inch in diameter, quite heavy and covered with a verdigris crust. When I scratched at the disc, it began to shine like gold! I rushed to show my treasure to Jim who quickly agreed that I had made a very important discovery – a piece of ancient money.

I took my trusted friend outside to see where I had found the coin. Shocked at the sight of the torn-up path, yet with a typical discretion, Jim said, "We must cover up all the holes quickly. No one must know where you have dug! There may be more coins. Only you and I will know the secret."

Quickly we covered up all the holes, scarcely finishing when the master, in his chauffeured car, arrived at the gateway of the residence. "Just in time!" said Jim, as he disappeared through the basement door, shouting to me, "You get cleaned up and ready for dinner."

When dinner was over, Jim placed the polished coin, on an attractive saucer, before the master. The coin, said Jim, had been found in the garden by Francis. My foster mother hugged me. "I would like the coin for a pendant!" she exclaimed.

Examining the coin with care, my foster father said, "It is a British coin and quite old. Tomorrow I shall show it to a friend, a collector of coins." He looked at me approvingly, "You have sharp eyes, Francis." Jim beamed with satisfaction.

When I am asked today how I first became interested in prospecting and mining, I usually tell, with a sly smile, of that little boy's discovery of that coin. That was one of my happier moments during the few months I was being considered for adoption. My foster parents seemed to feel that I would fit into their home, but I had grave doubts that I kept to myself. The wife became particularly attached to me –

and I to her – but I found the austerity of her much older husband somewhat frightening. My own mother, to my great relief, was finally opposed to any adoption. When she regained her health and strength my brother and I were once again reunited with her and we moved to a tiny cottage in Gordon Head, a small community some miles outside Victoria.

Sometime after I had returned to my mother, my foster parents separated. The woman went home to France; had I been adopted she would undoubtedly have wished to take me with her. There was no further communication between us, but fifty years later, while on business in Europe, I managed to trace her to a village in France, about an hour's rail trip from Paris. I visited, wanting to be sure that she was well and not in need, and our reunion was happy, though tearful.

At Gordon Head

In the early 1920s, Gordon Head was primarily an agricultural community with some mixed farming and animal husbandry. It had begun to establish a reputation for tree and vine fruits. Once again, we had Chinese neighbours – this time about half a dozen market gardeners who sold their produce, door-to-door, from huge wicker baskets which they took on balanced bamboo poles to Victoria once a week.

These gardeners worked, often on their knees, between tidy rows of vegetables from dawn to dusk each day. The only time they seemed to relax was at dusk on warm days. Then the five or six men in the group would sit together in a row against the outside wall of the shack in which they lived. There they quietly smoked their long, black, tubular, "bubbly" pipes. My mother, in answer to a question from either my brother or me about these curious pipes replied, "*C'est probablement de l'opium.*"

The Chinese were good neighbours. When our mother made bread, usually once a week, she gave two or three loaves to us to take to our Chinese friends. In return they invariably gave us a freshly killed chicken or a piece of pork to take home. While we grew some of our own vegetables and fruit, we kept no livestock, and the gift of meat was always welcome.

Such early (and continuing) associations with Chinese people have developed in me a great respect for them. I find their integrity, their philosophical attitude toward life, and their patience to be most impressive.

Some distance down the road from us lived Mr. Tracey, popularly known as "Crazy Joe." He was a tall, broad-shouldered man with reddish hair and pale blue piercing eyes. Usually he wore jeans, a short-sleeved flannel shirt, a thick old woollen sweater when the weather was cool, and a badly faded grey felt hat.

Joe Tracey was the first of many natural philosophers I was to encounter, listen to carefully, question, occasionally debate with, and learn from in my life. It is also likely that Tracey was the first prospector that I met. He introduced me to the small semi-precious pebbles, or agates, which were quite widespread in the soil of Vancouver Island, and which he searched for and recovered in considerable quantity with the same diligence as he harvested his various root vegetables. Initially, however, Mr. Tracey functioned as a primary source of encyclopaedic information for me concerning countless matters which arose in my mind and about which I was too shy to ask in front of a class in school. Mr. Tracey was the "oracle" who could answer a highly inquisitive boy's questions by drawing on his memory, his personal recollections, or by searching (often with me) through one of his many books. He also taught me much about the insect and bird life of the vicinity and introduced me to the whole range of animal life and the world of nature generally. He was both a thinker and a "hands-on" doer, a combination which I have regarded highly throughout my life.

Joe Tracey loved wild creatures and they loved him. The birds, squirrels, and other small wild animals ate from his hands. But his particular love and joy was his Jersey cow. He kept her stable as clean as a kitchen and she followed him around the farm like a pet. Occasionally he would place a coloured ribbon around one of her horns. As long as we lived nearby I went to his house every evening with our tin milk pail to get fresh milk from that cow.

The garden which Mr. Tracey kept had good, brown, sandy soil in which, besides vegetables and berries, he grew a profusion of flowers. When my brother or I took him fresh bread or some stew, to repay him for the milk from his cow, he would often say, particularly if the beauty of the flowers had been commented upon, "Take some home, but not the roses. The thorns spell misery and your poor mother has had enough."

Although we regarded Mr. Tracey as a good friend, and got on well with him, many others in the community viewed him as strange or odd. He was an intellectual and social rebel which may help to explain why he lived alone in the large house he had built for an Irish woman whom he had hoped to marry. When she had arrived in the remote community of Gordon Head, which bore no resemblance to her native Ireland, she had quickly decided to return to her homeland. I must admit that some of Mr Tracey's "spells" did trouble me. He would appear unpredictably on the front steps of the small local church to speak against the hypocrisy of the church and its false doctrine. While we did not go to church regularly, we respected its role in the community. I refused to witness any of Mr. Tracey's declamations against the church, even though they attracted lively public attention (climaxed on some occasions by his removal from church premises by the local constable).

To many he was "Crazy Joe" but to me he was always "Mr. Tracey," and he taught me a great deal during the time we lived at Gordon Head. He opened my eyes to a multitude of nature's wonders and developed in me a love of nature that continues to this day.

Another activity during this period was my participation in the Boys' Naval Brigade. One evening a week a group of about a dozen boys met at the nearby home of a retired naval captain to learn basic rules of seamanship, knot-tying, compass reading, signalling with flags, and other rudimentary naval activities. Each member of the Brigade was issued a naval uniform. I enjoyed wearing my uniform because it helped me overcome the occasional self-consciousness I felt about wearing patched clothing. Perhaps more importantly, it gave me the sense of being dressed as an adult. Moreover, the retired captain who trained us was a rare blend of majestic bearing, stern task master, and appreciative leader. When, after some group exercise he would exclaim, "Well done, men!" we twelve- to fourteen-year-olds would nearly burst with pride.

During my early teens I began to realize that I was learning as much, if not more, outside school as I was learning inside. My mother, of course, remained the central person in my life. Despite her frail constitution she was a stern disciplinarian. Increasingly she expected me to discharge my responsibilities as "man of the house." One of these responsibilities was to hand-deliver the monthly rent cheque to the landlord of the moment. Because of our financial circumstances, we were regularly forced to move in an ongoing search for suitable accommodation at the lowest possible cost. When I was about twelve years of age my mother decided that we should move to Mount Tolmie, a small Vancouver Island community not far from Gordon Head.

III
Classroom and Coalyard

Cedar Hill School in Mount Tolmie was one of several primary schools attended by my brother and me during our childhoods. After about three years at Mount Tolmie we moved back to Victoria where my brother and I attended Boys Central School to complete our primary education. At Boys Central School I attained a measure of stardom on the school's senior rugby team, where I was known as "Zoobie" by some enthusiastic fans. At the same time an accomplished art teacher exposed me to the world of self-expression through drawing and painting. So pleased was this teacher with my ability that he actually commissioned me to paint a set of porcelain tea cups and saucers for him during my after-school hours.

Reading – My Discovery and Continuing Delight

A major discovery and pleasure for me as a teenager was reading. I read as widely as possible and became enthralled by the works of George Bernard Shaw, Jack London, Brett Harte, Horatio Alger, and Robert Service. Stories about the gold rushes in California, British Columbia, and the Yukon fascinated me. By some means my mother acquired a selection of the the French classics including the works of Voltaire, Rousseau, De Maupassant, and Victor Hugo, and with her help I managed to read portions of them in the original.

My early attachment to books has never ended. Wherever I go I never travel without reading material. During the long years in which I was actively engaged in prospecting throughout Canada I became a standing joke as "the prospector who carries a book in his sleeping bag instead of a bottle of booze!"

If my reading as a youth did in fact influence my career, probably the poems of Robert Service, and the stories of Brett Harte did much to give me a glimpse of both the romance and the reality of life in mining camps. Even more important, however, was my absorption of the content and values of the books by Horatio Alger, the most popular author in the United States during the nineteenth century, and widely regarded as the most influential writer of his generation. Alger wrote stories of poor boys who, through their own efforts, went from "rags to riches." As I read Horatio Alger's novels, I quickly identified with his central characters. His stories stimulated me, on both a conscious and sub-conscious level, to be honest, persistent, cheerful, and to work hard at all times. What is significant is that I became convinced that individuals must and could enjoy success and good fortune, given the will and the effort. Curiously, about this time, my mother took me to a clairvoyant who said that I would win fame and fortune in "a field to do with chemistry" soon after I became forty years of age. My mother became certain that my day of fortune would come. I was skeptical until the forgotten prophecy was completely realized at age forty-one!

I Begin to Work

Before I was ten years of age, I was working at odd jobs to supplement the meagre pension my mother finally received as a war widow after she became a naturalized Canadian. In my late public school years in Victoria, I sold newspapers on the street.

As a newsboy I shared in the popular weekly Salvation Army "bean feeds" in what had once been a burlesque house. The Victoria newsboys, for whom these feeds were arranged, consumed huge platters of hot pork and beans and belted out inspirational hymns such as "Onward Christian Soldiers" to the accompaniment of the old theatre organ. This social event was the highlight of the week at that time in my life.

Another benefit came from the Chinese owner of the Purity restaurant. While on my newspaper rounds, I occasionally paid ten cents for a hot pork pie for my dinner at this restaurant. The Chinese owner-cook would give a large glass of milk in exchange for a copy of the *Times* and a brief explanation of what the headlines meant. I was convinced at that time that the Purity was the finest gourmet bistro in all of Canada.

During my early high school years, I delivered groceries by bicycle one or two hours every evening and on Saturday mornings. As delicacies were scarce at home, a fringe benefit to this particular job was the gift of cold meats, cheese, fruit, and pastries. In the days before refrigeration such food "would not keep over the weekend" and so was often given to me.

To share my solitary grocery rounds in the evenings, I would sometimes take my pet pigeon Peepo with me. She (or he, I never determined which) sat either on the handlebars of my bicycle or on my shoulder until I told her to fly home. I would perch her on the gatepost before approaching a customer's house to spare them any nervousness. Peepo was a most unusual pigeon. For example, I have no recollection of her ever having left any of the usual evidence of a pigeon's presence either on my bicycle, the groceries, or my shoulder. Peepo took particular pleasure in dancing and cooing on the outside windowsill of my bedroom window to music from my mouth-organ. Her enjoyment of this instrument was shared by our goat Nanette, whom I milked each day. Indeed I was greatly flattered to discover that Nanette's milk appeared to flow better to my music. I made a support for my mouth-organ out of a bent wire clothes-hanger so that I could play and milk at the same time. Nanette stood for milking on an old kitchen table under an apple tree to save me from kneeling or bending. While the neighbours and passers-by may have viewed us as show-offs, everyone seemed to enjoy the performances. Peepo, Nanette, and I simply enjoyed each other's company.

At Victoria High School

After Boys Central School, I enrolled in the technical course at Victoria High School. There I gradually learned how to absorb knowledge, retain it, and use it effectively. While I was a relatively slow learner, I retained a firm grip on what I had learned, and I usually ranked in the top third of the class. I was fortunate to have competent teachers whom I respected, in particular the school's principal, Ira Dilworth, who in later years made important contributions to the Canadian Broadcasting Corporation.

As a high school student I developed a reputation as an entrepreneur. In those days, skull caps, popularly known as "beanies," and pennants with the school initials and in the school colours, were popular with many students. Using my mother's foot-pedal sewing machine, and with the "hired" help of my brother and a number of other students to handle the sales, I made large quantities of beanies and pennants. Selling them was no problem. I simply invited students to sell ten of my beanies and receive a free one as commission. As word of my beanies spread, I began to receive orders from students in other schools.

My success in the skull cap and pennant business encouraged me to become involved in selling used textbooks. In this I teamed up with a classmate, Ken McKenzie, with whom I also studied later at Victoria College and the University of British Columbia. McKenzie and I found there was a considerable market for used textbooks, provided they could be sold at low prices. Together we opened a second-hand textbook shop in an empty space in downtown Victoria. At the end of the school year we invited students throughout Victoria to bring used textbooks to our shop, leaving them for sale on consignment. We undertook to sell these books at a profit, to them and to us. However, our very popular activities as used-book dealers quickly came to the attention of the commercially licenced new book dealers who did not approve of this type of competition. We had begun our used-book enterprise without realizing that we needed a business licence, and not yet being twenty-one years of age, we could not secure one. The established book dealers complained to civic authorities who ordered us to "close shop."

Principal of Victoria High, Ira Dilworth, who knew of my entrepreneurial initiative in regard to the beanie and used-textbook projects, felt that I might do well in the world of banking. At least when he was approached by a major Canadian bank for a recommended "short list" of eligible graduating students for training in that field, Dilworth called me into his office and asked if I was interested in being recommended to the bank. I was, of course, flattered by his proposal but after some soul-searching and the counsel of my mother, I declined. I had not, to that time, been happy in the world of numbers, and my mother rightly felt that I was too physical and more closely related to an outdoors discipline. How right she turned out to be. Even now, when I face a banker, I sometimes think "but for the grace of God . . ."

My Future is Decided

In the early summer of 1929, when I graduated from "Vic Hi," I had to find some job to help provide a steady income for my family. I felt good about my future in that highly optimistic summer of 1929, indeed, so good that for the first time in my life I took a two-week vacation, going with the family of a classmate to one of the Gulf Islands. Then I went job-hunting at two or three construction sites, soon finding work at one of the most publicized projects in Victoria – the construction of a new wing to the celebrated Empress Hotel. I was classed a labourer, and my particular responsibility was to keep a small number of bricklayers and masons supplied with cement and bricks. About three of four months later I became straw boss to a crew of three others responsible for the erection of the inside scaffolding for the installation of the brick and tile partitions. This promotion gave me a raise in pay to 80¢ an hour, more for overtime. Because I spoke French, my crew was made up of French Canadians who spoke little English. This ability was probably the reason behind my promotion. Not long after this, the project superintendent's casual inquiry as to whether I had plans to proceed to university (an undreamed of step for me to that time) made me decide to at least investigate the possibility.

Information I received from the Association of Professional Engineers of British Columbia and from one of the civil engineers on the Empress Hotel extension project confirmed that I could prepare for a career as a civil engineer through self-study, with on-the-job experience, and by passing the required periodic examination set by the Professional Engineers Association. This approach struck me as an excellent solution; I would be employed, thus maintaining my family's income, while I studied. I enrolled as an Association apprentice.

My Career in Construction

When I started work on the Empress Hotel extension in the summer of 1929, only the structural steel frame and concrete floors had been completed. Large openings, from top to bottom in the centre of the structure, had been left in the concrete floors to accommodate the elevators which were to be installed later. One day, while working on about the third or fourth floor, I decided to cross over the large opening for the elevator shaft by walking along a pair of 2" × 12" planks which had been placed across the opening for that purpose. Suddenly, as I was about mid-way across, one of the planks flipped over on its edge. Another workman behind me had struck the plank with a wheelbarrow and knocked it askew. I fell down the open elevator shaft.

I felt as though I was in a terrifying real-life movie. Everything was topsy-turvey as I plunged downward. I had no time to think or to sense fear. My fall ended abruptly. I wondered if I might be dead. I had felt no impact; I felt no pain – only a floating sensation. I was strangely relaxed, and wondered if I still had any feeling in my limbs. With some difficulty, but considerable relief, I moved my legs. They seemed to be entwined in a mass of soft material. I groped about for a while and shortly heard voices and the sound of heavy boots as rescuers came to my aid.

I had fallen into a huge pile of excelsior at the bottom of the empty elevator shaft. Fancy tiles for the hotel's bathrooms had been packed in this shredded wood product, and because it is highly inflammable it had been dumped into the elevator shaft as the safest place for temporary storage. That pile of excelsior had saved my life.

From that time on I always thought and looked carefully before taking a step in an unknown direction or area, and I walked before I ran. This practice of caution became subconsciously ingrained in all aspects of my life and has, I am sure, spared me and my companions from injury and death many times throughout an adventurous life.

Work on the Empress Hotel extension was completed shortly after the collapse of the stock market in late 1929. The Great Depression of the 1930s had begun. The construction company employing me had only one other contract in Canada, a bank building in Vancouver. However, it had bid on the construction of a hydro-electric dam in Colombia, South America. When one of the foremen asked me if I would work on this Colombian project, should they win the contract, I agreed and began night school studies in Spanish. After a month of soul-searching, I felt I should tell my mother of my plan. She was clearly shocked by the prospect of my leaving her and feared both for my safety and for her own health.

My mother had recently suffered a major disappointment when Gerald, my seventeen-year-old brother, had dropped out of high school and gone to sea as a cook on an international tramp freighter. He was following precisely in the steps of our father during his early years. It was clear that someone had to stay with our mother and care for her. As the older son I realized that the responsibility was mine and I accepted it. I informed the construction company that I could not accept the job in Colombia if the opportunity arose. Little did I realize then that forty-five years later, I would finally visit Colombia as a United Nations Technical Consultant to assist in that country's economic development.

Job-Hunting in the Great Depression

From 1930 to 1934, the depths of the Depression, I was constantly in search of employment of any type. Some jobs lasted only a few days, others a few weeks. I hitch-hiked to Surrey not far from Vancouver to pick hops and to the Okanagan to pick apples. I worked as a stable boy at the Willows Racetrack, near Victoria. On other occasions I was employed as a rough carpenter by a general contractor renovating old homes and, for a time, as a house and sign painter. When all else failed I joined the relief gang of the City of Victoria and dug ditches for water and sewer pipes.

In a Vancouver Island logging camp I worked briefly as a "bucker" and on a railroad gang as a "Gandhi dancer." In the early Depression years all the logging operations in the British Columbia forests were carried out either by hand or by steam power. The large rain-forest fir, spruce, and cedar trees were felled by two-men crews of "fallers" who used double-bit axes and felling saws. The huge fallen trees were then cut into certain standard lengths by two-men crews who operated the seven-foot-long "bucking" saws with a man at each end. I only worked briefly as a bucker since the job required men taller and heavier than my 150 pounds.

As a "Gandhi dancer" I removed rotted wooden ties, replacing them with new ones, on a short railroad line on the west coast of Vancouver Island. When the rotted ties had been removed, the new ties laid in place, and the rails spiked on top of them, the grade of the railroad bed had to be carefully adjusted by spreading and tamping the sand and gravel between and beneath the new ties. This was done by men using short-handled spades and their body weight as pressure in a rhythmic jiggling motion. Since East Indian indentured labour was widely used for this type of work in the early years of railroad construction in western Canada, and since there were many references in the popular press in the early 1930s to the Indian leader Mahatma Gandhi, members of the gangs who did such work were nicknamed "Gandhi dancers."

Later, back in Victoria, I found a job which offered me some continuity, at least during the winter months. I became a "sacker" and truck "swamper" for Smith and Sons, a small, family-owned and -operated, retail coal business. Using short-handled shovels, my fellow workers (usually Chinese) and I would unload a forty-ton rail-carload of coal from the Nanaimo mines once a week, and screen, shovel, and weigh it into burlap sacks weighing 104 pounds each.

But that was nothing compared to delivering the coal. This exhausting job saw us carrying two sacks of coal at a time, with a combined weight of 208 pounds, on our shoulders, sometimes up two or three flights of stairs. We delivered between ten to sixty sacks of coal to each address and there would be about a dozen addresses a day. Despite this arduous labour, I confess that my mate and I were shameless showoffs. On Victoria's downtown streets we carried on like a pair of jugglers, tossing loaded sacks of coal like dumb-bells from the truck into sidewalk coal chutes. Often our performance attracted an admiring audience.

As I worked in the coalyard beside my Chinese colleagues, screening, sacking, and lugging coal up flights of stairs, I began occasionally to spit blood. Alarmed, I went to see a doctor.

"An occupational hazard, Joubin," said the doctor. "Fortunately, coal dust is chemically inert, but a certain quantity of this can get into your lungs and, if you are exposed to it for long, you may be in trouble." Nevertheless, I valued my job with the coal company, and so, to deal with the problem on dry and dusty days, I tied a moistened handkerchief around the lower half of my face so that I could breathe through the wet cloth. Fortunately,the face mask was not necessary when delivering the coal. Had it been, I could have been mistaken for a hold-up man!

Some years later, when I worked at the Pioneer Gold Mine in the Bridge River Valley of British Columbia, I learned that the traditional way of settling silica dust in underground mines was to spray the freshly broken or crushed rock with water. The procedure probably helped, but not enough to prevent me from acquiring a weak silicotic shadow on one lung as a lasting record of my underground years.

Despite the hard and dirty work involved, I continued to work in the coalyard. The owner-boss was a kindly person and for me merely having a reasonably well-paying, all-winter-long job during the Depression was a considerable achievement.

The Victoria YMCA, *Wrestling, and Bike Racing*

While life during that period was difficult, the YMCA in Victoria provided opportunities and facilities for relaxation and recreation. Nearly every day after work, despite my labours in the coalyard, I would hurry to the YMCA on my bike. At the Y I showered, scrubbed the coal dust from my body, and engaged in a workout.

Through the encouragement and coaching of Lovatt, the excellent wrestling coach at the Y, I began to develop proficiency as a wrestler in the Greco-Roman tradition as practised in Olympic competitions. The Y's Greco-Roman wrestling team at the time was comprised of the two Loffler brothers, myself, and one or two others. Together we went to various communities on lower Vancouver Island to compete in weekend competitions with other aspiring wrestlers.

I occasionally visited a professional wrestling gym in Victoria, and on three occasions I was invited to wrestle professionally in preliminary bouts – until my alarmed mother ordered it stopped. These performances were designed to "warm up" the spectators for the main matches which followed. I was paid eight to ten dollars a bout, which was good money in 1933. I cultivated a variety of wrestling holds including the "Flying Scissors," a spectacular movement in which the aggressor leaps into the air feet first in an effort to tie both his feet around the head of his opponent in a headlock. It called, as wrestling usually does, for a high level of speed, agility, and strength; toughness also if you missed your target!

Wrestling developed in me a skilled and intuitive defensive mechanism that would serve me in good stead later in life.

I also enjoyed cross-country bike racing and tagged along with the celebrated Torchy Peden who, with Lew Rush and others, gained national renown as a Canadian bicycle racer and later as a champion of the professional six-day bicycle-racing circuit. On one occasion I entered the annual road race, sponsored by the *Daily Colonist*, one of Victoria's newspapers, which attracted riders from all over the west coast. I finished the race but trailed the leaders. It was neither wrestling nor bike racing, however, but my ability as a rugger player which resulted in my being offered a part-time position in the British Columbia civil service. This offer of employment came as a result of a chance encounter.

Introduction to British Columbia's Civil Service

One day, on the street in Victoria, I met a former classmate from Victoria High School and his father, the influential Colonel Philip Snowdon. The young Snowdon introduced me to his father, saying, "Franc is the fellow we called Zoobie. He starred on our team which won the Intercity Championship." The next day I received a message to go the Government Personnel Office to discuss a job opening.

When I presented myself at the Government Personnel Office, I explained to the one official there that I was working to support my mother and hoping to save sufficient money to move on from my part-time self-study program in engineering to full-time university studies. I was told there were no openings in the Public Works Department but that if I completed an application form, which he handed me, they would see what could be done for me. The official then excused himself, saying he had another appointment to attend to. He put on his hat, seized a covered tennis racquet, and hurried away. About a week later, I was told I had a position in the Department of Education and to report to the Deputy Minister's office. I did so and met there a kindly older gentleman who seemed genuinely interested in me. He said I would start as an inter-office messenger boy. I worked hard at my new job. It was menial but I wanted to prove I could work and keep my job.

The general attitudes toward work that I saw among the civil servants in the provincial government during the time that I held my summer job left grave doubts in my mind concerning the dedication to the public interest of a considerable proportion of those who were on the public payroll. This, I quickly realized, was a different world to the hustle and bustle of private sector industry, where the key word was *efficiency*. Nonetheless, I appeared to have made a good impression on some senior officials in the department because I was asked if I wished to apply for staff employment as a clerk. I turned down this generous invitation when at the same time I was offered a job in a fruit cannery on the lower mainland in British Columbia. This job promised more money and a more interesting work environment. That a position in the British Columbia civil service had been offered to me gave me some needed encouragement. That was not the first time I had received encouragement from an unexpected source.

When I had still been working in the coalyard, I was studying a prescribed engineering apprentice text during my lunch hour one day when a visitor entered the office and asked for the owner, Mr. Smith. The visitor was Mr. Morgan, owner of the largest coal company in Victoria and at that time also the mayor of the city. I replied that Mr. Smith would return shortly if he cared to wait in the office. He agree to that and after a moment or two asked me what I was reading. I displayed a mathematics textbook, explaining that my goal in life was to become a professional engineer.

Morgan looked me and the textbook over carefully. He doubtless noted my patched dust-covered work clothes. After a few seconds, he looked me straight in the face and declared, "You'll make it!"

Such assurance from the Mayor of Victoria to an unknown swamper in a coalyard made a deep impression upon me. For about a week the words "You'll make it!" echoed through my mind. Perhaps, I thought, Horatio Alger's stories were not all fiction. This surge of optimism made me all the more determined to accelerate my formal education.

One evening, not long after my encounter with the mayor, I pedalled homeward up the steep hill beside Boys Central School and looked, with greater interest than I had before, at the old Dunsmuir residence, Craigdarroch Castle, then occupied by Victoria College. I decided to visit the college during the following week and to learn more about it.

Working for a College Education in the Great Depression

In the midst of the many uncertainties of the early 1930s I was certain about three things: I was going to have to work hard to support my mother and myself and to survive in the world; I had to continue my education if I really wanted to make something of my life; and I could achieve these goals through a particular field of endeavour. What that field would be wasn't yet clear, but I sensed that it might be in some technical or scientific area. In the meantime I would attend Victoria College to help with my decision-making.

When I visited the registrar's office at Victoria College I learned that the tuition fees were about $150 for a year's study. I had saved that amount and had secured my high school graduation diploma which qualified me for admission to Victoria College, so I decided to enroll even though I still had to work part-time. I registered for my first year of study in the late summer of 1931.

Victoria College

Craigdarroch Castle, the home of Victoria College since 1921, had been completed in 1889, the centrepiece of the magnificent twenty-five-acre Dunsmuir estate. Its builder, the Honourable Robert Dunsmuir, had amassed a huge fortune through his activities in lumbering, mining, real estate, and transportation, and had spared no expense in the construction of his castle and the development of its gardens.

As I had spent all my life in modest surroundings, and not long before had been working in a coalyard, studying in such a magnificent building was an exhilarating experience for me. The castle had seven majestic chimneys soaring skyward. Its main tower loomed nearly one hundred feet above the ground. Its grand entrance, with *porte-cochère*, led to the vestibule of pink marble and sandstone and the incomparable panelling of the interior. There were eighteen carefully crafted fireplaces, a handsome library, and an elegant dining room.

Nonetheless, what I valued most highly were the intellectual opportunities offered by those around me. The privilege of acquiring knowledge and of sharing in the analysis and discussion of ideas with professors and students proved far more significant than the enjoyment of the physical beauty of the building and gardens. As I had begun to develop a particular interest in the sciences, I enrolled for a course in chemistry with Professor Savannah, who was one of the best known photographers and film-developers in Victoria. I also enrolled in French and economics courses and, although I had found it wearisome to the point of drudgery during my high-school days, I was also persuaded to include mathematics among my courses. This was one of the most fortunate decisions I made as a student as it brought me in touch with Walter Gage, a man who not only taught me mathematics but who encouraged me in a variety of ways and who years later became my colleague in a number of university development projects. Gage taught at Victoria College from 1926 until 1933, when he joined the faculty of the University of British Columbia (UBC). After a long and distinguished career as a professor and administrator he became UBC's president until 1975. He was not only a brilliant teacher and a highly successful administrator, but also a warm, helpful, and understanding friend of hosts of students. He was certainly a good friend to me.

Gage was precisely the type of teacher I needed to help me understand the logic of each step in the solution of a mathematical problem. His patience and willingness to explain details gave me the incentive to work hard in mathematics. And work hard I did. I was astonished and delighted by the grades I received in the courses I took with Gage at Victoria College. The study of chemistry under Savannah also inspired me; I even received a bursary of $25 for my performance in that subject – a substantial amount of money in the early thirties!

In 1931, unemployment in Canada stood at 17 per cent of the labour force; the following year it rose to 26 per cent – still lower than Germany's, but higher than the United States'. What was the source of the economic problems which were shaking democratic societies to their foundations? I was stimulated to take a particular interest in economics, which I studied with Professor P. H. Elliott, principal of Victoria College.

During the two years I had worked before enrolling in the College, I had often gone to an empty lot across the street from the government employment office (known less-than-fondly as "the slave market") to participate in public discussions about the pressing issues of the day. Groups of unemployed people and those sympathetic to them shared in these discussions during which individual speakers mounted an empty oil drum to express their points of view. On one occasion I gave my own analysis of the economic and political problems of the time. While I did not quite advocate overthrow of the government I came daringly close.

Basic social injustices, I declared while standing on top of that oil drum, including the manner in which economic life was structured and conducted, were the root causes of the economic problems plaguing the lives of individuals and communities throughout the industrialized world. These ideas were common early in the Great Depression and were outlined in detail by thoughtful clergymen from many church pulpits as well as by political reformers. The forceful advocacy of such reformist ideas troubled many in positions of authority in Canadian society: they sometimes spoke of the Bolshevik or Communist or "red" threat.

When I submitted an essay expounding on economic problems to my economics teacher, Prof. Elliott, I was given an A, but Prof. Elliott said to me privately, "Franc, perhaps it would be wise if you were to refrain from citing Karl Marx as a reference. As you progress through your university studies you will be exposed increasingly to Marxism and other socio-economic theories. Then you will be able to evaluate such problems more adequately. For the present, Franc, don't press his views too strongly."

My concern with political, social, and foreign policy issues prompted me to become interested in the International Relations Society of Victoria College. It had been established about the time I had first enrolled there, through the work of students and support from the Carnegie Institute for International Peace, and had given rise to a network of international affairs societies on various college and university campuses in the United States and Canada with which the group in Victoria was in touch. I became one of the first student presidents of the society at Victoria College.

The information I gained and the discussions in which I engaged through my work in the society seeded in me an interest in international affairs which has continued without interruption. For example, during my two years at Victoria College I became aware of the momentous historical events underway in the relations among the member countries of the British Empire, known later as the British

Commonwealth. The thoughtful relinquishment, without bloodshed, of political power by the British was, in my view, a major advance in the intelligent handling of international affairs. This highly significant development fostered my interest in the peaceful resolution of international issues which had originally been nurtured by discussions initiated in our home by my mother, and which later was deepened by my experience at Victoria College and the University of British Columbia. Given this background it is perhaps not surprising that years later I shared in the creation and raising of funds for the Canadian Peace Research Institute, participated in the Pugwash Conferences and the European East-West Round Table, and gave almost twenty years of voluntary service in various development agencies of the United Nations. The strong inner compulsion throughout my life to contribute to the advancement of peace among the nations of the world was nurtured in part by the stimulating discussions in which we engaged in the International Relations Society in Victoria.

As I became more aware of the major social problems and the suffering engulfing the majority of individuals throughout the world, I developed a simple personal philosophy. I knew that I had a sound physical body and reasonable mental health. Given these and the other privileges I enjoyed as a citizen of a country rich in resources and opportunity, I concluded that I owed a debt to society and had a responsibility to repay that debt. I determined to pattern my life and to conduct my affairs so as to leave, if possible, a few corners of the Earth better because I had been there. That general commitment became my guiding philosophy.

It didn't matter much to me whether I was asked to work with a shovel cleaning out a barn or whether Walter Gage asked me to solve a mathematical problem. To achieve the best possible results, not primarily for myself but for the overall good of whatever particular enterprise I might be involved in became my fundamental objective in all my activities.

At Victoria College I enjoyed the intellectual challenge I lived, to a greater or lesser degree, as a free spirit reading and studying in those fields which intuitively appealed to me. Increasingly I became conscious that learning occurs in three particular areas of human life: individuals can engage in formal learning through the taking of courses of study in school, college, or university; they can learn through informal education, by studying on their own those subjects which are of particular interest to them; and finally, individuals can, or should, learn through life experience. I also began to realize that I could learn and improve through careful analysis of my failures. Properly viewed, I concluded, failures could provide memorable lessons and lead to ongoing success.

Another lesson I learned was the value of friendship. My friendship with Kenneth McKenzie, begun at Victoria High School, was a singularly helpful and enjoyable friendship. Ken, who went on to Victoria College with me, excelled in the "hard" mathematical sciences and demonstrated early that he was a person of unusual intelligence. Through Ken McKenzie I learned of the developing world of electronics. Not long after we first began to discuss scientific matters and well before the advent of radio and television, Ken explained to me that electronic systems would some day be devised to record and transmit sound and pictures. His understanding and explanation to me of the role electronics was to play in the future greatly stimulated my thinking and years later produced results which neither of us could have anticipated in the early 1930s.

University of British Columbia

When I was a student at Victoria College it was a two-year institution. Graduates who wished to proceed to academic degrees had to transfer for the final two years to a university. The natural choice in my case was the University of British Columbia. As Ken McKenzie also wished to go on to university, the two of us went to Vancouver to hunt for inexpensive living accommodation near the university. This we found in the modest yet comfortable home of the widow of a medical doctor, Mrs. Moffatt, not far from the entrance to the main campus of the University of British Columbia.

I was greatly impressed by the natural magnificence of the Point Grey campus area. To the north, across English Bay and Burrard Inlet, I could see the coast mountains covered, during much of the year, with snow. To the west and south was the Gulf of Georgia. The view across the Gulf on a clear day was glorious. I could see not only the islands in the Gulf but also the outline of Vancouver Island's mountain range nearly one hundred miles away.

In that autumn of 1933, there were only three or four permanent and a number of semi-permanent buildings to serve the sixteen hundred or so registered students. The school's annual grant from the government of British Columbia had been reduced by over 50 per cent. In company with most public institutions in Canada at the time, UBC was experiencing the severe economic and financial problems caused by the Great Depression. Because of the relatively small enrollment, we came to know our professors personally, as we had done at Victoria College. We were not turned over to junior faculty members or graduate assistants. Students discussed courses in which they were interested with the senior professors.

The first difficult question which I had to resolve on arriving at UBC was whether I should enroll for a degree in pure science or in applied science. As a result of careful inquiry and consideration, I concluded that I should prepare for a degree in pure science. In my first year I studied biology, mathematics, zoology, chemistry, geology, and physics. I did rather well in all of the science subjects but ran into difficulty in the mathematics course. That I survived in my study of mathematics and physics at UBC may be attributed in large measure to the help I received from Ken McKenzie. He explained mathematical problems in terms and at a speed which enabled me to understand. Ken subsequently became one of Professor Gordon Schrum's most gifted physics students. He went on to advanced studies in the physics laboratory at California Institute of Technology, which was headed then by the world-renowned American physicist, Robert Andrews Millikan, who had won the Nobel Prize for Physics in 1923.

While Ken specialized in mathematics and physics I was attracted increasingly to the study of geology. Much of my initial interest in this field was inspired by Professor Schofield, who introduced me to the study of geology in a deliberate, methodical manner which I found most helpful. Schofield's patience and sensitivity my have stemmed in part from the illness which he had contracted on one of his field expeditions carried on during vacation periods, primarily in Asian countries. He had been afflicted by sleeping sickness, transmitted by the tsetse fly. It involves the brain and spinal cord and leads to creeping paralysis and eventual death. When I first began to study with Professor Schofield he was already suffering from this disease which in due course took his life.

With my interest in the study of general geology stimulated by Professor Schofield, I subsequently enrolled for related courses in paleontology with Dr. M. Y. Williams, minerology with Dr. Harry Warren, and economic geology with Professor Henry Gunning.

Like Professor Schofield, Dr. Williams was an exceptional person and brilliant teacher. The grades I achieved in paleontology were so high they startled me, but I wondered whether this was really me. I drew back from the prospect of spending my life in a dusty corner of a museum, cracking rocks and peering through a microscope at the fossilized remains of creatures many, many millions of years old! However, I became a complete devotee of Professor Williams as a fine professor and friend.

Harry Warren, a Rhodes scholar and a British Commonwealth running champion, was a dynamic, brilliant teacher, a most genial friend of students. Fifty years later, in the 1980s, he was still a stimulating professor at UBC and a voluntary "guru" to hundreds of his past graduates who sought his advice regarding professional problems.

Henry Gunning was highly gifted both as a teacher and practising geologist. The geological mapping in which Gunning engaged included, among other regions of Canada, the Cadillac, Malartic, and Rouyn-Ungava areas of Quebec, which have proven rich in gold and nickel. In 1932, Gunning had mapped the Zeballos area of Vancouver Island where, six years later, a gold rush and boom occurred in which I participated as a scout and prospector for Pioneer Mines. I had the extraordinary experience of finding, beside a wilderness foot-trail into the Midas claims, a small draughting instrument – a protractor – lost six years earlier by one of Gunning's geological survey assistants. Shortly before I picked up that instrument I had lost an identical instrument and was desperate to replace it. When Gunning learned later of this incident, he simply shook his head in disbelief and added, "some prospector!"

Step by step I became completely "hooked" on geology and began to dig deeper and deeper into its literature. While I completed my undergraduate studies at UBC with chemistry as my major field of study, in due course I would proceed to advanced studies in geology.

Financing my University Studies

As my academic confidence developed, my primary problem was no longer passing examinations but earning enough money to support my mother and pay for my tuition, food, and accommodation. Ken McKenzie had the same problem.

Our landlady Mrs. Moffatt and her daughter Margaret, a nurse in one of Vancouver's hospitals, were determined to help us in every way possible. Mrs. Moffatt loaned us an electric hot-plate for our one large room in her attic, on which Ken and I took turns preparing meals since we could rarely afford to eat even in the low-priced university cafeteria. Our usual meal consisted of a stew of vegetables, meat, and skimmed milk. Some of the vegetables were supplied by one of our Victoria College classmates, Russell Twinning, whose father, a cannery owner, arranged for several cases of canned vegetables and fruit to be sent to us.

Once a week either Ken or I cycled downtown to Blackburn's Market where three pounds of fresh hamburger could be purchased for 25¢. For another 25¢ we could buy assorted vegetables: potatoes, a big turnip, a bunch of faded carrots, or a couple of Spanish onions. In our attic room we cut up these vegetables, added the meat and skimmed milk, and made our weekly stew, which on a dignified French menu might have been listed as *Ragoût au lait* Moffatt. Occasionally we each enjoyed a luxury. For Ken this was usually a raw apple. I had a more exotic taste, and would splurge 5¢ on a coconut.

Our supply of clothing was equally as limited. We did all our own washing, pressing, and mending. Despite the poverty of the mid-1930s, students never wore jeans, T-shirts, or sneakers at UBC as they do on college and university campuses today. The wearing of a shirt, tie, and jacket or pullover sweater was the standard attire of almost all male students. At lectures all professors wore academic gowns.

It might be assumed from these sartorial comments that UBC in the midst of the Great Depression was an elitist institution, a place primarily for the education of the children of wealthy families. This was certainly not true either in my case or in Ken McKenzie's. I did not attend the convocation to receive my Bachelor's diploma in 1936 because I did not have the extra $35 to pay for my diploma and because I lacked what I regarded a "proper" suit to wear. There was another practical consideration. By not attending I gained a one-week headstart on my fellow graduates in the search for job.

During our two years at UBC Ken McKenzie and I constantly had to devise new ways to make money so that we could pay our fees and meet our living expenses. Between and after lectures and laboratory sessions we engaged in many money-making activities; we sold magazines door-to-door, but most of our endeavours were rather more unconventional.

Ken secured a part-time position in the physics laboratory and found in the physics building a considerable supply of quarter-inch aluminum tubing which appeared to be surplus to the needs of the department. He cut some of this material into six-inch lengths which he carefully bent into S-shaped pieces. Then he drilled a tiny hole in each piece. When this little gadget was placed properly in the top of a bottle of whole mile it could be used to separate the cream. Ken and I sold these devices to women who wished to skim off the top layer of cream from the bottles of milk delivered to their doorsteps by milkmen. McKenzie's handy-dandy cream separator did not challenge Vancouver's appliance dealers' market but its sale did provide more apples for Ken and some coconuts for me.

We also resorted to serving as professional blood donors to the Vancouver General Hospital, earning when we did so what was for us "big money." At that time, acceptable suppliers were paid (if my memory serves me correctly) $20 for one-half litre of blood, the normal quantity taken from a donor at one time. Today's system of voluntary blood banks had not yet been developed. Nor were arrangements for blood transfusions as professional as they are today. Indeed, transfusions then were rather rare. When a hospital had need for blood of a specific type a telephone call would be made to those on the list of available "suppliers" kept at the hospital. The names of Joubin and McKenzie were on such a list at the Vancouver General Hospital. When one or other of us was called to give blood we would immediately go to the hospital at any hour of the day or night, usually by bicycle.

At the hospital a sample of blood was taken quickly and tested for type and purity. If the test was passed the supplier would be taken directly to the patient's room. A cloth curtain separated the supplier from the patient requiring the transfusion. The two persons were connected by a rubber tube equipped with a simple valve. Usually the transfusion was supervised by a doctor. When the brief procedure was completed the supplier would be given an ounce or so of brandy and encouraged to rest on a cot for half an hour before returning home. Before departing from the hospital the supplier would receive on-the-spot payment for his blood. Then, in our case, the return ride on the bicycle would begin. Sometimes it was a shaky ride. Which caused the shakes – the brandy or the loss of blood – we were never sure.

Later I became a voluntary blood donor for many years. When our daughter Marion had to undergo open-heart surgery about 1950, and the procedure was still in its pioneering stage, I experienced in a more personal way the importance of blood transfusions. It was one of the rare occasions in my life when I experienced fear. My wife and I were profoundly grateful to the various blood donors and the medical brilliance of Dr. John Keith and Dr. William Mustard of the Hospital for Sick Children in Toronto, whose medical skill made possible a normal life for our daughter.

My First Prospecting Job

Before I had completed my first year at the University of British Columbia I had begun to hunt for a summer job, a necessity if I hoped to return to university in the autumn. My inquiries led me to a young mining promoter, a key figure in the Yorkshire Prospecting Syndicate, who apparently concluded that my experience in high school when I had panned gold in my summer holidays, might be particularly valuable to his syndicate. The Yorkshire group took me on, along with a classmate of mine, Don Summers, agreeing to pay us a monthly salary, to pay for our supplies, and to give us shares – a unit or two each – in the syndicate if we found anything of value.

Don and I went to work for the Yorkshire group in the late spring of 1934 as a helper for Joe Marron, an able and experienced prospector in the Bridge River area of British Columbia, west of Lillooet. This gold-mining area had been discovered first by placer miners who searched for grains and pellets or nuggets of gold which had been loosened from their source rock and mingled in the sand of streams, by sifting sand and water in a "gold pan." At that time the Pioneer and Bralorne mining companies were in the early stages of their production of lode gold which eventually proved to be highly successful. Lode gold is found in its source rock, usually quartz, which most commonly occurs as a vein or sheet and fills a fracture in a barren host rock.

Whereas placer miners work in the valleys of rivers or streams panning their gold, Don and I helped Joe Marron prospect the peak area of Mount Ferguson, not far from the developing Pioneer and Bralorne mines. We worked at an elevation of about seven thousand feet above sea level, well above the timberline.

Joe Marron was entirely different from the charming, fast-talking young promoter who had hired Summers and me. He was a small, muscular, quarrelsome individual with a shrill voice, who chewed "snoose" or smoked a cutty pipe, either of which he could and did employ with emphasis when he spoke. Joe shared with us the experience he had gained as a prospector working in the wilderness. He taught us how to identify specific types of rock and mineralization, what we should look for and how not to be fooled by what we thought we saw.

The three of us erected the Yorkshire camp near the summit of Mount Ferguson after we had made our way to the mountain-top level by a zig-zag foot-trail over which we climbed wearing shoulder packs. Most of the terrain was loose sand with small-to-large-sized angular pieces of rock which had slid down the face of the mountain. It took at least two hours of climbing to reach our camp site. But the straight-line trip down could be completed in about half an hour by sliding, seated on a small hand shovel and holding the handle between our legs.

The Yorkshire camp included a rectangular canvas tent supported by spruce poles. We slept in hammocks on which we spread a blanket or two, and cooked over open campfires, using the roots of juniper shrubs as fuel. A kerosene lantern was available for emergencies during the night. The camp, which was comfortable and easily portable, was also highly inflammable, which eventually led to its being destroyed by a fire caused by Joe Marron's lighted cutty pipe, left on his hammock and overlooked for a moment.

Our principal foods were rolled oats, rice, dried beans and dried fruits, bacon, and flour for sourdough hot cakes. Our water source was puddles left by melted snow. Our utensils were a tea pail, a frying pan, tin plates and cups, and a couple of tin basins for washing. Joe Marron also insisted on another utensil – a small but heavy cast-iron pot with a lid. In this Joe occasionally baked beans and bacon in a night fire pit, a shallow hole dug beside or beneath the campfire. The last glowing embers of the campfire were placed beneath, around, and over the "bean pot" which was then covered with soil and left to simmer during the night. The use of the bean pot in this manner produced what I came to regard as the most delectable gourmet meal available on any mountain top, a meal whose quality was universally recognized by all prospectors, as well as the occasional grizzly privileged to enjoy it at the prospector's expense.

During the summer of 1934 I was the only one of our group to discover a "showing." I found a three-inch-wide band of quartz sprinkled with a mineral closely resembling the gold-bearing material of the Pioneer and Bralorne mines. This showing was the edge of a vein of such material filling a vertical crack in the dark green "host rock" that formed, at that point, the mountain top. Such showings or veins, if they contained sufficient gold and were over three feet in width, formed the commercial ore-bodies of the district. They normally varied in width, and the narrower sections were called "stringers." I tended to be optimistic and without difficulty could imagine that my stringer would widen from three inches to three feet at greater depth and would contain adequate gold to constitute a commercial deposit.

When I first saw the stringer close to the ridge top of Mount Ferguson, I studied it carefully and then knocked off fragments and scrambled back to the Yorkshire camp. When Joe Marron examined the fragments I had brought back he was enthusiastic. Later, the assayer confirmed that the specimens I had secured contained appreciable gold.

Unknown to the three of us on Mount Ferguson, however, the Yorkshire Syndicate was having trouble raising the money necessary to keep us at work in the field. Since we were completely unaware of these financial difficulties, Joe Marron, Don Summers, and I continued to charge our groceries at the Ogden store in the Bralorne community. When the storekeeper complained that he was not receiving payment from Vancouver, Marron wrote to his family and learned that his paycheques had not arrived. Nor had Summer's. Nor had mine. And a telephone call brought the troublesome news that the charming Vancouver promoter had disappeared without a trace.

Marron, Summers, and I went unpaid for the work we had done over several months. Our immediate concern, however, was our debt for the groceries we had bought. Our troubles deepened when our camp was destroyed by fire. All our personal effects were lost, including, alas, a diary I had kept scrupulously for the preceding five years or so.

Summers, understandably, gave up in despair. But Marron and I continued to be enthusiastic over what I had found.

"Franc, your discovery could lead to something – maybe we could do it on our own," said Marron. "I'll be the promoter. You and I will form a new syndicate, 'The Summit Syndicate,' because it's up at the summit. We'll raise the money, we'll go back and open it up!"

Marron and I learned that the promoter of the Yorkshire Syndicate had failed to provide the government with reports of the assessment work which had been done. Thus the claims lapsed and were no longer reserved for the Yorkshire syndicate. Others could now re-stake all or part of the same area, so Joe and I completed a partial re-staking of the Yorkshire ground, five or six miles from the Bralorne and Pioneer mines where we hoped to raise money for our venture.

The Bralorne Mining Camp

During its early days the Bralorne camp in British Columbia's Bridge River Valley, about one hundred miles north and east of Vancouver, was much like other mining camps. It was a development of wooden shacks, strung out along both sides of a crushed-rock road from "outside" which ran roughly parallel to the Bridge and Hurley rivers at right angles to Cadwallader Creek, leading to the mine and its plants. The buildings owned by the mining companies were the only well-built and painted buildings in the camp. Beyond the road front-age, up and down the mountain side, hardly visible from the road, were the shacks, lean-to's, and tents of the seasonal mine workers, prospectors, and job-seekers.

Camps such as Bralorne, Pioneer, and others occurred at irregular intervals along the main access road. Their location was determined by the boundaries of mining properties and the availability of streams for water supplies. Apart from the developed mineral prospects, which were being readied for gold production, there were scores of adjoining prospects with small temporary camps strung out along the roadside for those prospecting in such specific locations.

In discreet semi-isolation but also handy to the main road were the "relaxation" or "entertainment" facilities common to almost all mining booms – the brothels, the poker dens, and the bootleggers. These entertainment centres provided a nightlife for the population – practically all male – of the Bridge River Valley. They also provided material for much of the daytime conversation and joking. The mad-ames all had colourful names and were themselves colourful extro-verts. Still, they and their ever-changing girls or, as they sometimes were known, "ballerinas," were rarely seen or even identifiable in public.

Such establishments were relatively well-built, resembling over-sized houses, and were usually well, if not tastefully, furnished. The truckers handling the freight from the railroad to the mines frequently grumbled about the awkward, garish, over-stuffed furniture they had to lug to these "goat ranches." Drapes in bright hues hung from their windows and music from gramophones and radios often drifted out. Some had front porches with flower boxes while others were known for their food and well-equipped kitchens. Occasionally a miner would say (not always in jest) that "the best roast pork in town comes from Zada's kitchen."

Help from Zada and her Friends

The social environment in which Joe Marron and I set out to raise money for our new Summit Syndicate was one in which individuals had grown accustomed to risks simply by living with them, consciously or unconsciously, every day. Marron, twenty years older than I, had long experience as a prospector, and he took the lead in raising funds for our new syndicate. He would go to people he knew had money, were near the scene of action, and "had the gold fever." His first approach, he told me, would be to Zada, the Madame of the local "cat house." If Zada were willing (or "game," as Marron put it), she might help to find other buyers for units in the new syndicate.

In addition, of course, there was Zada's "guy" down the road at Ogden. He ran the poker den and served as the bouncer in Zada's house. Joe would go to him – if Zada approved. A commonly heard phrase in the Bralorne camp at that time was that "Zada is a lady," unlike her competition down the road who was known as the "Canyon Cat." Given my upbringing and essential preoccupation with the securing of jobs so that I might continue my education, I had no personal knowledge of Zada or the Canyon Cat or, indeed, of any girls in their profession. Joe, however, a much more worldly character, insisted that I accompany him to Zada's to sell her some units.

I felt quite self-conscious climbing the half-dozen steps to Zada's house in the full light of day. Joe, however, didn't hesitate in the slightest and brashly led the way. Rapping loudly on the door and getting no immediate response – it was about mid-morning – he muttered to me, "probably ain't up yet."

Eventually the door opened slightly, and a woman with tousled reddish-blonde hair surrounding a plump matronly face poked her head and shoulders out. It was Zada. Blinking, she asked, "What's up, Joe?"

"I've got a grubstake deal on my mind that I thought could interest you. This is Frenchy Joubin, my partner and a geology student. It'll only take a minute to give you the pitch."

"Okay." said Zada, looking me over. "He looks like a nice kid; let him sit outside on the step. He'll come here on his own, if he decides, when he's good and ready. Joe, you come in and tell me what's on your mind."

Before too long, Joe emerged from the brothel. "Not often a guy goes into Zada's place without money and comes out with a bundle!" he boasted to me as we set off down the road. Joe had received $200 cash from Zada for two units in our Summit Syndicate. She had told him that we should go to see her guy. We did: he also bought a unit in the syndicate and then gave us the names of other potential investors. After two days of "rustling up money," Marron and I had raised $600. With a case of blasting powder, fuses, and caps, along with some grub, we again made our way up Mount Ferguson to our Summit claims.

In the days and weeks that followed we worked hard with pick, shovel, hand drill, steel, and dynamite. We blasted a trench in the loose slide rock to reach the solid source of our prospect. Then we blasted the solid face to remove all rust and to expose the vein to view. It was heavily mineralized but, to our despair, it was still quite narrow. Nonetheless we broke off pieces and took them down the mountain to show them to the geologists at the Bralorne and Pioneer mines. In the Depression, however, prospectors had to have a highly promising prospect to command attention. Despite our hard work and the initial financing provided by Zada, her guy, and other venturers, we had to abandon our efforts when snow arrived in the late fall of 1934.

What a story it would have made, I later thought, if our Summit Syndicate, financed by Zada and her clients, had succeeded. What headlines Joe and I would have made! I could see them in my mind's eye:

ZADA AND FRIENDS GRUBSTAKE LATEST GOLD STRIKE
  ON MOUNT FERGUSON.
HUGE DISCOVERY BY JOE MARRON AND FRENCHY
  JOUBIN.

But alas, it was not to be.

I had gained much practical experience of considerable value through my association with Joe Marron, but I had lost a considerable amount in wages during the summer of 1934. As a result I had no money: I would be unable to help my mother or to return to UBC. I began to look for work, taking various odd jobs offered to me. While I was searching for the best possible solution to my financial problems, governments throughout the world were doing the same in their spheres.

One of the early steps taken by the Congress of the United States to deal with the profound economic problems confronting the country at the time Franklin Roosevelt was elected in 1932, was to pass the Gold Reserve Act. This authorized the president of the United States to revalue the dollar. Subsequently, President Roosevelt took action which resulted in a rise in the price of gold. While this did not contribute appreciably to the resolution of the economic problems of the United States, it provided a major stimulus for gold-mining in that country and in Canada. Thus it seemed logical, as I searched for employment in 1935, for me to return to the Bridge River Valley.

To Bridge River in a Model-T Ford

In the spring of 1935, I persuaded three of my university friends from the previous year to join me on a job-hunting expedition to the Bridge River area. These friends were: Art Irwin, who later became a key official in the federal government's Department of Indian Affairs; Hugh Hamersley, who distinguished himself as an officer in the Royal Air Force before losing his life during the Second World War; and Nick Rodin, who served in the Royal Canadian Air Force during the Second World War, surviving an adventure-filled period as a prisoner-of-war to later become a brilliant professor in the United States. My three colleagues and I were thoroughly compatible. Although our resources were severely limited, our motivation was high.

Hugh Hamersley, a cultured, tall, athletic young Englishman, had an old Model-T Ford which he suggested we use to get to the Bridge River. It was a long drive on a terrible road, through Chilliwack, Yale, and Hope, then north to Lytton and on to Lillooet, the entrance to the Bridge River area.

The trip from Vancouver to Lillooet was a journey of about two hundred miles. Today, such a trip could be completed easily in several hours. In 1935, however, the road was a twisted ribbon of crushed stone, rock, rubble, and dust or mud. It took us about three days. We had repeated troubles with the car's tires and springs. Lacking service stations and, above all, money, we had to improvise constantly. When the brakes of the Model-T began to wear out, we developed an original braking system. It must have been one of the most unusual braking systems in the history of the automobile.

Before descending a steep hill, two of us would get out of Hamersley's car, take an axe, and cut down a large evergreen tree. The tree was then tied to the back of the car with a strong rope. The drag of the tree, supplemented on occasion by the body weight of one or two healthy young passengers, provided additional braking power. Going up a hill the car's small radiator tended to boil and steam, and water had to be found regularly to replenish it.

Completely exhausted at the end of each day, Hamersley, Irwin, Rodin, and I slept wherever we could rest our heads comfortably. One of us usually slept in the back seat of the car, the others on canvas sheets underneath. Sometimes we might find an empty shack along the road in which we could sleep, or, best of all, some dry hay or straw in an abandoned barn.

After three long days and short nights, the four of us arrived in Lillooet, a community at the junction of the Fraser and Bridge rivers. Lillooet had been developed on the site of an Indian settlement and had become first an important base on the Cariboo Gold Rush Trail and later a key stop on the Pacific Great Eastern Railroad. In the mid 1930s it was a frontier community of perhaps five hundred people, the majority of whom were Indians and Métis. The main economic activities of the community were connected with the railway, hydroelectric power generation, and some lumbering. Lillooet was also the last major centre through which materials and equipment were taken for the development of the mining properties in the Bridge River region.

When my colleagues and I arrived at Lillooet it was the end of the road. If we had wished to continue by car we would have had to put the car on a train or ferry and go to Shalath, where an extremely rough road continued the few miles over Mission Mountain to the mine sites in the Bridge River Valley.

Before we arrived in Lillooet, none of us knew about its central character, Ma Murray. In later years Ma Murray became known through her country newspaper as one of Canada's most forthright political and social commentators, a kind of Canadian equivalent of the American humorist Will Rogers. In the spring of 1935 she was well known throughout the Bridge River area.

Ma Murray had grown up in Kansas, a tall, blonde, gangling girl with a masculine frame. Later, she described her youth in graphic terms. "By the time I was eighteen or nineteen I was a crack shot with a rifle. I could rope cattle and brand them. I was the best hired man on the ranch. Then I decided I'd go to Canada and find me a big, good-looking mounted policeman and marry him, or a wild game hunter. I planned to marry a real he-man. I looked at the prospects in our town. I couldn't see the type I really wanted. So I headed for British Columbia."

When Hugh Hamersley drove his car into Lillooet he stopped near one of the few illuminated places to be seen, a house. Unknown to any of us, it was the home of Ma Murray. We began setting up our tent and stretched a ground sheet under the car. Suddenly the back door of the house was flung open. A women's commanding voice asked "What you doin' out there?" Hamersley, the spokesman of our group because he was tall and distinguished looking, approached the intimidating voice.

Hamersley tended to stutter when he was nervous. This usually disarmed the other person. As he walked into the light of Ma's back porch – Ma had her own little gas engine which generated enough power for a few light bulbs – Hamersley wrung his hands and began to speak. "Well, well, w-w-we're university boys. We're, we're, we're going to look, to look, look for work at, at, at, the m-m-mines!"

"Stop right there!" said Ma. "Have you et yet?"

I answered. "No, but it's all right. We still have some bologna and a loaf of bread."

"That won't do, an' fer a damn-sure!" announced Ma. "You all come in, in fifteen minutes. How many are you?"

"Four."

"All right, come in, all of you, in fifteen minutes."

We completed setting up our tent and were soon "hollered in" to Ma's kitchen. She was frying pans full of potatoes, ham, and eggs, and a pot of coffee was bubbling merrily.

Needless to say, all four of us were instantly impressed that night by Ma Murray. Her concern and curiosity about each of us, coupled with her brusque acceptance or dismissal of a suggestion, with "fer a damn-sure" added for emphasis, heightened our interest in her.

She scolded and pampered us like children at this first encounter, but our respect and admiration for her, apparently mutual, grew through the years. For several summers afterwards, Art Irwin and I secured work in the Bridge River mines. On each of our returns to Lillooet there would be a boisterous reunion with Ma.

Later, during the early years of the Second World War, the Pioneer mine in the Bridge River region became my base of operations for the strategic mineral exploration in which I was involved. There was much coming and going to and from Lillooet during those years by my colleagues and I. Gradually all of us became full members of the large and extensive clan which Ma Murray called "my boys." Ma Murray kept tab on at least some of her "boys" in later years and we received news of her through her weekly newspaper, *The Bridge River Lillooet News*. This unusual paper was printed in Ma's big house – the largest in Lillooet – where she lived and shared in the work of its printing and distribution with two or three co-workers.

Ma's pungent editorials questioned the integrity of premiers and cabinet ministers, the administration of justice, or any issue of social justice or hypocrisy that caught her eye or ear. But she could be lavish in her praise also. I was greatly embarrassed some thirty years later, when I returned to Bridge River to merge and revitalize the once-great but seriously languishing Pioneer and Bralorne gold mines, to be described in her widely read weekly as "the Messiah." Ma was a remarkable and unforgettable individual – "fer a damn-sure!"

The next day, we bade farewell to Ma Murray and completed our trip to the Bridge River Valley. We were quickly swept up in the mining boom that was underway. There were three mines in the valley: the Lorne Mine (known later as the Bralorne); the Pioneer, which was a couple of miles away; and the Bradian, between the Lorne and the Pioneer. The Lorne and Pioneer had built new, modern mills and were already producing considerable bullion. Their vertical mine shafts were being rapidly deepened and major construction was underway on the surface.

Each morning, before the day shift, a single-file line-up of ten, twenty, perhaps even fifty men hoping to be selected for work stood at the mine entry office. The mine foreman and the construction foreman walked down the line looking over the newcomers. They and the shift bosses were always on the look-out for men who could increase the productivity of their work gangs. At the end of each shift – the mines operated day and night with three shifts – the men coming

off work would pass a "shifter's office" on their way to the shed –
known as the *dry* – where they removed and hung up their work
clothes, took their showers, and changed into their street clothes. If
a miner passing through the shifter's office was told to "see the time-
keeper" by a shift boss, it usually meant that the man's work was
regarded as inadequate and that he was about to be fired. A new man
from the daily line-up would be given a trial. The foremen who looked
the line-up over might stop to ask a question or two and then say,
"Report to the shifter's office." This was usually said to those whose
appearance gave the impression that they could handle the hard work
involved in mining – larger, strong-looking men. Of the four of us,
only Hamersley was a big fellow, over six feet in height. Before long,
however, we had all secured some type of work in the valley, although
this took perseverance.

Several times I went through the line-up, but my size and inex-
perience in underground mining worked against me. In desperation
I made a direct approach to the chief geologist and general superintendent of the Pioneer Mine, Dr. Howard James. Dr. James had been
at the Pioneer for about a year. During that year he had resolved a
number of major problems for his company and had guided the development of the Pioneer to the point where it was then becoming
one of the richest gold mines in North America. The Pioneer Mining
Company had just finished building Howard James a fine house in
the Pioneer community in the valley. I thought perhaps I might be
able to secure a job landscaping the grounds around Dr. James's new
home. When Dr. James learned that I had worked occasionally with
Japanese gardeners landscaping properties in Victoria, he arranged
for me to be employed by Pioneer as a surface worker, landscaping
around his new residence. I terraced the ground around the house
and then had trucks haul rocks from the waste dumps of the mine
for the dry walls which I built to retain the terraces. These I planted
with local shrubs chosen carefully from the nearby bush. Dr. James
was so impressed by what I had done that he asked me to do the same
around the hospital, the office, and the community cookhouse.

While I was disappointed that I couldn't get a job in the mines,
I was glad to get work at all. Unknown to me at the time, the personal
relationship which I established with Dr. Howard James was to pay
handsome dividends in the future.

One of the first dividends resulted from a suggestion by Mr. Udall,
Pioneer's plant manager, that I might like to make some extra money

by "twilighting" as a stationary engineer and night watchman on the "graveyard shift." I agreed and began to stoke the steam boilers which provided the steam power for the mine and mill, and the central heating for all of the Pioneer buildings. I was also responsible for ensuring that the boilers operated properly during the night. As night watchman I patrolled and punched the clock around the mill and certain other Pioneer facilities where security was important. One of these facilities was the bullion smelter, which was operated only during the day, when those responsible for the smelter prepared bullion and delivered it to those who stored it in the safes in both the general office and the bullion room. On my rounds as night watchman I kept a close eye on these areas to ensure that no thefts occurred.

Work on the graveyard shift was not as arduous as one might imagine. I had a comfortable cot in the warm boiler room, and a good alarm clock to arouse me for a twenty-minute work period each hour of the eight-hour night shift. The Pioneer mine and mill operated, as did the other mines in the valley, twenty-four hours a day, every day, save for statutory holidays, of which there were few.

Given the relatively primitive working conditions which then prevailed in the mines in British Columbia, it is not surprising that efforts were made to unionize miners. While the miners did all the hard physical work and risked their lives in the mines, they had no status within the company. By banding together in a union and seeking collective bargaining rights they could gain official status if their bargaining unit were recognized. I understood the need for the miners to work together and was sympathetic to their objectives. However, the route by which I had gained employment with Pioneer, by directly approaching Dr. Howard James, and the nature of the responsibilities assigned to me, put me more in the category of a staff person than of a regular employee. In addition, I felt, at that time, those organizing the union were too aggressive. Still, I was sympathetic to the needs of ordinary working men and have continued to be throughout my whole career in the mining industry.

A quarter of a century after I secured my first job with Pioneer, I, with several associates, acquired control of and consolidated the Bralorne and the Pioneer mines. After we had acquired control, my colleagues and I sat down with our mine managers and the leaders of the union responsible for contract negotiations. There were five members of the union bargaining committee. Two of the members of that committee recognized me as one of their fellow-workers from years before. They came over to me, and shaking my hand warmly, asked with mock surprise and considerable respect, "Joubin, you union 'double-crosser.' What went wrong in your life? When did you go over to management? We always thought you were one of us!"

Underground Working Conditions in the Mid 1930s

In the mid 1930s a fully qualified miner earned $3.20 for a seven-hour shift underground. Each pair of miners was required to complete an established quota during each shift. For production above the quota a bonus was earned. A miner and his helper, taking heavy portable drills and drill steel with them, would go down into the mine to a specific *face* or *stope*. There they used crowbars to pry down the loose rock slabs above their heads before drilling twelve to sixteen holes in the rock. Each hole was drilled six to eight feet deep and loaded with explosives which were ignited at the end of the shift. With that work done, a miner and his helper had finished their daily quota of work. Given trouble-free working conditions, a good miner, with a competent helper, might be finished his quota in five hours. Usually, however, it required the full seven hours. They then had to get away from their workplace since "blasting" throughout the mine would soon commence. Blasting, of course, sent rock flying in all directions and produced thunderous noise. It filled the workplaces and connecting corridors with fumes that produced nausea and terrible headaches.

At that time the Bralorne and Pioneer mines each had two shafts to between one thousand and fifteen hundred feet, and were hot at these depths. The mines were ventilated by air pressure from the surface to keep them as cool as possible. The ore was siliceous, like crushed glass. Since the miners could and often did become victims of the lung disease silicosis, water was sprayed with pressure hoses from the surface to settle the silica dust from the atmosphere. Such spraying increased the humidity which contributed to the enervating heat. Heavy hard hats were worn, with a battery-lamp attached, replacing the earlier open-flame carbide lamps. Accidents occurred – some fatal. The most common were from rock falls and "bootlegs." If a miner and his helper did not carefully check the new face before starting to drill, an explosion could occur if the drill bit touched any unexploded powder from an earlier hole. This was a bootleg.

After the drilling and blasting shift, the piles of recently blasted rock would be ventilated by pressurized air introduced from the surface for two hours or so, then "mucking shifts" would go to work. The muckers would proceed to the freshly blasted face to "scale down" loose rock slabs from the roof and walls and to lay a short length of narrow gauge track to permit the removal of the freshly broken twenty tons or more of rock or ore. This was done by two men hand-shovelling the material into one-ton dump cars. These were pushed to a particular location where a *trammer* with a small battery-powered *lokie* (locomotive), would haul the load to an *ore* or *waste pocket* or *chute*. Miners and ore were raised to the surface by mine hoists, usually in different shafts.

My first underground job with individual responsibility was as a *sampler*. I had secured this job because I had gained, by that time, some experience in various aspects of the mining operation and as a student of geology I had developed ability in the identification of rock formations and specific minerals. As a sampler I had to visit the working areas after blasting to examine the fresh rock faces. I would crawl over the broken rock piles to examine quartz fragments and the quartz "veining" in the face, to note any visible gold. It was my responsibility to collect representative chip samples of the rock for assay. At the same time, I was on the alert for any bootleg holes. When I found such holes I circled them with bright-coloured crayon to warn the muckers and drillers who followed.

On a few occasions, I came upon an obviously rich distribution of gold in the broken ore. When this occurred I promptly informed the shift boss that there was "high-grade" here. The shifter, sometimes with my help, would then rough-pick the high-grade lumps from the broken muck as it was shovelled into the dump cars. One such memorable occasion at the Pioneer mine produced nine empty powder boxes filled with high-grade, weighing approximately 450 pounds and containing a total of 1,540 ounces of gold, the present day value of which would be in excess of $900,000 (Cdn.). I looked at the filled boxes with wonder and thought, "How little time it took to fill those boxes with gold. How bountiful nature can be to those ready to struggle patiently and risk their lives in the search for such treasure."

The wilderness beauty of the Bridge River Valley in the 1930s – flora, fauna, and the physical features of the mountains, streams, and lakes – brought me great delight. I roamed the valley with friends,

enthralled by the world of nature. My interest in rocks of all kinds
was greatly heightened. Even the topsoil of the region was unique
and fascinated me. Much of it was a clinkery, volcanic pumice or ash
erupted and carried by the wind in relatively recent geological times
from the nearby volcanic crater of Whistler Mountain in the Garibaldi
Park Reserve.

I began to develop the ability to read the rocks in the same way
that curious people pick up and scan a page detached from a newspaper or book. But reading such detached scraps of the story did not
satisfy me. I was eager to learn the entire story of the creation and
evolution of our remarkable planet in all its organic and inorganic
aspects.

Because of my employment at Pioneer mines during the summer
of 1935, I was able to register for my final year of undergraduate
study at the University of British Columbia. The experience gained
that summer also accelerated my conversion to geology. Thus my final
academic year for the Bachelor's degree was divided between chemistry and geology.

My Introduction to Radioactivity

Through the courses I took in chemistry, physics, geology, mineralogy, and paleontology, I gradually gained knowledge of the history
of the Earth's formation and of the composition and structure of its
many varieties of rock. The interrelationships between rock formations and environmental and climatic influences became clearer, as
did my understanding of the evolution of both animate and inanimate
organic life on our planet.

My new studies greatly increased my appreciation of the role of
time as a factor of change. I learned that an increasingly detailed
geological record of planet Earth has gradually become available over
a three-billion-year period, within a universe even older. Undoubtedly, time has been one of the most, if not *the* most, critical factor
in those "miracles of nature" evidenced by our Earth's surface, in
both physical and organic form. Since the normal personal experience
of time is less than one hundred years, few individuals develop a
comprehensive concept of time and its powers, although the anthro-
pologist's time-frame of "human occupation of this planet" is probably in the order of 300,000 years. Fortunately, the geologist and

paleontologist are able to develop the necessary awareness. The paleontologist, however, has knowledge of several great organic kingdoms, each of which has evolved, climaxed, and disappeared with little more than a fossil trace over many millions of years. I began to realize that humans are brash latecomers and that mankind's preoccupation with forceful means of controlling his environment will, in all likelihood, only accelerate his self-destruction and early demise.

From the beginning of human history individuals have sought to control the environment and to harness energy in its various forms in the hope that doing these things would improve their prospects for the future. With the discovery of radioactivity and the realization that matter is congealed energy, toward the end of the nineteenth century and the opening years of the twentieth century mankind entered a new era. During the first four decades of this century, there was widening interest in radioactivity and the power of the atom. Radioactivity, expressed as X-rays, was widely discussed in both scientific and popular circles. In my study of physics I learned of the work of the American, Danish, English, French, German, and Italian scientists who had made and/or were making important contributions to the advancement and application of knowledge concerning these matters.

Through reading about these scientific developments I became more aware of the advantages of X-ray diagnosis and the use of radium in the treatment of cancer. This began to focus my interest in the fascinating element, uranium, and the geological formations in which it could be found. I learned that the principal source of uranium, a material called *orangelb*, *pitchblende*, *iron pitch ore*, or *black tin ore* had been known to miners of silver, gold, tin, and other metals for several centuries. It had been recovered and used in the colour-glazing of pottery in Europe.

The precise nature of this pitchblende ore was unknown until 1780. In that year Martin Klaproth, a German chemist, analysed and described in some detail a material from Joachimsthal, in what is now Czechoslovakia. Klaproth proposed the name *uranium* for its principal element and accurately suggested it was associated with lead. Some fifty years later, a French chemist, Eugene-Melchiar Peligot, established that the substance Klaproth had analysed was actually uranium oxide.

In 1861, the Russian chemist, Dmitri Mendeleyev, in formulating his periodic table, concluded that uranium was the heaviest of the elements. Three and a half decades later a German physicist, Wilhelm Roentgen, discovered X-rays. In 1896, Henri Becquerel, a French scientist, discovered radioactivity and found it to be a characteristic of uranium in any form. Within a year or so, Marie Curie, a Polish-born French scientist, had isolated radium and coined the word *radioactivity*. About the same time, Ernest Rutherford, a New Zealander in England and a student of J. J. Thomson, who had discovered the electron (the basic unit of electrical current) was beginning his amazing scientific career. He discovered, through his study of uranium, alpha and beta particles. Rutherford developed the nuclear theory of atomic structure.

Early in the twentieth century Albert Einstein set out his scientific theory that all matter is congealed energy and that the mass/energy relationship can be expressed in the formula, $E = Mc^2$, which implies that a vast amount of energy is contained in a small amount of matter. Soon a variety of brilliant researchers, men and women in different countries, examined carefully and demonstrated, step by step, the correctness of Einstein's theory and his calculations, and set out in detail the implications of his ideas.

Studying such events in the history of science fostered my interest in uranium and helped me to realize that radioactivity, a characteristic property of uranium, could, like magnetism in iron ore, be identified through the use of a special instrument. Through discussions with Ken McKenzie, I learned that natural deposits of uranium minerals, such as pitchblende, should be detectable by some adaptation of the Geiger counter for detecting atomic particles, which had been first developed in Montreal and refined later in Germany. Ken agreed to make enquiries.

When he asked his friends in the physics department at UBC, Ken was told that Professor Shrum knew about Geiger counters and had an interest in the development of a device for studying radioactivity. Shrum had already been working on the development of a Geiger counter for use in prospecting, but the device which had been developed was barely portable, since it was rather unwieldy and weighed about seventy pounds. Professor Shrum brought his Geiger counter into a physics class one day. It was an innocent-looking electronic apparatus mounted on a first-aid stretcher and powered by lead storage batteries which contributed greatly to its weight. A prominent goose-neck horn, probably taken from an old phonograph machine soared above the assembly. This electronic device was designed to respond to radioactivity by emitting sound to indicate its presence.

Professor Shrum's interest in a portable Geiger counter had been stimulated by the report that uranium had been discovered on Quadra Island at the north end of the Strait of Georgia, between Vancouver Island and the mainland of British Columbia. Doctors who had bought property next to the supposed Quadra uranium site encouraged Shrum to develop his portable Geiger counter, providing him and his associates with funds to develop the equipment and to take it to Quadra. The machine failed to detect any uranium there. However, when a piece of rock known to be uranium was brought near the device and the power turned on, the presence of radioactivity in the uranium was clearly detected. The device worked, but it was unwieldy and Shrum knew that it required improvement. He encouraged Ken McKenzie to take steps toward that end.

Ken and I responded to the challenge and soon a division of responsibility was established. Ken would work on improving the device and I (as the one interested in prospecting and geology) would undertake a detailed search of the literature concerning all known deposits of uranium to learn the details of the geological environment in which uranium occurred. We knew that in order to search for uranium, it was essential to know where it was likely to occur. A prospecting instrument helpful in its detecting would be of immense value.

There were not at that time many known uranium occurrences in the world which had been identified and described. I noted that the majority of those deposits were found in association with nickel, cobalt, and arsenic in the form of nickel/cobalt arsenides. Reflecting on this, the mining districts of Sudbury and Cobalt in northern Ontario naturally came to mind as logical areas in which to search for uranium. Sudbury had been established in 1883 after men working on the Canadian Pacific Railway line had come upon copper/nickel deposits. Twenty years later, crews building the Temiskaming and Northern Ontario Railway – later the Ontario Northland – discovered silver on the shore of Long Lake. A stampede of prospectors followed and the town of Cobalt was incorporated in 1907.

This spare-time project, on which Ken and I worked during the 1935-36 academic year, was of continuing interest to me, but I also had other concerns. I had to complete my academic studies and continue with part-time work to finance them. However, another UBC student, Carman Ridland, improved on the design and miniaturization of the device. He demonstrated its field applicability over the Great Bear Lake pitchblende in the conduct of research for his doctoral degree from Princeton University. In the course of his work Ridland tracked not only the known pitchblende deposit at Great Bear Lake, but identified others there also.

Fifteen years were to pass before the search for uranium would lead me from my first musings as a student to Bancroft, Ontario, then to the north shore of Lake Superior, to Athabaska (Beaverlodge), and finally to the Blind River region of Ontario – less than one hundred miles from the Sudbury/Cobalt region. My early interest in a device that would be helpful in the location of uranium deposits was sustained. When, in 1948 I think, Electronic Associates of Canada, Limited, became the first Canadian company to mass-produce a portable Geiger counter, I was the first non-government person to buy one. I purchased the sixth instrument produced by that company; the first five were distributed to the Geological Survey of Canada and the National Research Council.

Although I have followed with interest and encouragement the continued refinement of radiation-detection instruments, I have never personally, in all my prospecting field work, used a more sophisticated instrument than this simple, hand-held, flashlight-battery-powered, total count Geiger unit. This unit is a small metal box about half the size of a cigar box. It contains a screened open edge through which any radioactive gas particles and/or rays can flow. An argon-filled Geiger tube assembly, a small amplifier, and an earphone complete the assembly. This device is designed to detect radioactivity from all sources and to convert that energy to a clicking sound.

Before Ken and I discussed the possibility of developing and using a portable Geiger counter in the mid 1930s, awareness of its value in economic terms had already become apparent through the dramatic financial success of the discoveries of rich uranium and silver ore at Great Bear Lake. While Ken was primarily interested in the scientific aspects of radioactivity I took a special interest in the subject as an exploratory tool.

Activity in Social Issues Continues

During my two undergraduate years at UBC I engaged in various extra-curricular activities both on and off campus. In the midst of the Great Depression, many of these activities reflected the continuing economic and social despair of the period.

With two or three fellow students of like mind I attended public evening lectures on social issues at the International Workers of the World (IWW) or "Wobbly" Hall on Cordova Street. Meetings of the Socialist Party of Canada, of the League for Social Reconstruction, and youth rallies held by the CCF all attracted my attention and often my participation in debate. I also attended various churches to hear the sermons of forward-thinking clergymen such as the Reverend Andrew Roddan. Little did I realize that one of the choir girls in Reverend Roddan's church would later become my wife.

On campus, usually with my friend Nick Rodin, I attended occasional meetings of the Student Parliamentary Forum, and sometimes engaged in the free-for-all debates on economic, social, and political issues. One participant in these debates was a bright-eyed younger student, Davie Fulton, who defended the traditional ideology of the conservative right while Rodin and I vigorously supported reform proposals of the left wing, to the delight – if not the enlightenment – of on-lookers and the occasional embarrassment of Professor Day, who presided.

There were frequent noon-hour gatherings in the university's assembly hall at which invited guest speakers addressed students on matters of public interest. I remember one particular speaker, Howard Scott, a charismatic figure in his mid forties, an engineer who had played a central role in the formation of the Technocracy Movement which burst upon the American scene in the early 1930s.

This movement had originated early in the decade as a study group in New York City, drawing, in substantial measure, on the ideas of the American economist, Thorstein Veblen. Veblen sought to demonstrate the sharp contrast between the rational attitudes adopted in industrial development and production and the irrationality of the finance of business enterprise and conduct of individuals who acquired money and power. He argued that control of economic affairs should be placed in the hands of those best able to solve economic problems. According to Scott and his associates, engineers and industrialists were best equipped to deal with such problems. Although Scott had come for only a noon-hour address, his overflow audience, including Nick and I, flooded him with questions until late in the afternoon, disrupting university lectures for the rest of the day.

I Meet My Mary

While academic work, extracurricular activities, and the constant struggle to earn enough money to support my mother and pay my expenses filled my time during my two undergraduate years, there was one seemingly everyday occurrence which was to completely change my life.

Not long after Ken McKenzie and I moved into Mrs. Moffatt's home in the autumn of 1933 we were invited for Sunday dinner at the home of the Reverend Mr. Osterhout, the minister of Mrs. Moffatt's church. The minister's daughter, Mildred Osterhout, a graduate of UBC, was, like her father, a sensitive helpful person, active in the improvement of individual and social life in Vancouver. Mildred had gone to considerable lengths to ensure that the dinner would be excellent. When the time came for dessert, she brought out some magnificent lemon pie. At the time, she did not know that lemon meringue pie was my favourite dessert. Neither Ken nor I had eaten lemon pie for weeks and the pie served in the Osterhout home was superlative! Realizing that it was freshly baked, I congratulated Mildred on the pie's magnificence, assuming that she had baked it.

"Oh, no. I didn't bake the pie," said Mildred. "Would you like to meet the cook?"

"I certainly would," I replied.

A lovely girl with wonderful blonde hair peeked around the kitchen door.

"Don't be shy, Mary," said Mildred. "Meet our guests."

Mary Torvinen was introduced, a girl with a warm, dimpled smile and delightful presence. She had prepared the entire dinner, including the delicious pie.

A day or so later, after overcoming my bashfulness, I asked Mildred Osterhout about Mary Torvinen. She had been born in Finland and had come with her family to "homestead" in Canada. They had settled in a small north-central Alberta community and become well-established farmers. Mary was a good student. After graduating from a teachers' training college she was fortunate to receive a teaching position in Wetaskiwin, an Alberta community not far from her family home. There, for seven years, she taught all eight elementary grades in a one-room school. As the economic depression wore on, however, employment opportunities even for teachers began to decrease.

As one of the older members of a rather large family, and one of the few with a paying job, Mary had assumed some of the responsibility for supporting her younger sisters and a step-brother. Frustrated by the lack of opportunity in Wetaskiwin, she had moved to Vancouver. To her dismay she found that her Alberta teaching credentials were not recognized in British Columbia. In her typically resourceful way she promptly found work with a candy manufacturer and completed a program of business college training during the evenings. While searching for secretarial employment she had been helping with the household cooking for the motherless Osterhout family to earn her board.

In Vancouver, Mary had become an active participant in the life of the remarkable downtown church where Andrew Roddan was the minister. Since she enjoyed music and had a lovely singing voice, she became a member of the choir. When I learned that Mary sang in the choir, the church became doubly attractive to me. I was already attracted to Roddan's church services, as he was a socially concerned preacher who could relate Christian teachings to contemporary events.

After several of the Reverend Roddan's sermons and time spent watching Mary sing, I gathered sufficient courage to go to the door where the choir came out. I was unable, however, to persuade Mary to ride with me on my bicycle across town to her home with the Osterhouts. However, on future Sunday evenings we pooled our money to travel together by streetcar and bus. That was the way in which my friendship with Mary began.

After Mary and I had come to know one another relatively well, I took her to meet my mother. Their first meeting turned out rather unhappily. Mary was upset, understandably, by an early, blunt, and acerbic lecture from my mother. Nothing, no, not even a lovely girl like Mary, was to stand in the way of the completion of my education. All thoughts of marriage had to wait until I had completed my education and was well established professionally. Mary was taken aback by my mother's unexpected and stern position.

My mother's determination that I proceed to the highest possible level of educational achievement, as unfettered as possible, was no doubt based on her own experience. She knew, from what had happened in her own life after she had eloped with my father, how the power of one's emotions can overcome one's better judgement. She was determined that my affection for Mary would not stand in the way of the realization of her aspirations for me. To my great sorrow, that initial lecture by my mother made a lasting impression. Regrettably, a total rapport between Mary and my mother never developed.

Mary and I agreed that we would not marry until I had received at least my bachelor's degree. I got that degree in the spring of 1936 and began full-time employment with Pioneer Gold Mines the following year. We decided that we had met my mother's minimal requirement, and, on December 21, 1937, about four years after we had first met, we were married in the home of the Reverend Mr. Osterhout and his daughter, just a couple of steps away from the dining table where, under the influence of her delicious lemon pie, I had first caught a glimpse of Mary.

When Mary and I were married I was employed by Pioneer Mines at Zeballos, at that time a gold-rush boom town on the west coast of Vancouver Island. I felt that Zeballos was too wild a place, given the rough accommodation available and the general character of its social life, for me to take Mary there immediately. Thus, she remained in Vancouver while I returned to Zeballos to complete the construction of a home for us.

About four months later Mary arrived in Zeballos. During those months I had experienced a number of hair-raising encounters. There were more throughout our period there together. There never was a dull moment in Zeballos!

V

Adventures on Canada's Pacific Rim

I graduated from UBC in the spring of 1936, and spent that summer working for the Geological Survey of Canada, an experience that has served me well ever since.

The Geological Survey of Canada was established in 1842 to assist in the gathering and sharing of knowledge concerning the mineral resources of Canada and in the ongoing development of the mineral industry in Canada. Morris Zaslow's 1975 book, *Reading the Rocks*, properly directs attention to the Survey's impressive achievement and the realization of its original objectives. Although not widely known among Canadians, the Geological Survey is one of the most influential – and oldest – of Canada's scientific societies. Many of Canada's unsung heroes made significant contributions to the work of the Survey, opening up Canada, in the geographical and geological sense, not only to Canadians but to the world. The earliest officers of the Survey were hardy, venturesome, multi-talented explorers or geographers. Early Canadian geologists were, in many cases, also anthropologists, botanists, and zoologists. They observed and reported on all natural features of the resources of Canada. Their breadth of interest and documented observations were, and remain, the primary foundations of scientific knowledge concerning our vast country.

Members of the Geological Survey of Canada had completed a wide variety of surveys of awesome dimensions on foot and by canoe during the ninety-four years before I joined it. As a student of geology I had learned of the work of the Survey from distinguished geologists such as Professor H. C. Gunning at UBC, who himself had made important contributions to its work. Comprehensive knowledge of mineralization in Canada had been developed by the Survey long before such mineralization could be exploited. That knowledge greatly facilitated the work of those engaged in mineral exploration and in mineral development. I became acutely aware of this in 1950 when I depended upon one of the Survey's maps, then thirty years old, in regard to a major staking program.

While employed by the Survey in 1936 I was involved in the

geological re-mapping of the Greenwood-Grand Forks area of south-central British Columbia. To that time only sketchy geological information had been recorded on that area, although several important copper deposits had been discovered and exploited on a large scale prior to the First World War. It was hoped that more detailed mapping would lead to the discovery of other deposits.

The chief of the Survey party to which I was assigned was Duncan McNaughton, a man who had recently won the Olympic gold medal in the high jump. McNaughton was an amiable, hard-driving individual who had had previous experience with the Survey in northern British Columbia. The area of south-central British Columbia in which we worked was near the American border. The climate there is temperate and semi-arid. The terrain is a mixture of rugged rocky hills covered completely by brush that rose for several hundreds of feet above the bottoms of the river valleys where agriculture was carried on.

Working under McNaughton's direction, I learned a variety of practical lessons which were highly significant in my development as a geologist. In my efforts to become an effective geologist, I was constantly seeking to find, map, and describe mineral occurrences accurately, tending to pay little attention to non-mineralized formations. That was heresy with the Geological Survey; all rock formations were to be considered with equal care. From that time onwards I knew that if I really wished to be a successful geologist I must not merely be a prospector. I must gain thorough knowledge of the geology of whatever area in which I worked.

Another practical benefit which resulted from my summer's work with the Geological Survey was my acquaintanceship with Bert Locke, a remarkably good camp cook. Later Locke served as my cook in many of the prospecting camps which I managed over the next decade in various places in British Columbia. The more experience I gained in the mining industry, the deeper my appreciation grew of the value of an excellent cook in a mining camp. Mining camps are almost as dependent on good food as they are on good ore!

In the hills of the Greenwood-Grand Forks area, where we were working that summer, there were rattlesnakes and in the lowlands there were wood ticks. Fortunately none of the Survey group were snake-bitten, but the ticks caused problems. Tiny creatures which burrow into the skin to feed on human blood, wood ticks were a considerable nuisance. My colleagues and I removed the ticks from one another's bodies as we showered at the end of each day. If the ticks were not removed alive, their blood-bloated bodies could cause blood poisoning, which in some cases is known to be fatal.

The six of us in McNaughton's party worked in pairs, examining and recording the identity of rock outcrops as we traversed sections of the Greenwood-Grand Forks area on a carefully planned basis. One man in each of the pairs would walk ahead pulling the end of a measuring chain while the second man, standing with the other end of the chain, secured a compass bearing of the man in front. All of the data gained through the examination, identification, and measurement of rock outcrops was carefully recorded. Each evening the data was plotted on a master map of the specific area in which the project was being carried out.

A Brush with Death

One of the responsibilities of a Survey party is to gain information on mining properties which have previously been worked. The examination of such abandoned sites can, as I learned to my horror, involve major hazards.

I had gone underground with McNaughton in an old silver mine abandoned some years earlier. It was necessary for McNaughton, as chief of our party, to ensure that reports on existing mineral properties in the area we were studying were complete. Earlier reports concerning this property indicated that rich ore still remained in the mine, so we had been told to determine the accuracy of these reports. This particular property was owned by a family known as "The Crazy Maddens," who had recently re-opened a portion of it without modern equipment. McNaughton and I had to take extreme precautions as we proceeded down the mine shaft since the ladders installed by the Maddens some years before had become badly rotted.

We had notebooks and pencils to record the details of the rocks and minerals we observed on the walls and roofs. I walked ahead, one end of a steel measuring tape attached to my hand through a loose ring on one of my fingers. When I came across something which I thought should be noted, I called back to McNaughton. He read the distance on his tape and made an entry in his notebook.

We had proceeded cautiously down the old shaft and were about two hundred feet below the surface entry. I called back that I had reached a horizontal corridor or *drift*, with a footing of loose, broken rock. The mineralized vein had been blasted out and removed from below. We were standing on broken waste rock on the edge of a steep slope which had been the original wall of the extracted vein. Much of the material which had filled the large vein crevice had been removed for recovery of its silver content.

In the blackness, illuminated only by the tiny flame of my lamp, I gradually became aware that the narrow ledge, or *stope*, on which I was walking was not entirely solid. Later I learned that the fragmented material on which I had walked was broken rock which had failed to slide down with the rest of the material into the bottom where it would have been drawn out.

Groping my way across this material with the aid of my lamp I tapped and probed carefully with my pick to be sure of the direction in which I should go while I dragged my end of the steel measuring tape. McNaughton was following cautiously. We called back and forth to one another to express caution or reassurance in the pitch-darkness. Finally I shouted that I had come to the end of the open stope and was on firm footing.

Suddenly, there was a great sweep of wind. The steel tape attached to my hand by the loose ring was torn away. I realized immediately that the path of loose rock I had just crossed over had been swept into the cavern below. Where was I? What had happened to McNaughton? Had he been swept down into the cavern below? I shouted, but the only answer was the echo of my own voice. I became alarmed, not only for McNaughton, but for myself. Had that rocky path been the only route by which I could return safely to the surface? Now that it had disappeared how was I to get out? In shock, I sat down to decide what I could do.

I shouted again, and heard nothing but resounding echoes of my own voice. I sat and waited, trying to quench my fears. Then, in the distance, I heard faint shouts. Was that the word *raise* (an opening to the next level, either vertical or at an incline)? It was. I knew that McNaughton was alive somewhere on the other side of the chasm.

I re-lit my carbide lamp by adding fresh carbide, wetting it with spit and igniting the gas with the flint. Then, cautiously, I moved ahead. Soon I found the raise, the shaft going upward. The air in the raise was fresher, and I knew that it must lead to the open air. The wooden ladders were intact but badly rotted, so I cautiously made my way upward, slowly, assisted by my prospector's pick, hooking it into the crevices of the rock. It seemed anxious hours before I reached the next level, where McNaughton was waiting for me.

When the ring had been torn from my fingers, McNaughton had almost lost his balance because of the abrupt pull on the chain caused by the volume of sliding rock striking it. Fortunately, however, he had managed to make his way back to the entry shaft.

We lost no time in climbing out of that mine. Back at the safety of our base camp, McNaughton opened a large bottle of whisky and set it and two glasses between us on a folding card table. "Let's settle our nerves!" he said.

Never having developed a taste for Scotch or for firewater of any type, I don't think I settled my nerves to the extent he intended, but I fully approved of his concern. My nerves, though not shot, were badly frayed. I silently offered thanks for my survival.

Hand-Mining with Dutchy

After my work with the Geological Survey finished, I decided to remain in the Greenwood area of the Boundary District for the winter. With a practical miner named Dutchy Streider, I ventured into small-scale hand-mining as a partner and as a lessee of abandoned, formerly productive, smaller silver and gold mines.

Dutchy was a short, muscular, somewhat weather-beaten individual, twelve or fifteen years older than me. His years of practical experience in the day-to-day work of mining had made him an expert in both *single-jacking* (a miner working alone holds a steel drill rod in one hand and drives it into the rock with an eight-pound hammer held in his other hand) and in *double-jacking* (one man holds a steel drill rod with both hands while squatting or kneeling, and the other, standing upright, swings a ten- or twelve-pound sledge-hammer). Working with Dutchy made me realize how strenuous was the labour in which miners had engaged for centuries before the advent of modern mining equipment.

During my time with the Geological Survey I had identified a number of properties on which I judged some ore remained. Dutchy and I leased one of these, a property called The Bay, a gold prospect with a hundred-foot-deep inclined shaft put down by those who had developed the property earlier. They had followed the gold-bearing vein down but had done practically no work on the sides of the shaft.

We decided to do this lateral work since we could see gold in the vein matter.

The lease which Dutchy and I arranged on The Bay granted us the right, at our own expense, to mine the sides of the shaft only but not to deepen it. We were required under the lease to mine and ship not less than thirty tons of gold ore per month to a custom smelter at Trail, B.C. Twenty per cent of the sum paid to us by the smelter was to be paid to those who granted us the lease. Thanks to an increase in the price of gold, Dutchy and I were able to operate for some months at a modest profit, while sharing many memorable experiences.

A small but rich shoot of gold ore which Dutchy and I had developed and were mining underground, attracted the interest of Dr. A. H. Lang, an officer of the Geological Survey. He visited The Bay and expressed an interest in examining the deposit. Invited to "get into the bucket," however, he balked. He looked down at the forty-gallon oil drum which served as our elevator cab, and then at the rusty cable from which it hung, he surveyed with his eye the rebuilt automobile engine we used for hoisting, and he peered down to the one small, flickering light at the bottom of the 120-foot shaft. He looked further down to the twenty-foot-deep sump, full of water. Then he turned to me and said emphatically, "You want me to go down in that bucket? Never!"

I believe Dr. Lang took a few specimens of ore from our stockpile. He may also have photographed our "haywire" plant, peed beside a nearby shrub, waved us goodbye, and left in a hurry. But he never forgot his visit to The Bay! During the ensuing forty years of our friendship, Dr. Lang regularly reminded me of the invitation I had extended to him and how he had declined. He viewed it as a miracle that Dutchy and I had survived probably over two hundred trips in that "bucket."

Our discovery of high-grade ore at The Bay aroused the interest of the smelting company in Trail, and they sent a senior engineer named Davis to examine the mine.

Like Lang, Davis refused to trust our "hoisting" system. Tediously, he descended into the mine by wooden ladders, accompanied by me as his guide and helper. When we reached the ore section, he peered at the mineralization and exclaimed, "What attractive steel galena!" Galena is a lead mineral. I was too embarrassed to correct him. It was not galena that had provoked his remark but telluride minerals, which accounted for the very rich gold and silver content of the ore.

In chipping his general samples, Davis seemed to delight in throwing disproportionately large amounts of what he mistakenly thought was "steel galena" into the empty container I was carrying for him. I became alarmed, realizing that his samples would assay several ounces of gold per ton, as opposed to the actual average of about one ounce per ton. If he took such rich ore back with him, the logical conclusion of his superiors would be that his samples had been salted, or tampered with, probably by me! There was only one course to follow, in my view, if I was to protect Davis from himself. I would have to discreetly "de-salt" his samples. To do this, I simply added pieces of barren rock to the material he had selected. This was the only occasion in my entire career when I have ever tampered with another person's samples. The irony of this "reverse-twist" greatly amused Davis when I confessed it to him several years afterwards.

The Zeballos Gold Rush

After a strenuous seven or eight months as a small-mine lessee with Dutchy, during which I developed better arm muscles from many hours of "single-jacking," I returned to Vancouver where, in early 1937, I was fortunate to gain permanent employment as a prospector/ geologist with Pioneer Gold Mines. My first assignment was to go with several others to the remote gold-rush boom-town of Zeballos, at the head of an inlet of the Pacific Ocean on the west coast of Vancouver Island, sixty or seventy miles, as the crow flies, due west of Campbell River.

The Zeballos delta was almost always gloomy since it was dominated on both sides by steep, forested mountains, rising to about three thousand feet above sea level. The sky over the delta consisted usually of low rain clouds. Zeballos, a drab, wet place with mud everywhere, is in the British Columbia rain forest where the rainfall can reach 180 inches a year. Prior to 1936 there had been only one log cabin on the mud delta of the Zeballos River. That cabin had been shared by three men – Bird, Bloom, and Smith. All three lived off the land, earning a meagre cash income as trappers.

The first important discovery of gold in the Zeballos region was made by a mystical character named Ilstad who lived in Quatsino, a community on the west coast of Vancouver Island, fifty or so miles northwest of Zeballos. He was a tall, slim, white-haired wiry man who seemed withdrawn and nervous. Looking at him, one might imagine that he was a clerk or office employee rather than the agile bushman that he was. While Ilstad's methods of prospecting were unorthodox, it was his discovery which sparked the Zeballos gold rush. I met him later and asked him how he had made his discovery. He told me that he had "done it all with trigonometry." With ruler and pencil he had linked the highest mountain peaks selected from topographical maps of Vancouver Island into triangles. Then he would investigate the valley centres of his triangles by panning the streams for gold. Thus he had located the outcropping which later became The Privateer, the first and most important of the three or four Zeballos mines.

I do not know whether Ilstad had employed other triangles prior to his work in the Zeballos area. In any event, I was convinced that his theory for the location of mineral deposits was highly dubious. By the time I met Ilstad I had learned that many prospectors had theories, many as fantastic as his. All such theories served one useful purpose, however – they motivated prospectors to go into the field, both to make a discovery and to prove their theory.

Later I became acquainted with Bird and Smith and asked them if they knew of Ilstad's "theory." Their answer was blunt. "The old bugger may be crazy. But he found the mine." Then they told me their side of the story.

Bird, Bloom, and Smith occasionally panned gold as they trapped along the Zeballos River. They had found notable placer gold but the patches were small and they could see no nearby outcroppings. Then one day Ilstad appeared at the mouth of the river in his boat. After a brief conversation with Bird, Bloom, and Smith about nearby trails, he headed along the river, axe in hand and pack on his back. Later that same day he returned, even more uncommunicative than he had been earlier. Declining to have dinner with them, he rowed out to his motor boat, spent the night anchored offshore, and departed early the next morning.

Bird, Bloom, and Smith sensed something unusual had happened. After Ilstad left, Bird went up the river. He came to a point where soil on the opposite bank had recently been disturbed. Crossing over on a wind-fallen tree, he scrambled to the place where strips of moss had recently been torn from the rock. A rusty one-foot-wide quartz vein was exposed. With his axe Bird knocked off a piece of the vein and examined it. While he could see no visible gold, he nonetheless put the piece of rock in his jacket pocket. Then he saw, a short way up the hill, two freshly cut claim posts. He examined them and found they were Ilstad's.

"And what happened then?" I asked Bird.

"I headed back, worried," said Bird. "I had a hunch we'd lucked out."

After supper that night, Bird dropped his piece of rusty quartz into the coals of the fire. Next morning Smith was up first. He ground and panned the roasted quartz. There was a fine "tail" of gold in the pan.

"And that," added Bird, "was why Bloom shot himself. He just couldn't take it. Ilstad, that crazy old bugger, had struck it rich. We had nothing. Bloom became depressed and in a week ended it all by blowing himself to hell."

A gold prospect which later became a rich gold mine had been just up the river from the cabin Bird, Bloom, and Smith shared. Ilstad had staked a gold mine from under their feet. To make matters worse, Bloom had argued that "tie-on" claims were not worth the trouble, although after Bloom's death, Bird and Smith realized a few thousand dollars from the rush.

When I arrived at Zeballos with my two Pioneer colleagues, Ed Lovitt and Eric Parr, we found the log cabin which Bird, Smith, and the departed Bloom had shared. In mining communities the word *camp* implies order and structures. Neither of these were present in Zeballos save for this one log cabin and the tents which had begun to appear on the "beach," as the relatively dry river delta was known.

Although we were among the early arrivals at Zeballos, we did not arrive sufficiently early to acquire any of the more important claims for Pioneer. Thus Lovitt and Parr soon left, and I remained alone. My job as a scout-prospector for Pioneer Gold Mines was to discover on my own, if I could, mineral prospects which Pioneer might develop. I was also to encourage prospectors to show me their discoveries, and to option them for Pioneer if they showed promise. They did occasionally, and I probably examined two or three new "discoveries" each week. These were usually within a walking radius of about five miles. Occasionally I would travel farther if part of the trip could be made by boat to some coastline point from which we could walk to the prospect. Between visits to such discoveries I was out prospecting on my own with my backpack. If I made a discovery while on my own, I was entitled to an interest in it in addition to my regular basic salary.

After it was decided that I should remain in the area, Pioneer built one of the first wooden buildings on the beach where the community of Zeballos later developed. Our wooden building consisted of one large room which served as office, medical centre, warehouse, and bunk space for six. While the Pioneer building might be regarded as merely a shack when compared with buildings in the usual Canadian communities, in the tent community of Zeballos it was one of the earliest and primary focal points. The Pioneer building was noteworthy in that it featured the first enclosed privy in Zeballos! In addition, I believe we were the first to bring a Coleman lamp and radio transmitter to the beach.

Our First Home

Although it wasn't easy in the almost constant rain of Zeballos, I soon set about building a home to bring my new wife to. For $59 I secured a shipment of planed green lumber from a sawmill about ten miles down the coast and arranged for it to be brought to Zeballos by a fish trawler. This green lumber was all freshly cut and, naturally, wet from moisture and sap. Normally lumber is stacked outdoors to dry, or dried in a kiln, before it is used. Green lumber has a tendency to shrink, warp, or split. But I was anxious to complete a home for Mary as speedily as possible and green lumber was the only lumber I could secure quickly, so I decided to go ahead and use it. I had the two-by-fours, shiplap, and shingles sent to the site I had chosen.

Fortunately I was able to secure the help of Fred Luddit, an excellent but unemployed camp cook who was also a good carpenter. Fred and I, with the assistance of a couple of labourers, built the house in two or three weeks. It contained a kitchen, a living-dining area, a bedroom, and a bathroom equipped with a chemical toilet. After we had the structure closed in, it took a month of heating from the inside to sweat the water out of the lumber. The entrance was at the back, a door which opened onto a porch which visitors reached by walking up five steps. For some reason, Fred Luddit did not build these steps. I took on the task myself, assuming that my abilities as an amateur carpenter would be equal to the task. I was mistaken.

Friends who used the steps said that I had not measured with sufficient accuracy. The rise from one step to the next was not uniform. As well, some steps sloped out while others sloped in. These technical inadequacies were accentuated by the constant rain, and the greenness of the lumber made each of the steps quite slippery. Even though I was familiar with them I usually tumbled every third or fourth time I used them. They were so bad that our house was named "The Bear Trap." My colleagues were convinced that I had intentionally made the steps hazardous to ensure that wife Mary would not be bothered when I was away.

Since Zeballos was on the edge of the ocean, rain was the primary source of fresh water. It was collected in large galvanized tubs, in our case on the back porch. Usually a tub would be completely filled to overflowing each morning. On the very rare occasions when we had a rainless day in Zeballos, we would walk two or three hundred yards down the dirt road and fill our pails with water from a little stream which flowed down the mountain.

In 1938 as soon as I had the little house ready I set off for Vancouver to bring Mary to Zeballos. We would travel to Zeballos by ship – the *Princess Maquinna*. This two-hundred-mile journey along the magnificent west coast of Vancouver Island was to be our honeymoon voyage.

The trip was leisurely and interesting with frequent stops at coastal communities where the main activities were fishing and/or forestry. The accommodation on the ship was splendid and the food magnificent. The passengers were an interesting mixture of individuals who worked in manual trades along the coast of Vancouver Island, a few professionals (government officials, doctors, and clergymen as well as managers of fish canneries or small sawmills, or directors of the companies which owned them), and bankers coming to visit businesses to which they had made loans or to investigate development opportunities.

Among the most popular passengers were Jack and Gordon Gibson, frequent travellers on the *Princess Maquinna*, and the sons of an early West Coast "timber baron" who held huge timber limits and cutting rights in the Gold River basin not far north of the Zeballos delta. When the Gibson boys, who greatly enjoyed throwing a party, learned that there was a honeymoon couple on the vessel, they immediately commenced celebrations. They already knew me as a "hustling prospector" and were delighted to learn that I had taken a bride. What better cause for a celebration! They neglected to take into consideration, however, one crucial fact. The Pacific Ocean had a roll.

Like any good prospector I am used to walking on rough, but always firm ground. I am not at home on the rolling sea. As the waves of the Pacific began to mount, I quickly left the dining room and went directly to our cabin where I stretched out flat on my bunk. In common with most of the other passengers I ceased to have any interest in the magnificent food available in the dining room. Mary and the Gibson boys, however, were not in the slightest troubled by the increasingly rough seas. Practically alone in the dining room with steward and musicians, they danced the evening away while I languished on the bunk in our stateroom. Some honeymoon voyage! Soon, however, my condition improved and I began to enjoy myself.

About mid-morning on the second or third day of our voyage, we stopped at Tofino, a fishing and fishboat-building community down the coast some distance south of Zeballos, whose citizens were primarily Japanese Canadians. As Mary and I leaned on the railing of the vessel watching cargo being loaded and unloaded, I saw on the wharf about a dozen small, heavily filled jute sacks of the type normally used for shipping mineral ore or concentrate. I left Mary, went ashore to examine the sacks, and found they contained ore which appeared to resemble the type of high-grade gold ore we were trying so hard to find in Zeballos. When I asked the ship's officer supervising the handling of the cargo for details I learned that the ore was being shipped to a smelter in Tacoma, Washington, by a young prospector who, at that moment, was walking along the road away from the wharf. He was pointed out to me and I ran after him.

When I was close enough I called out to stop the man. I introduced myself. In a strong Irish brogue he told me his name was Patrick McCrory. His shipment of ore was, he explained, from a discovery he had made some two months earlier "up the Bedwell River." I asked what the gold content of the ore was. He drew from his pocket a soiled copy of a certificate with about three assays on it, ranging between 4.5 and 7.0 ounces of gold per ton. The sample material, he said, had all been taken from a single trench with a vein about one foot wide.

McCrory told me that he had worked briefly at The Privateer mine in Zeballos where he had learned what he knew about prospecting. Then he had set out to find a mine of his own. The material from the Bedwell River vein was being shipped to secure some money so that McCrory could continue trenching his first discovery, which he had called The Musketeer. We agreed that I should go to his prospect with him immediately, if my wife did not object to continuing her honeymoon voyage alone.

To support me in making this most unusual request, I asked McCrory to return to the vessel with me. After introducing him to Mary I asked her if she would feel comfortable in continuing the voyage alone while I went into the bush to examine McCrory's prospect. I would then go north by aircraft and be on hand to meet her in Zeballos when she arrived on the *Princess Maquinna*. She agreed.

Mary arrived somewhat apprehensively in Zeballos. Since no wharf facilities yet existed, ships had to anchor offshore. Passengers and cargo were taken by barge from the vessel to the edge of the mud flats where the real struggle began. When the tide was in, the flats, which consisted of two to six inches of sticky mud and boulders, were about one hundred yards wide. When the tide was out, the flats widened to three hundred yards or more. The unloading of larger vessels, such as the *Princess Maquinna*, was efficiently co-ordinated by Captain Nicholson, the B.C. government agent-for-all-problems based in Zeballos.

The periodic arrival of the *Princess Maquinna* was a major event. Her shrill steam whistle was blown with frontier abandonment as she approached, its echoing sound prompting individuals to scurry from their tents and shacks in the surrounding hills and head for the beach. Even the half dozen or so males usually to be found having a casual smoke and gossip, among other bodily functions, at the communal outhouse rail beside Captain Nicholson's shack would rise, hitch up their trousers ("tin pants" of rubber layers and canvas, for the rain forest) and join the gathering throng of ship-greeters waiting at the beach. Most of those greeting newcomers had empty packboards slung over one shoulder for the load of supplies they would back-pack to their camps.

On such a day I waited nervously among the throng for the arrival of my bride. To my dismay, the tide was out. I knew that those three hundred yards of mud flats would create problems, but I had come prepared. As soon as the barge from the *Princess Maquinna* reached the flats, I joined the rush. I was wearing hip waders. I picked up Mary in my arms and carried her unfalteringly back to the dry land. A rousing cheer went up from those watching, prompted, no doubt, as much by Mary's beauty as by my display of strength and gallantry.

Mary's first view of our new home did nothing, I feel certain, to dispel her anxiety. There it stood, a rectangular wooden box, entirely unpainted, with its rail-less balcony at the front and those hazardous, amateurly crafted steps at the rear! Although she may well have wondered what on earth she had come to, she gave no indication of concern of any type.

Gifted with an outstanding ability to adjust to any and all circumstances, Mary constantly sought to improve whatever conditions surrounded her. This was her way throughout her life. During that summer of 1938, wooden shacks were being built day and night on the beach, and by the autumn Zeballos had a population of about five hundred (double that on weekends when the men came to town from the outlying camps). Mary soon noted a dozen or so school-aged children in the mushrooming shacktown. No school had yet been organized or built. Within a few weeks Mary had an effective school system organized and in operation!

All the children in Zeballos came to Mary's "school." If they had books, scribblers, pencils, and pens, that was fine. If they didn't, Mary provided them with help from others. She taught the children herself and her days were filled with noisy activity.

As a scout for Pioneer Mines I came and went constantly. Often I had to leave at dawn on two- or three-day trips. During my absences, Mary, of course, was busily occupied with her school, while several prominent citizens and new-found friends watched out for her. One of these was the chief of police, a man who had headed the police force of a major mainland community. Sadly, however, his alcoholism had led to his dismissal there. He and two or three other men, including Captain Nicholson, a leading figure in Zeballos, served as a voluntary committee helping to ensure that Mary's school had all the supplies it needed. They handled her mail and happily performed countless chores for her.

Soon Mary's school included three or four grades. In wet weather, the classes were held in a quiet corner of the separate Pioneer warehouse, but on dryer days, classes were conducted on the large front balcony of our home, which soon became not only "The Bear Trap," but also "Mary's Schoolhouse."

A year later, when formal classes were set up in some rooms in a newly built hotel and three professional teachers arrived, there was a lively "kids' rebellion" in Zeballos. The pupils unanimously declared that they preferred "Mary's school!"

Mary's was a delightful, different school. Almost always she had an interested audience of fascinated and amused prospectors surrounding her and her pupils while she taught. Their voluntary participation in her classes was not uncommon. Among such participants was "Haywire Alex," who became popular with all the pupils and was cautiously accepted by Mary. He was a prospector of ripened vintage and a stifled poet. With Mary's permission, he occasionally recited his latest poems with vigour, while a blend of beer and tobacco juice trickled from the corner of his mouth.

Even years later, when we lived at the much larger and well-developed Pioneer village in the Bridge River Valley, Mary's teaching abilities, particularly in art and handicrafts, were recognized and enlisted. She also became one of the three regular Sunday School teachers. Her Sunday School classes soon became so popular that they were crowded with practically every four- to eight-year-old in the camp. During one class Mary led a discussion on the 23rd Psalm. She asked some of her students to memorize the short passage and to recite it at the following class. Several children recited quite well, then it was Sally's turn. Sally was a lively, bright eight-year-old extrovert, the natural leader in the class, and popular with everyone despite her often untidy appearance caused by the neglect of her alcoholic parents. Sally sprang to her feet with her usual bounce and looked defiantly around her. With the hint of tears in her eyes she said, "Mrs. Mary, I'd have memorized every single word in that Psalm if only there was a God-damned Bible in our home."

In the several reasonably settled frontier camps where Mary, and later our daughter Marion, could join me – Zeballos, Tofino, Pioneer, and Fort St. James in British Columbia, and Goldfields in the Beaverlodge area of northern Saskatchewan – Mary quickly found herself a socially useful role and soon was universally admired. Only once can I remember her asking pensively, "Characters, characters everywhere, will we ever again live with ordinary people?" Even after we had returned to the routine of city life, Mary did not change. She continued to serve others, however and wherever she could.

The Girls of "Hollywood"

Not all the characters in and around Zeballos were men, nor were men the only ones anxious to find a stake through an ancient profession. The girls in "Hollywood," on the edge of Zeballos, were equally determined.

In the very early days of the Zeballos camp, when the beach was still a collection of tents and before Mary had arrived to join me there, I was approached, confidentially, by Dr. Kelly who had recently arrived in the community. He asked to help him solve a problem.

Kelly received a retainer from some provincial medical agency to keep a close check on venereal disease in Zeballos, particularly among the girls at Hollywood, the villa of the local "ladies of the night." Its name had been chosen by one of its more artistic residents, who had hand-lettered *Hollywood* in rainbow colours on a board and nailed it to a tree beside the trail leading to the villa. But Dr. Kelly wished to provide these women with health care more comprehensive than simple disease treatment. He had agreed with them that they should have an automatic electric record player and he had come to me because I was known to have a reasonably well-organized catalogue purchasing and transport system. I protested that my purchase of mining tools, blasting powder, wheelbarrows, and camp grub could not include the purchase of a record player. My protests were in vain.

Our compromise was that I would order the outfit through Pioneer's purchasing system, but that I would advise the company that it was being purchased for Dr. Kelly personally. He would pay for it.

In due course, the equipment arrived and was delivered to Hollywood. Two of my men in town from the bush announced that they were going to the "opening music party" the next night, and from them I heard all about the evening's events. Nothing about the automatic record player had worked properly. The Hollywood girls had been terribly disappointed when it broke down and failed to provide the mood music they had anticipated. At the party, Kelly had repudiated all responsibility and told everyone in Hollywood to go to hell before storming out of the place.

Fortunately, neither Pioneer Mines nor myself were mentioned in the course of the "music party squabble," however, I was worried and vulnerable. Could I be seen in some way to have been trying to promote prostitution in Zeballos? I told Kelly to come to my office – he had gotten me into this mess and we had to find a way out. We decided to split the cost and give the record player to Hollywood as a toy.

Three months later, when Mary had arrived and met Kelly, I told her the story. She was not amused. Raising her index finger in the manner of the grade-school teacher she had been, she said, "I hope that teaches you a lesson!"

The heavy and almost constant rain over Zeballos and the natural constriction of the flow of water through the gorge-like Zeballos River sometimes had dramatic consequences. Occasionally when the rain was heavy and prolonged, the single road beside the Zeballos River was covered with water to depths of several feet or more. Sometimes the flooding rose to the level of the cross-arms on the short telephone poles. This created a dangerous problem for Hollywood, since it was situated on the low-elevation river flats.

During such floods, the Hollywood girls were forced into the attic of their wooden building. There they waited and waited, until it occurred to somebody to rescue them by removing them, usually feet first, through the attic windows at the end of the house, with no concern whatever for their dignity.

Such problems stimulated Hollywood's madame to attempt a better solution. She arranged for two nearby four-foot-diameter cedar trees to be felled. The house was jacked up and these logs were placed beneath it so that, it was hoped, the villa would become a houseboat during a flood. The madame's enthusiastic volunteer squad decided, however, that this new arrangement would not be sufficient. There was a risk that the houseboat might rise so high that it would float off its foundation and down the river, perhaps even as far as the next cove where the girls might float into the embrace of the uncouth group of fish-cannery employees who lived there.

To guard against this terrifying risk the volunteers secured some heavy log-boom chains and attached them to one end of the platform and to the two huge cedar stumps nearby.

The floods soon reappeared and the flood waters quickly rose. To the surprise and shock of two voluntary watchmen, only one end of the building rose with the water level. The other end rose to the short length of the chains and hung firmly, under ten or twelve feet of water. Hollywood assumed a forty-five-degree angle with all the contents and the residents sliding around as gravity took over. Drastic rescue measures were again required.

But the fiascos involving Hollywood were not the only amusing and sometimes disturbing events in my life in Zeballos before Mary arrived. One which I vividly recall was a truly bloody affair.

Black Angus and Blood Everywhere

One evening at dusk during the usual downpour, there was a loud banging on the door of the Pioneer office. At the door was Haywire Alex, the alcoholic poet-prospector.

"What's up, Alex?" I asked.

"Black Angus," he replied. "Cut himself with an axe. Blood everywhere!"

"Bring him in," I said.

Black Angus was an almost entirely silent man, who, when he spoke, did so in a nervous staccato voice. He was called Black Angus because of his heavy black beard and bushy eyebrows. Haywire Alex followed Black Angus into the shack. Haywire peeled off his heavy, muddy slicker and kicked off his rubbers before helping Angus gingerly to remove the left sleeve of his slicker. Only then did I see Angus's wound. His hand, held upright, was covered with blood streaming from his index finger. My stomach churned as I looked at the wound.

Angus had been splitting kindling in the rain. The axe had slipped and cut off half of his index finger on his left hand near the centre knuckle. Haywire Alex had heard Angus make a strange sound and rushed to him. Seeing the blood spurt from Angus's finger, he had wrapped it with the woollen tam that Alex had had on his head. Now, in the Pioneer shack, the blood-soaked tam was on the floor and I was holding Angus's hand upright.

"Get the first-aid kit!" I shouted to one of my men who had been dozing on a bunk. "And bring a roll of bum-wipe! Someone find Dr. Kelly!" We applied a tourniquet to Black Angus's forearm and wrapped his entire left hand in fresh toilet tissue to "clot" the blood flow.

"I need some booze," was Angus's first comment. We sat him down and poured him a generous portion of rum.

"I need a drink too," said Haywire. I frowned, but one of the other Pioneer men said, "Haywire should get one too," and poured him a drink.

At this point the man I had sent for the doctor returned. "Kelly's not in town, not in his shack, and not at Hollywood. The girls say he's been at the sawmill down the inlet all day but will be back soon. They're cooking his dinner."

So we waited for Dr. Kelly and sipped our rum with hot water. Black Angus's hand, wrapped in blood-soaked tissue, looked like a squashed pomegranate. But the bleeding gradually stopped, and we loosened the tourniquet.

Kelly soon arrived, hatless, dishevelled, and drenched. He had rushed directly to our shack over the mud flats from the sawmill launch on which he had returned to Zeballos. Expertly, he removed the toilet paper from the injured hand.

"Not bad," he said. "I think I can handle it okay." Rather sheepishly he added, "I left my kit at the sawmill, but let's get cracking." Looking at me, he said, very professionally, "Need boiling water, sterilize a couple of new razor blades, a hacksaw blade, a big sewing needle, a pair of scissors, a sharp pocket knife. Get me some strong button thread, any colour, clean gauze or cotton. Got iodine or boracic acid?

"Move that card table under the Coleman. Cover it with a towel, a clean one. Just keep pouring the booze to Black Angus – wait, I'll have a belt myself. Let's go."

Half an hour later the surgery was complete. The bone and the flesh of the finger were trimmed back neatly to the knuckle, with a skin flap sewn over. The rum bottle had been emptied and we'd had to send to the bootleggers for a second. Black Angus, at Kelly's insistence, had to remain with us. He had been lifted to an upper bunk in an aura of rum, and was snoring loudly. The medical team – Kelly, my two companions, and I – sprawled comfortably on other bunks in relaxation, but not for long.

Another loud knock on the door. I rose to open it, flashlight in hand. The rain was still pouring down.

It was Haywire Alex. Somehow, during surgery, he had slipped away unnoticed. "Guess what I've found?" he asked, with obvious pride. Before I could answer he flicked open his hand, less than a foot from my face.

On his palm in the beam of the flashlight rested the severed portion of Black Angus's finger. Suddenly I felt dizzy. I grabbed the door-jamb for support.

"Just bugger off," were the only words I found strength to say.

Paddy the Hoot and Haywire Alex

Paddy "The Hoot" Craig was another delightful Zeballos character. An older man, he was pure Irish, with the brogue to prove it. At unpredictable times, but usually to display delight or anger, alone, or in company, he would suddenly emit two or three loud "hoots" like an aroused owl. Hence his nickname.

Paddy, who had been well educated and apparently had trained for the church, viewed himself as a prospector. While he had partici-pated in many rushes to stake claims his principal avocation was that of a philosopher. Stretching his lanky frame and sitting in the rare sunshine with his corncob pipe, he loved to philosophize, either to himself or an audience. Quotations from the Bible with chapter and verse flowed in his clear ringing Irish voice to illustrate some moral point under contemplation. He also quoted widely from classical En-glish poetry and prose.

My introduction to Paddy occurred one day as I sat beside him on a log at the edge of the mud flats, waiting for the tender to unload a coastal vessel. It was a rare rainless day. Across the flats struggled a single file of sturdy young men, most of them in hip waders. Some were stripped to the waist. They were back-packers.

There were still no vehicles in Zeballos and horses could not be used because of the mud and tangle of roots on all the trails. The human back-packers had loads of sixty to one hundred pounds on their packboards. To that point, Paddy and I had simply exchanged nods. He was surveying the scene of human activity carefully. Sud-denly, startling me with a couple of wild hoots, he jabbed in the air with his pipe and said, as much to himself as to me, "Sure, 'n look at thim sturdy lads, all strugglin' wi' their great loads, 'n not a brain in their heads to baither them."

Some in Zeballos might have put Haywire Alex in the same cate-gory as Paddy put the back-packers. But Alex was more wily than they knew, and I had first-hand evidence of this.

One day Haywire made his "strike." No one knows quite how it happened, since Alex seemed to devote his entire time to hanging around the growing village simply nattering and spearing drinks. Not only had he slipped away alone and made the discovery on a small stream a couple of miles from the beach, but he had staked it intelligently, calling it, appropriately, The Beanpot. Somehow he had contacted an eastern mining company whose representative had slipped unnoticed into Zeballos, looked at the discovery, and promptly optioned it. Alex received a "down-payment" of two or three thousand dollars and, to all intents and purposes, was "rich" before any of the story became known to the camp.

I had befriended Alex and was dismayed that he had neither taken me into his confidence nor offered me an early opportunity to examine and deal on the property. I chided him on the matter. His frank explanation was, "The Beanpot ain't going to get me very far. It's a blow-out and don't go nowhere. You're smart and you'd know that. Most any smart guy around here would. Then you don't pay "early money," but the Americans and the easterners do. Besides, it's a company with a name I liked. It could be lucky for me."

"And what," I asked, "is the name?"

"Inspiration Mining," replied Alex with a twinkle in his eyes.

Haywire Alex's assessment of how I would have viewed his discovery was probably correct. I was energetically examining many old properties and new discoveries in and around the district, and developing confidence in my evaluations. My work as a scout also involved the supervision of several small groups of prospectors and hand-miners on a number of prospects optioned for further sampling. None of these became mines despite optimistic names such as Midas, Golden Horn, and The Friend.

Spud Huestis

One of the prospectors in Zeballos was H. H. Huestis, known to everyone in the mining world as Spud. Huestis's Bethlehem copper prospect in southern British Columbia became Canada's first porphyry copper mine in the 1950s. He was a short, stout but muscular man with a ruddy complexion, blue eyes, a round face, and a bald head surrounded by a fuzzy white fringe. Although he was very independent and sensitive, Spud was a wonderful colleague and companion. While quite literate, he rarely put pen to paper, but instead spoke directly to anyone to whom he had something to say.

Spud sought me out in Zeballos for two reasons. He wanted to look me up because we had worked together in the Bridge River district of British Columbia, and also he now had an option on a new gold discovery near Zeballos which he hoped Pioneer might consider developing. Naturally I was pleased to see him, and naturally I agreed to examine the showing.

We set off together in the Indian fishing boat he had rented. After a trip of about fifteen miles our boat approached one of a small group of islands. We tied up to a small landing where a neatly dressed, middle-aged white woman, who had heard our boat's engine across the water, awaited us with a boy of about ten and a dog. Spud introduced me. Together we climbed to a clearing among the trees along a path which led to an attractive log cabin. "As pretty as a dollhouse," Spud observed. We entered and, despite Spud's protest that we did not have much time, spent a half-hour chatting and drinking tea. The woman, who was the owner of the discovery, told me the story.

A month earlier, Spud had pulled into her landing to check on the best passage between the islands to reach Zeballos. On that occasion her husband, a fish-cannery official, was with her. They gave Spud directions and walked back with him down the rock-bordered path to the landing. Spud noticed that two or three of the rocks were oxidized or rusty.

"That's what we prospectors look for," he said, pointing them out. The woman and her husband and son paused and looked at the rocks. Spud also looked more carefully. Pointing to a particular rock he said, "That white rock is quartz, in which we sometimes find gold."

The boy picked up the rock, put it in Spud's hands and said, "Mummy found that where we go for picnics."

Spud peered at the rock closely, saw that it was well-ribboned and thought it should carry gold, although he saw none. "Far from here?" he asked, and was told about one mile. They agreed to go there.

When they reached the place where the family went for picnics, Spud realized that the source of the rock he had examined earlier by the path was a piece of "float" or detached loose rock. Similar pieces lay in the bottom of the stream. Spud broke a piece, examined the fresh surface and thought he could see a tiny speck of gold, but was not sure. He said nothing, but walked with the husband along the stream for about one hundred yards. There they approached an almost vertical cliff of rock, parallel to the stream.

Spud pulled the thick moss from the rock face. A four-inch-wide quartz vein was exposed. He broke off some chips of rock, examined them with his hand lens, and said, "I'll take some samples, but in any case we ought to stake a few claims now. If you agree, we'll be equal partners if I can make a deal for the development of this site."

Six claims were staked by Spud and his new-found partners. Spud proceeded to Zeballos where the samples were assayed. Some showed appreciable gold content.

After our tea in the woman's log cabin Spud and I and the boatman proceeded to the showing. Spud led me to the outcrop. It was just as he had described it. We tore away the moss and examined it at several other points. It contained visible gold but it was fine and irregularly distributed. What we saw indicated that the gold content was low, not comparable with the richness of the "bonanza" ore of Zeballos, so we passed it by. Nonetheless, this incident is noteworthy as a valuable glimpse into the way in which mineral deposits are sometimes discovered by an observant and curious amateur. Some such discoveries have become great mines.

Those who wish to be successful as professional prospectors must know what they are looking for and where they are likely to find it. They must be constantly curious about all rocks they see. When they see something which they believe should be investigated they must scratch, dig, and often break off and show a piece to some higher authority for appraisal. Success as a prospector requires one other quality. One must never be surprised when unexpected events occur. Mother Nature, like Dame Fortune, is a capricious mistress and can tease and reward everywhere and in many ways, even in the rain forests of Vancouver Island.

Salmon from the Trees, the Sky, and Guddling

One September, when I was based in Zeballos, over eighty inches of rain fell. That record rainfall – nearly three inches of rain every day during the month – coincided with the spawning run of the salmon on the Zeballos River and also with an equinoctial tide. During a single day and a night the Zeballos River rose by five or six feet. Its width was swollen perhaps ten times the normal. The record rainfall and the swollen condition of the river, combined with the extra high tide, apparently confused the salmon as they were swimming upstream. The morning after the storm subsided, I picked two large salmon, one dead, the other still alive and quivering, out of the low branches of some trees! That was not the only occasion on which I had a most enjoyable meal of salmon "caught" in a highly unusual way.

One rare, lovely, sunny day I went with a local prospector, Andy Morod, to examine an iron-ore deposit he had discovered. (Subsequently, it was brought into commercial production as an iron mine.) On this occasion, Andy, who was a good climber, suggested that we climb and prospect above his iron-ore deposit to the top of the mountain, about two thousand feet above sea level. There we could enjoy a good view of the region while we ate our lunch.

No sooner had we reached the top of the mountain and sat down on a patch of moss, when suddenly a shadow passed over us. Andy leapt to his feet. He ran quickly toward a group of scrubby trees from which had issued a thump and fluttering sounds. As he approached the trees, a large eagle rose from the ground and soared toward the sea. I saw Andy draw his prospector's pick from his belt, kneel and strike a sharp blow at something on the ground. With a triumphant cry, he rose to his feet gripping a large salmon in his hands and exclaimed, "Fresh salmon from the sky for dinner tonight."

I not only saw salmon caught in trees and dropped from the sky during my time on Vancouver Island – I learned how to catch fish with my bare hands. This is the art of "guddling." It was taught to me by a European geologist named Bernischke, with whom I prospected briefly, and I employed the technique on several occasions on both Vancouver Island and the Queen Charlotte Islands.

Bernischke and I were prospecting various coastal rivers as the salmon were moving upstream to spawn. During the spawning, the eggs are laid in sandbars which may be a foot or two below the surface of the river. After they mature in the ocean, adult Pacific salmon are compelled, it seems by instinct, to return to the rivers and tributaries where they were born and to which they come to spawn and later to die. The returning hordes of salmon come in dense schools; they struggle upwards through rapids and leap high falls until they reach the shoals of their spawning grounds. In some cases these schools of salmon may constitute a mass up to twenty feet in width.

Both Bernischke and I were utterly amazed by the numbers of salmon we saw struggling upstream. We decided that we should take a good supply of fish and have them smoked for future use. Bernischke suggested we try guddling, an art which he had learned during his boyhood years as a poacher on the estates of wealthy Austrians.

We waded into the water, to knee-depth or more, found a sandy shoal, and strode over it in a stationary forward-crouching position, with both arms submerged in the water at least to the elbows. The salmon favoured such sandy shoals to pause for a rest before swimming further upstream to spawn. To my surprise I learned that I could reach about under water, touching the fish and testing them for firmness of flesh to select the most desirable – all without frightening or even disturbing them. Only when I quickly closed my one-handed grip around the fish's tail and jerked it out of the water onto the river bank, would the fish have a sense of danger, usually too late.

The Friend Mine

The Friend was a gold prospect optioned by the Pioneer Company on which great hopes were based. Unfortunately, after six months of hard work, it failed and did not make a mine. It was located about seven miles by boat from the Zeballos beach, thence about three miles back in the hills. A visit to The Friend always required at least a full day.

We had built a simple one-room overnight shack at the boat-trail connection site, called the "Trail Camp." There was a difficult up-and-down overland footpath between this camp and the mine site over which I occasionally back-packed three cases of mine powder at a time, for a total weight of 180 pounds, when my regular back-packers, who normally carried much less than that, failed me. I never let this feat be known around Zeballos for fear my sanity would be questioned and my newly acquired registration as a professional engineer placed in permanent jeopardy.

We started building a new mine camp on the mountain-side near The Friend gold discovery, since the decision had been made to explore the vein outcrop underground, and we expected to be there for at least six months. Large old red cedar trees lay fallen on the ground nearby, and I decided that we would use them in the construction of our buildings. We cut the fallen trees into six- or eight-foot lengths, then slit the wood along its grain with a simple hammered tool. In this way we obtained the boards we needed. I marvelled at how well this method worked with good red cedar. Under ideal conditions we could produce boards of our choice, resembling huge red cedar roof shingles, from ten inches to sixteen inches wide, up to eight feet long and of uniform thickness – from one-half inch to two inches – at the rate of probably one board every five minutes, when pressed for time.

The cookhouse, with a den for the cook, was the first building we put up. I had a good, versatile crew of about six men, mainly Scandinavians. The work went well and quickly. By late the first day we had the cookhouse foundations, floor, frame, roof, and three walls erected. We decided to sleep on the new floor that first night. A large circular, air-tight, woodstove heater made of tin was installed on a temporary basis to provide warmth and on which to cook our meals. We ate, stoked the heater with wood for the night, spread our seven sleeping bags on the floor, and crawled in to enjoy a well-earned sleep.

Toward the middle of the night, I came half-awake – unusual for me. I started sniffing. Yes, I smelled smoke. Suddenly I seemed to be wide awake. I glanced in the direction of the heater – a crimson inferno! *"Fire!"* I shouted. *"Jump!"*

Immediately seven strong men leapt up. In the darkness they became confused and collided with one another as they hurried to escape. The air was filled with shouts and curses. All was bedlam. I picked myself up off the ground about twelve feet from the building on the wall-less side, one leg still tangled in my sleeping bag, and struggled to take stock of the situation.

I suddenly realized that I was wearing my crimson woollen bonnet, a garment knitted by my dear mother which I always wore when sleeping outdoors. Before falling asleep I had pulled it down below my chin. I took off the bonnet and looked back toward the heater. It was now a gentle pink colour.

Sheepishly I climbed back into the cookhouse frame. Except for about a dozen boards torn off the sides as the men jumped to escape, no great damage had been done, and no bones were broken.

I felt an explanation was due the gang but was too embarrassed to tell them the whole truth. "Guess I had a nightmare, fellows," I said. "Sorry." But one of the group, McGibbon, the oldest of the crew, a wonderfully versatile woodsman and prospector, who on many occasions was as protective of me as a grandfather, examined the heater carefully, and said, "Maybe it's as well we woke up. The heater's too close to the wall and charring the boards behind. I'm putting it out." This he did, and we crawled back into our sleeping bags and soon fell asleep again.

We had a fine camp at The Friend and a good crew. Unfortunately our cook became bored and one day drank all the flavouring extract for its alcohol content, then soon told us loudly that he was quitting. This was an occupational hazard with many fine camp cooks in those years.

We were faced with a critical emergency, one so grave that I left the camp to resolve the problem myself at Zeballos beach. My first inquiries, addressed, naturally, to the tavern owner, the bootlegger, and the local constable, in that order, revealed that no unemployed cook was around. I sent one of my packers to scout out all other options. After several hours of loitering and beer-drinking at the newly opened beer parlour, he rushed to me with the news that the best cook in the whole of Zeballos, then the chief cook of the largest mine in the camp, The Privateer, was in the beer parlour, drinking.

"You don't mean Ed Able!" I exclaimed. "Ed's not only the best camp cook in these parts – he's probably the best in British Columbia. I don't know him, but I've heard of him all over the province from Stewart to Rupert and Bridge River."

"Yes, I mean Able," the packer said. I asked if he had quit at The Privateer and was told, "No, but we might persuade him to quit!"

I naïvely said, "Okay. Bring him here for a talk."

But my packer, aided, if I recall properly, by one of my young engineers, a man who later became one of British Columbia's most distinguished mine inspectors, said, "No, let us persuade him our way and at the beer parlour." I nodded, and they disappeared.

About four hours later, the young engineer returned to report progress of a questionable sort. Able and our packer were both almost too drunk to stand. They were hanging onto each other and singing. So he felt "everything was turning out okay." He would get our company boat ready, take extra fuel for the "kicker" engine, some grub and extra sleeping bags and thus be able to get away – "if necessary" – in about an hour.

"But it'll be dark," I said. "We've never made the trip in our small boat at night."

"Able might change his mind by morning," was the muttered response. I said no more.

The next morning, when I appeared at my beach office shack at seven o'clock, a scribbled note was on my desk. Its message was clear and informative. Our company boat had left about midnight. The tide was out and it was tough going. It had taken three men to carry Able over the mud flats to the boat and two more to carry the packer. I read the note with mounting concern. For the first time I wondered if Able had been aware of what was happening at any point in the persuasion process. No word came from our trail or mine camps the following day.

On the second morning, our boat and boatman returned. He reported that the night boat trip had passed without problem, but carrying the fellows had been difficult. Finally, everyone had crowded into the trail shack and slept soundly until noon the next day. Then they all got up. After an hour of drinking coffee "the two mine fellows and the new cook" started up the trail on foot. They had covered only the first hundred yards or so of the three-mile walk, when the new cook, Able, felt that his head was "so big" he "couldn't safely squeeze it between the big trees" which bordered the foot trail. So they all returned to the trail shack. There they rested in the bunks and drank coffee until dark.

At one point, Able's head seemed to clear. He asked, "Where the hell am I?"

The young engineer replied – with poetic license, "about forty miles from Zeballos."

To the question, "How did I get here?" the engineer had not committed himself, beyond saying, again with poetic license, "by boat." They all slept soundly the second night, so the boatman decided to leave early that morning to return to the Zeballos beach. He did so before the "new cook" was up.

Two days later, I summoned enough courage to visit The Friend's mine camp and face a sober Ed Able. To my surprise, he was in an amiable mood. He liked the clear air, the quiet nights, even the mountain view, and he had found among the miners three old friends with whom he had worked in other camps. We talked of mutual friends in various mining camps where he had worked.

Able could remember none of the circumstances of how he had

left The Privateer and come to The Friend. Fortunately, he asked no questions, so no information was volunteered. He gave me a list of the supplies needed for the cookhouse, which I agreed to secure quickly. It was a strange beginning to what became a long and mutually respectful friendship and professional association in several subsequent mining camps.

The "persuasion" – more truthfully, the "kidnapping" – of Ed Able to become the cook in The Friend's camp became part of the folklore of the mining industry of the west coast of Vancouver Island during the late 1930s. And such accounts must not be brushed aside as inconsequential. Mining-camp cooks were key individuals in the frontier camps of that period. For mines to be developed the companies bringing them into production obviously had to have competent, usually all-male, workmen. Unless the food was good and plentiful a company could not retain its crew. In the days of which I write, there were few, if any, other pleasures or diversions save cards and, if the mining camps were sufficiently large, perhaps one or more villas with "girls" for companionship. There were no portable radios, no TV. Food was central in the life of mining camps, and those which were well-managed provided fresh meats and fish, fresh fruits and vegetables, freshly baked bread and pastry. In the late 1930s a mining camp like The Friend worked largely on its stomach.

Thus when our efforts on The Friend prospect were abandoned, I was relieved and flattered that Ed Able and all my excellent hand-miners who had worked on the prospect decided to remain with me in the employ of Pioneer Mines, accompanying me and my wife Mary to the Pioneer Vancouver Island base in Tofino to develop Pat McCrory's Musketeer property.

The Musketeer and Hand-Mining

Bringing the modest Musketeer mine into production was a source of great satisfaction for me for several reasons. Its development provided clear evidence of what a motivated young prospector could achieve. McCrory, a young Irish immigrant, found employment in a mine within a year and a half of coming to Canada, and, through the process of self-education there, became sufficiently informed and motivated to make a discovery of economic importance. Although the venture's success was prematurely interrupted by the Second World

War, it nonetheless brought McCrory a lump sum of $25,000 in cash, and shares in the company from which he would realize much more. It also gave him the self-confidence and financial momentum to push on to even greater mining achievements.

The Musketeer project was of particular interest to me because Tofino was so different from Zeballos. Tofino, a pleasant open community on the west coast of Vancouver Island about 130 miles northwest of Victoria, is set amidst relatively low hills and lovely sandy beaches. When we moved there in the late 1930s it was a tidy village of less than two hundred – Japanese fishermen and their families and a small group of Scandinavians who built the fishing boats for the Japanese. There was also a fine English couple, the Sharpes. Mr. Sharpe was the official agent in Tofino of the government of British Columbia. Most of the colourful, semi-permanent cottages had attractive gardens. The community, which was industrious and well-kept, reflected the Japanese and Scandinavian ethnic and cultural influences. Mary and I enjoyed the time we lived in Tofino immensely and made several lifelong friends there.

An unusual feature of The Musketeer mine development was my decision, based on economic and time factors, that much of the underground work would be done by hand-mining. This program, probably approaching nine hundred linear feet of tunnelling and raise-mining done during 1938-39, may have been one of the last of the larger hand-mining projects in Canada. Given the problems of road construction, the mountainous terrain, and general rain forest environment, the mine could not then have been developed as quickly or as inexpensively by other means.

The removal of huge trees from virgin forest, the necessary rock work, the bridges required across flood rivers, the lack of readily available sand and gravel in the necessary quantities, the ever-present mud (often a foot deep) and tangled roots, all of these rendered road construction costs unjustifiable, particularly in the absence of an identified ore body. The unpredictable and torrential rivers made the use of canoes and boats totally impracticable and the mud and roots made it equally impossible for pack horses. The era of the helicopter had not yet arrived!

In that pre-Second World War period, the only feasible means of doing the preliminary work to develop The Musketeer were the arms, legs, and backs of men. My crew of about twelve were excellent all-round workmen. They had proven their worth to me in Zeballos and had volunteered to come with me to Tofino and The Musketeer. Six or seven were exceptionally able hand-miners.

The miners also did their own mucking. This involved removing broken rock by rubber-tired wheelbarrow. Fortunately, the need to install timber beams to support the roofs and sides of the workings was minimal. The Musketeer hand-miners worked in two seven-hour shifts per day with three men to a shift. Two men would handle the hand drilling and blasting. The third man sharpened the steel, mucked, and occasionally took the place of one of the two miners. Each team averaged about three feet of advance per shift. All the men worked under a plan of guaranteed wage plus a bonus incentive for footage driven, above the minimum required figure.

Our men at The Musketeer were mainly muscular Scandinavians. Despite the rugged work in which they engaged and the physical energy it required, they were artists. The rhythm and grace and seeming casualness with which they drove steel drills into the rock on a carefully calculated pattern and sequence, loaded the holes, fired them, and mucked the rock, gave every appearance of a highly trained team of athletes. Not surprisingly, they greatly enjoyed their work. I praised them with a sincerity they understood because they knew that I had also served an apprenticeship in their art.

While I was the general manager of all activities at The Musketeer, with the help of a junior engineer and an accountant, our miners needed little supervision. The miners, the cook Ed Able, and my small staff and I were all one team.

Life was simple and uncomplicated in the mining camps on Vancouver Island in the 1930s. The miners worked six days a week and did their laundry and other simple chores on the seventh. A few who had hobbies found time to carve in wood or engage in leather work. Others simply explored the nearby bush with fishing rod or gun. The only communication with the outside world was a good, one-way, battery-powered radio kept in the cook tent. Television had not yet arrived nor had the two-way radio. Following supper, most of those in camp would huddle around the radio to hear the news. Probably the most popular evening recreation was the card game – poker – almost always played for money.

Mail from the "outside" arrived weekly, coinciding with the weekly trips of the coastal steamer, usually the *Princess Maquinna*, to Tofino. The miners, in the main, were not letter writers. Not many read to any great extent. Reading, of course, was difficult. The lighting system was inadequate, consisting only of a number of flickering Coleman lamps. The mining crews were primarily men from forty-five to sixty years of age who had not been exposed to city and family life, with their complexities, or who had outgrown or rejected one or both for a simpler and more isolated environment and slower pace of life.

To many, the external urban community meant trouble. Often, on their rare visits to civilization, and in their efforts to find the conviviality of the small male group to which they were accustomed in the camp, they would make their way to a tavern or a bootlegger's. Usually, too, the miner would be "staky," that is, he would have a few hundred dollars or more in his pockets. The cash attracted the card sharps, the pimps, and the prostitutes. The unlimited flow of alcohol after weeks or months of drought (no alcohol was allowed in camp) would make the miner irrational, and often the only news I would receive from a "holidaying" miner was a call from the police or hospital to "come and collect him." After paying property damages and other costs, I would take the miner back to the camp.

The miners regarded the camp as their home and one of the few institutions they could trust. If miners ran into trouble while they were away, their bills would be paid and their trips back to the camp would be arranged. When they returned, the quiet sympathy of all the others in camp awaited them. After a short "drying-out," they returned to the life of the camp. But it was not always necessary to go totally outside to meet with trouble.

One time, one of our workers was about to start a holiday outside. While soberly waiting for the coastal vessel to pick him up in Tofino rather than taking a small, pontoon-equipped, bush aircraft to go to Vancouver for some real excitement, he was struck from behind on a narrow footbridge by a bicycle. The blow toppled him into the rock-strewn stream below. The result was four broken ribs, a dislocated hip, and two weeks in hospital. After his return to camp he was seriously admonished by one of his mates who told him, "You should have flown to Vancouver or Alberni and gone straight to a poker den or a whorehouse instead. It wouldn't have been as dangerous!"

Samples: Salted and Sugared

While I was overseeing Pioneer's development of The Musketeer project, I continued my work of seeking out and examining other prospects for the company. In some instances I accompanied prospectors to the sites of their discoveries. Occasionally, mineral specimens were brought to me.

When prospectors brought collections of rock fragments to me in Tofino to examine and have assayed, I followed a simple procedure before their eyes. The entire collection of rock fragments was dumped upon a flattened sheet of clean newspaper. This was to ensure, as far as possible, that rich fragments of Zeballos ore had not been inserted – or *salted* – into the collection by the prospector or any unscrupulous third party. I would separate these "foreign" fragments, usually few in number, from the larger collection, asking, in mock surprise, "How did these become mixed?" If I were certain of my identification, I might even add, "Have you also prospected in the Zeballos district?" Nonetheless, even when my suspicions were aroused and tended to influence my assessment, I tried to ensure that such suspicions did not govern my thinking. Thus, I usually sent the residual material to be assayed after removing any identifiable high-grade which appeared to have been introduced from a different source.

On one occasion a sack of rock samples was brought to me at our home by a stranger who told me he was an evangelical coastal missionary. While he chatted with Mary I subjected his sample to the newspaper-sheet scrutiny and was instantly shocked at what I saw. Two or three fragments of obviously Zeballos-type ore were among a dozen or so rock fragments of nondescript appearance. I elected not to embarrass or even discreetly challenge the "missionary." I simply said his material called for an assaying test before I could judge it. This was done after removal of the salting material. Later, he was incredulous when told that his sample was valueless.

One day a local resident brought me a small sack of three or four pieces of mineralized rock which he had found while hunting. The mineralization was of unusual appearance and I was at a loss to identify it. At that time it was necessary to assay for certain specifically named elements. The present broad-based investigative techniques made possible by X-ray and atomic analysis came much later. So, as a starter, I sent the sample for assay, initially for copper and gold, with a note to the assayer, George Eldridge in Vancouver, stating my perplexity and asking for his guidance in having additional assays made.

The first report indicated high copper and evidence of nickel. It also reported "no gold" but a substantial quantity of a silvery metal, insoluble in the strongest acids. I thereupon asked for a nickel assay and a platinum assay. The next report indicated high nickel and added that there were no dependable assay facilities in western Canada for platinum. The best facilities for such rare assays were probably in the eastern United States. I requested that some of the sample material be sent there and that duplicate copies of the assay reports be sent to the office of our eastern Canada exploration associate in Toronto as well as to my employer, Pioneer Gold Mines Limited.

Before I received the assay reports through the once-a-week coastal steamship mail service, two telegrams arrived in Tofino. The exploration chief for our eastern associates, Cy Stewart, then acting for Anglo Huronian Mines, was flying from Toronto to Vancouver to Tofino immediately, and my chief in Pioneer Gold Mines, Howard James, was flying separately from Vancouver to meet me in Tofino. Stewart was the first to arrive.

I was on the small dock at Tofino to greet Stewart when Ginger Coote, one of B.C.'s most able and colourful coastal bush pilots, delivered him there through turbulent leaden skies and occasional showers. It was my first introduction to Stewart. He descended from the small, single-engine, pontoon-equipped plane on very wobbly legs. He grasped my hand and asked immediately for a drink. "I've never had a plane ride like that before in my life and never want another." Later I learned that he had been a distinguished air force officer in the First World War.

When Stewart was warmly settled in our home in Tofino, his nerves relaxed with a hot drink of rum, he suddenly exclaimed, "Some platinum results, eh!" To his surprise, I told him that I had not yet learned what they were. He searched through his briefcase and brought out the assay certificate. It reported almost one ounce of platinum-group metals to the ton. I read it and whistled. Beaming, Stewart asked, "How soon can we see the showing? Is it staked?"

I replied, "Yes, I advised the young logger who brought the samples to me to do so. He has staked four claims to cover the showing, which he has called The Flybite."

"Copper and nickel too!" Stewart exclaimed.

"Yes," I replied, "about 10 per cent of each."

"My God!" he exclaimed. "Mary, pour me another drink."

We were up very early next morning. The storm had cleared and the sun was about to shine. "Terrific," said Stewart.

"A lovely day," I responded.

"No," added our prospector-guide, whose name was Knott. "If it gets much warmer, the black flies will eat us alive. I had good reason for calling the claim The Flybite."

Boarding Knott's small fishing boat, we set out on our journey. Two hours later we were in a small sheltered cove. From there we had to climb a most difficult half-mile up a steep mountainside to reach the outcrop.

It was a small rounded knoll about twenty feet in diameter, slightly *gossaned*, or rusty, with a single small, freshly blasted two-foot deep hole in the centre. The sides of the hole and fragments from it were heavily mineralized. Stewart examined it carefully and collected several chunks of rock to take with him.

"Funny looking stuff," said Stewart. "But who's going to worry about appearances if there are a couple of million tons of 10 per cent copper, 10 per cent nickel, and in addition, an ounce of platinum-group metals here!"

He asked if I had prospected for other outcrops on my earlier visit. I told him I had, but without success. The area was totally covered with moss and tree growth. We agreed that it was probably a blanket-form deposit.

Stewart concluded that it should be diamond-drilled after more surface trenching had been attempted. The latter would show the readily determinable extent of the mineralization. I agreed and added that I would also bring a couple of my hand-miners over from Musketeer to blast a pit down into the centre to determine its thickness. Once again, however, Fortune proved to be a fickle Dame! After a week of blasting, it was clear that the deposit was not of significant size despite the richness of the mineralization.

When Dame Fortune says "No" it is always a letdown, a vertical drop without a parachute. The Flybite prospect, did, however, produce some attractive mineral specimens. And much more intriguingly, Professor Gunning later suggested to me, upon examining my specimens, that The Flybite may have been near the point of collision of the Pacific oceanic and the continental land-mass plates. This was a highly interesting observation for geologists and others who study the Earth's crustal plates.

The Flybite, which had brought Stewart and James to Tofino with high hopes, was quickly relegated to that long list of broken dreams which every prospector and scout accumulates in his lifetime. Fifteen years later, however, Cy Stewart and I would share a dream that became a realization more momentous – he was the first company scout to walk with me over the Blind River uranium outcrops in Ontario.

A Close Call

One wintery day while I was developing The Musketeer, my time-keeper and accountant Alan Thompson and I set out with heavy packs on our backs to walk seven difficult miles through mud and slushy snow, sometimes up to our knees. We had to ford the icy-cold, bould-ery-bottomed Bedwell River. The turbulent spring runoff had started and the river water was from knee- to hip-high. In Indian fashion, we each had a rigid board on our back with straps around the shoulders and our loads of supplies and other material strapped to the boards. We were in mid-stream when my companion, who was slight and not particularly strong, stumbled, lost his balance, and fell. It happened so quickly he was unable to rid himself of his packboard. Although he was a good swimmer, he was helpless in the turbulent water and slowly but roughly was tumbled downstream. I did not lose my foot-ing, perhaps because I practically never go anywhere in the bush without a roughly made staff like a shepherd's crook. To me it's a third leg.

I quickly scrambled up the river bank, threw off my packboard, and hurried through the underbrush downstream alongside the river, fervently hoping that a shallow shoal would halt Thompson and enable me to grab hold of him. I hadn't run far when I came to a huge tree which had collapsed partially across the river. It almost, but not completely, spanned the river. I crawled my way out to mid-stream upon this fallen tree. My companion was spread-eagled on his back, flailing his arms, and being bumped along the bouldery river upstream from me. When he came near, I lunged out from the tree trunk and seized him. He still had his packboard on his back. By this time, his sleeping bag, which had been the top load of his packboard, was soaked with water. This added another twenty pounds to his body weight and ensured that his head was going to sink first. I cut his pack off and dragged him along the fallen tree to the shore. His face was nearly blue.

I shook him and rubbed his head and hands. Slowly he began to revive. I reached for the "first aid kit," a "mickey" of rum in a small flat glass flask carried in the hip pocket of my tin pants. Most prospectors along the west coast of British Columbia carried such "medicine" to keep us from dying of pneumonia.

My semi-frozen fingers couldn't unscrew the cap. Something had to be done quickly. Fortunately, I had become adept in sculpting rocks and mineral specimens with my prospecting pick, always at the ready in my belt. With a blow of the pick I sliced the top off the bottle. The edge was jagged, but the bottle was open. Thompson was slumped on the ground. I propped him up, pried open his mouth with my thumb, and, for better or worse, poured the rum – I don't know how much – into his system. Slowly it brought him around.

When Thompson regained enough strength we stumbled the remaining one-half mile to the mine camp without further incident. As that day came to its end we knew that it was one we would not soon forget.

The days which remain forever fresh in the memories of prospectors each have a character all their own. Some are days of dramatic discovery, of new wealth, of disappointment, of new hope, of danger or disaster, experienced alone or shared with others. Several days which are forever fresh in my memory were shared with two sincerely religious brothers in the late summer of 1939.

Prospectors and Armageddon

The two brothers were prospectors in Kyuquot Sound near Gold River, north of Zeballos, on the Pacific Coast toward the northern tip of Vancouver Island. In letters they wrote to me they described a gold discovery they had made near their cabin. They were unknown to me but their correspondence was intelligent and their rock specimens intriguing.

I chartered a pontoon-equipped bush aircraft to fly from Zeballos to an inlet on the ocean beach where the brothers would meet me. From there we were to follow a foot trail to their camp and mineral showing some three miles inland. In due course I arrived over the beach area as planned and after "buzzing" their log cabin to announce my arrival, awaited their appearance at the beach. I confirmed arrangements with the pilot for my return to Zeballos a week later. He agreed to pick me up at the same beach and in the same aircraft.

Despite the isolation in which they lived, the two brothers were cultivated, soft-spoken men. They looked like twins, both short, stocky, well-tanned, muscular outdoorsmen with short, carefully trimmed beards. After leading me along a pleasant forest trail the brothers brought me to their well-built, tidy log cabin which was quite near their mineral discovery. It was late afternoon but still daylight when we arrived at the cabin.

My curiosity prompted me to suggest a quick preview of their discovery before dinner. But they said politely, "No, a service of thanks to the Lord is needed first." I was highly flattered when they thanked the Lord, aloud, for bringing me safely to them and for His choice of such a fine young geologist. But the service continued for an hour and most of a second hour, to my increasing frustration. During that time, it grew dark. Candles were lit. In the flickering light, I could see occasional drops of perspiration fall from the eyelids or tips of the noses of this devout pair, as their entreaties to the Lord persisted and, indeed, increased in fervour.

The main thrust of the service was that mankind had sinned and sunk beyond redemption. With this, to a large degree, I silently agreed. But when they went on to assure the Lord that they and their new-found friend felt the day of Armageddon and Redemption had now come, I was, silently, less certain. Then they explained to the Lord that they and their new-found friend were ready for His judgement. The brothers took turns addressing the Lord. Both were silent at intervals as they waited for Him to "speak" to them. I, personally, had difficulty in hearing His replies. But during one of the silent periods when a sharp draft extinguished both candles, I felt that it was His signal that He had the message!

At long, long last, dinner was finally prepared. By that time I was famished. I had had no lunch, and spiritual nourishment alone had not filled the void within me. After dinner, we retired to sleeping bags spread on comfortable bunks. I was soon asleep. Suddenly, I was awakened by a shout. In the pitch darkness one of the brothers was again calling out to the Lord. The theme of his prayer was generally the same as that of the evening service.

This pattern of direct address to the Lord continued for four nights and four days. I became so finely tuned to the coming of Armageddon I felt it was upon us each time I heard a dead limb crack and fall in the forest, an owl screech, or a seagull cry!

During my jittery stay with the brothers, I completed my examination of the several trenches they had dug to reveal the extent of their showing. My conclusion, on the visual evidence, was one of disappointment. Samples were taken; assays would provide the crucial answer. But I asked myself, by this time in all seriousness, "If Armageddon is about to strike at any moment, should we be wasting our time examining this, or any other, mineral prospect?"

There was no reading material in the cabin, no radio, no news from outside. When I attempted to start on one of my normally popular "campfire lectures" on the origin of mineral deposits such as their own, I was quickly reminded that "it was all the Lord's work."

My jitteriness, as we waited for Armageddon or the seventh day of my visit, whichever occurred first, continued. I had urgent need of a change of company and a change of conversation. Early in the morning of my departure day, I assured the brothers that I could find my way down the trail alone. I would wait, as planned, for the pontoon-equipped aircraft to pick me up precisely as I had arrived, "the Lord and Armageddon permitting," I thoughtfully added. I noted that both brothers smiled in appreciation at the last phrase. In their eyes, they had succeeded. In the service of the Lord they had won a convert. I said goodbye to each of them and started down the trail.

I practically jogged, with the heavy sample-laden pack on my back, the three miles or so to the beach, in order to escape the foreboding I felt. Finally, I reached the beach and my pick-up point. The tide was out. I took off my pack and began to indulge myself in two of my favourite pastimes while near the sea – beachcombing and exploring the crawly creatures of the muddy seashore – the littoral where all life began. The first few hours flew by quickly.

Soon it became noon, there was a clear sky and yet no sign or sound of my pick-up plane. Afternoon passed. I slept soundly in my sleeping bag beside a log on the beach that night. By noon of the second day, still with a clear sky and no plane on the horizon, I began to doubt that the Lord was co-operating. I had no shelter on the beach, only a large driftwood campfire and my sleeping bag, and nothing to eat save plentiful clams. But even this, I felt, was better than being "saved again" for destruction by Armageddon.

It was mid-morning of the third day when an Indian fisherman cruised into sight on the inlet in his trolling boat. I signalled him to come ashore. He anchored his boat and rowed to the shoreline in his skiff. He spoke no English but by repeating the Indian name of a fish cannery I knew to be in the inlet, I was able to explain that I wanted to travel there. Two hours later the cannery came into view. To my dismay it appeared to be totally abandoned.

The Indian brought his boat alongside the wooden wharf, which was riddled with broken and rotted planks. He kept his boat engine idling and indicated clearly that he did not want to tie up or remain there. Displaying some alarm when he realized that I intended to stay at the wharf, he hastily sped away as soon as I had paid him for his help.

Slowly and cautiously I picked my way, with my packboard on my back, avoiding the holes and rotted planks on the pier, toward a cluster of large, old, unpainted, wood-frame buildings. All of them seemed abandoned but one which had a smoking chimney. I headed toward it. As I approached, a wild din greeted my ears. It seemed beyond explanation. My first impression from the babel of noises, voices, and music, was that a wild drunken party was underway in the building. Perhaps, I thought, this is why the Indian fisherman departed with such haste. I removed my pack and left it on the ground for greater agility, if necessary. Slowly I drew near the building from one side so that I could peer through a window rather than approach from the front entrance.

Through the window I saw a store-like counter and shelves littered with large tins, jars, cartons, and wooden crates. There were also hardware supplies. In one corner was a big iron heater and nearby a pile of firewood. Beside the stove, huddled in a tattered old chesterfield armchair with his back to the front door, I saw a man. To my surprise, a single electric light bulb and an electrical cable hung from the ceiling. Attached to the cable were three or four extension cords to each of which a radio was connected. All the radios seemed to be blasting away at full volume, apparently each tuned to a different station. This was the source of the ear-shattering din!

Somewhat reassured by the presence of a single person, I went to the front door and hammered on it. As I had expected, there was no response. Nothing could possibly have been heard in that shack. I tried the handle, the door was unlocked. I opened it and stood on the threshold for a few seconds. I did not wish to startle or alarm the odd occupant. I left the door open and went to pick up my packsack.

As I returned slowly toward the building with my pack, the man's figure appeared in the open doorway. He was old, bearded, and unkempt, with wild staring eyes. As I approached, he extended both arms to the sky and screamed, "Armageddon! It's here! It's here! Armageddon! Armageddon!"

He retreated into the building and I thought to myself, "My God, not another one!"

Cautiously, I passed through the door and dropped my pack to the floor. I approached one of the radios and turned the volume down. He did the same to the others. When we could hear one another's voices he said more calmly, "Yes, it's Armageddon for sure. Hitler's armies are on the march. Poland has fallen. The British, French, and Canadians have declared war. This is the end." It was the first week of September 1939.

The aircraft which was to have picked me up after my visit with the two prospecting brothers never arrived. The outbreak of the Second World War brought into play new regulations concerning aircraft flights along and across Canada's long coastline. The largely uncontrolled coming and going of aircraft, which had been an increasingly accepted way of life among the rising generation of geologists and prospectors, had come to a sudden end. I had to make my way back to Mary in Tofino as best I could.

The advent of war and the inconclusive, though generally encouraging, results of the exploratory work done on the Musketeer property by late 1939, raised questions concerning the desirability of continuing its development. The decision was taken, however, to carry forward the project to its logical end, and on the basis of this additional work, a plan was put in place to bring the property into production in a modest way in the fall of 1941. The Musketeer was in full production for only about one year, with a fifty-ton per day mill processing one-ounce gold ore. The end came dramatically.

On the evening of June 20, 1942, the mine and mill crew of about twenty-five were in the cookhouse dining hall listening to news of the war. Over the radio came word that an unidentified alien submarine, presumably but never proven to be Japanese, had surfaced beside a lighthouse at Estevan Point, on the west coast of Vancouver Island, about twenty miles up the coast from The Musketeer. An attempt had been made, apparently, to destroy the lighthouse by shelling from the submarine. This news prompted almost the entire crew to quit their jobs and the camp and go to Vancouver.

I had left The Musketeer long before the crew ceased to work there in mid 1942, however. I abhorred the idea of war. But mankind, unfortunately, had developed no other effective means for removing tyrants and controlling their followers. So I tried to contribute, as best I could, to the struggle for a better world. Whether it would emerge through war, I was by no means certain. I still had the taste of the First World War in my mouth and it was exceedingly bitter. My father had died from war injuries incurred during that war. Years later my brother would die from an injury he received during the Second World War.

In 1939 I was nearly twenty-eight years old. Mary and I had been married slightly less than two years and were expecting our first (and only) child. Our life in British Columbia progressed almost normally during the war, brightened by the birth of our daughter Marion, but far removed from the untold tragedies experienced by so many millions in Britain, Europe, North Africa, and Asia.

While I knew personally the human cost of war I decided to become directly involved only in 1942, after I had completed my Master's degree in geology. To my great surprise I was rejected for military service on the medical grounds that I had "flat feet." This puzzled me at the time since I had never had difficulty in athletic contests, in the various types of heavy physical work in which I had engaged as a miner, nor in walking and climbing many hundreds of miles as a prospector in the mountainous regions of British Columbia. Probably, a graver defect of which the authorities may have been aware but made no mention, was a "silicotic shadow" on one of my lungs, which I had acquired through my work as a miner.

Throughout the Second World War I worked for Pioneer Gold Mines in the search for strategic minerals and the development and production of metals essential to the allied war effort. Occasionally, my employment with Pioneer involved my secondment on special projects for the Geological Survey of Canada. In addition, largely through the support and encouragement of my boss Howard James, and due to the seasonal nature of my field exploration duties, I was able to continue my academic work at the University of British Columbia beyond the Master's level.

VI

Armageddon and the Search for Strategic Minerals

When I heard the word *Armageddon* from the lips of the two religious prospectors and that strange character in the abandoned cannery near the northern end of Vancouver Island, I knew what it meant. It is used in the last book of the New Testament as the name for war so overwhelming in its slaughter and destruction that the continuance of military conflict becomes impossible. That point was reached – at least for rational human beings – when Hiroshima and Nagasaki were bombed in early August 1945.

Henceforth, war in its traditional form – people using their most destructive weapons against each other – would lead only to massive international destruction and radiation sickness. This entirely new situation in human history was reached through the application of science, in increasingly sophisticated ways, in the resolution of military problems and the development of indescribably powerful deadly weapons.

Before the news of the bombing of Hiroshima was flashed around the world I knew little of the mammoth increase in the destructiveness of the weapons being used in the war, but I had gained considerable knowledge concerning some of the metals which were urgently required for the successful organization and conduct of the war effort of the Western Allies.

When the Second World War began, the primary sources of several critically required metals essential to the Allied war effort were in the hands of the enemy. Co-ordinated action had to be taken to find new sources of such strategic minerals in Canada, if possible.

The federal government gave the Honourable C. D. Howe, its effective Minister of Munitions and Supply, responsibility for mobilizing Canadian efforts to overcome these shortages. Mr. Howe was a gifted engineer who was widely praised for his ability "to get things done." In 1940 he appointed Dr. George C. Bateman as Wartime Metals Controller and established a War Metals Advisory Committee to assist in the resolution of problems involving strategic metals. The remarkable prospector and mine developer, Viola MacMillan, who later served for twenty highly successful years as the president of Canada's Prospectors and Developers Association, was the only woman appointed to this senior governmental committee.

A list of about fifteen "strategic" metals was compiled for high-priority action. Practically none of these had been produced previously in Canada although there was evidence that certain of them might be present in economic quantity. This list of strategic minerals informed and guided mineral exploration efforts throughout Canada during the war years and was highly influential in the allocation of manpower, supplies, and equipment.

From 1939 until 1941, Dr. Chris Riley and I served Pioneer Gold Mines as exploration geologists and prospectors. During the next two years I served as Pioneer's Chief Mine Geologist and Exploration (Strategic Metals) Geologist for western Canada. It was during the winter months of this latter period that I completed my graduate studies at UBC.

Although I remained directly responsible to Howard James, Pioneer's chief executive officer, he, in turn, was working with Dr. W. E. Cockfield, western representative of the Geological Survey of Canada and the British Columbia Ministry of Mines. The program was that during the summer months I would lead a small group of experienced prospectors and work in the field with them in various areas of British Columbia believed to offer potential for one or more of the strategic minerals sought. Among the federal Geological Survey and provincial officers who did field work and provided direction to others in this effort were J. G. Gray (Pinchi Lake, mercury); Dr. J. E. Armstrong (Endako, molybdenum and mercury); Dr. C. S. Lord (Takla Lake, chromite, asbestos); Dr. H. M. Rice (Takla region, chromite); Dr. John Stevenson and Dr. Joseph Mandy (tungsten, antimony, and mercury). Working in their respective areas of specialization these men either identified the presence of strategic metals or sought to gather and collate data concerning the specific locations in which they could occur. We followed in their footsteps to do the actual prospecting. Other advisers who assisted during this period were Doctors Victor Dolmage, Henry Gunning, and Harry Warren, with all of whom I worked in my post-graduate studies at UBC during the winter months.

My work with Pioneer during the Second World War was solely in British Columbia. I was searching principally for mercury, antimony, chromium, and tungsten in a wide strip of the province north and south of the Canadian National Railway line between Prince George and Prince Rupert, with a northern arm extending from Vanderhoof to Takla Landing. I worked also in the Princeton–Kamloops –Nelson triangle, the Grand Forks boundary area, and on the west coast of Vancouver Island and Queen Charlotte Island. When I was not engaged in these more remote areas, I participated with other prospectors in the evaluation and some development of various mercury, tungsten, antimony, chromite, and cobalt occurrences in the Bridge River–Ashcroft sector.

Normally I worked in the field with crews of two to six prospectors. Local prospectors were often included in my parties, either on a formal or informal basis. I cherish the memories of those days for the camaraderie and mutual respect as well as the tremendous physical hardships and risks we shared. Among those whose names readily come to mind are Spud Huestis, Cliff and Buster Harrison and Shorty Haven, Sammy Craig, Dan and Manuel Rottacker, Arthur Irwin, Gordon Hilchey, and "Stampede John" Stenbratten.

Occasionally we shared base camps and information concerning the geology of the area in which we were working with others involved in the strategic mineral search. Among those with whom I worked during this time I particularly remember Karl Springer and Dr. Desmond "Cap" Kidd in north-central British Columbia, and Egil Lorntzen and Ed Phillips in the Bridge River area. We often met around campfires at day's end and talked shop. Occasionally someone would dream aloud about the years ahead and how he would strike it rich when the war ended. The dreams of some of these men were not idle: their hard work eventually transformed their dreams into reality.

All of us who shared in Canada's search for strategic minerals worked hard during the Second World War and gained valuable experience and knowledge, but, in truth, our searches were not outstandingly successful. Nevertheless, the group with which I worked did develop and produce a modest amount of antimony from The Snowbird mine near Stuart Lake and tungsten from scheelite in the Bridge River Valley.

At the time we were not certain how antimony was to be used since there was tight military control of such information. Later on we were told that it was used as a pigment in camouflage paint since it could foil certain types of specialized photography used by the enemy. I recall with amusement the wry complaint, made to me by the agent who purchased antimony for the British government, concerning impurities in the antimony we were producing. "Too much selenium and too much gold!" he grumbled on one occasion.

We also produced modest quantities of tungsten from the custom milling of ore from various Bridge River prospects. My crew and I made determined efforts to supplement the mercury production from the newly discovered Pinchi Lake mine in north-central British Columbia, but were unsuccessful. With the occasional help of grizzly bears (principally in accelerating our rate of travel), we tracked the remarkable Pinchi Lake fault structure for an additional forty miles south-easterly from its earlier recognized limits. Despite frequent traces, however, no other substantial concentration of mercury (cinnabar) could be found. In this work we sought to enlarge upon the earlier and brilliant work of a Geological Survey of Canada officer, J. G. Gray, who first identified this structure and the cinnabar within it.

In the difficult Takla–Tezzeron Lakes terrain, we worked vigously, but in vain, to confirm the theory of another able GSC officer, Dr. C. S. Lord, that chromite could occur in that section of British Columbia. In the Vanderhoof–Endako area, Dr. J. E. Armstrong established the presence of a molybdenum-bearing rock formation but we searched without success for concentrations of this metal. Twenty years later, however, in the same area, my friend and colleague, Dr. Chris Riley, with the spare-time help of a local farmer and his road grader, trenched into view the present remarkable Endako mine deposit of molybdenum.

A Serendipitous Discovery

An unexpected discovery, made by accident or what I regard as an act of serendipity, occurred during this period. Dr. James had asked me, following a suggestion by Dr. Cockfield of the GSC, to discuss with prospectors in Burns Lake reports that they had discovered a tungsten deposit. Accordingly I visited Burns Lake and met Cliff and Buster Harrison and their companion Shorty Haven. They showed me pieces of "slide-rock" that appeared to be scheelite, a tungsten mineral. Although it involved a long trip, mainly by water and pack-horse trail, I agreed to visit the source of the mineral specimens shown me.

On the second or third day we finally reached Lindquist Lake.

We had visited various lead and zinc mineral showings along the way despite my efforts to make my companions realize that my sole objective was to see their tungsten deposit! Still, their dawdling was pleasant. Shorty Haven was colourful and entertaining. Under the stress of portaging, Shorty appeared to be the toughest of the group even though he was clearly much older than the rest of us. When Shorty admitted to being over eighty years old – "He's been eighty for the past five years," threw in Buster – I asked what his secret for strength and longevity was. Shorty replied in a conspiratorial whisper, "It's the hot springs at Lakelse in winter and the granite water I drink during the summer."

It was late afternoon by the time we had walked over the portage from Little Whitesail to Lindquist Lake. We were just at the timberline rimming the small valley filled by the lake. Immediately above us, perhaps fifteen hundred feet higher in elevation and on the same slope, I caught sight of a white slope-line near the mountain top, resembling a rock ledge supporting a remnant of snow.

"What's that?" I asked Buster.

"That's the Bull Quartz vein," replied Buster. "Nothin' in it. I've cracked it lots of times. Good trappin' though. I sometimes set marten traps up there."

"And the scheelite slide," added Cliff, "is off to the left of it about half a mile."

Since it would be a couple of hours before the campsite and dinner would be ready I decided to go for a climb.

"Keep in the open away from the scrub," counselled Buster. "Grizzlies!"

With my pick in hand I began a zigzag climb up the steep slope toward the Bull Quartz outcrop. Finally, I reached its lower end. It was quartz, as Buster had said, but it contained faintly perceptible wavy ribboning and faint beige-coloured patches which intrigued me. So I chipped away at some of these patches as I slowly progressed up-slope along the several hundred feet of exposed length. The mass of quartz had a gentle dip into the mountain and appeared to be from eight to eighteen feet wide or thick.

At last I came to a patch where my first pick blow dislodged quite a large chunk of quartz. To my surprise the fresh underside was rose-coloured. As I examined it under my small 10-X magnifying glass I saw, for the first time, small grains of fresh "non-rusted" mineral. I kept cracking and examining fresh pieces until finally a larger flake was revealed. It could be molybdenite, I thought, a mineral of molybdenum, since it was flaky and lacked the typical crystallinity of galena, a mineral of lead. It had the same colour and sheen. I scratched the flake with my pocketknife and examined the scratch. The mineral was very soft and the scratch colour "streak" was not that of molybdenite. The best and most optimistic opinion remaining was that it was a flake of telluride.

I had had no previous practical experience with the rich gold-silver tellurides. All I knew about them was from my reading and the examination of various museum specimens. Tellurides were little known in British Columbia but were common in the great gold-silver mining camps of the western United States. My curiosity grew. I scrambled to crack off more rock fragments. Suddenly two rifle shots from the camp below told me that dinner was ready.

That night as we were unrolling our sleeping bags, Cliff asked, "See anything up there?"

"Yes," I replied, with a sense of pride. "I found some mineralization in the Bull Quartz!" and handed him a small piece of rock.

"The hell you say!" exclaimed Buster, "is it 'moly'?"

"Don't think so," I replied. "I'm not sure what it is. We'll figure it out in the morning."

After breakfast, Cliff and Buster prepared day packs for the hike to their tungsten slide. But I said, "Before you go there I want you to help me sample the Bull Quartz vein."

"Why, it's a half-mile from the tungsten," protested Cliff, "and that's what we're here to see. What's in it for Buster and me if there are values in the Bull Quartz?"

"Same thing," I replied. "If the Bull Quartz kicks, you stake it and give the Pioneer the same terms we've agreed on for the tungsten. And you take care of Shorty."

"Okay," replied the others and we set off.

During the next five hours we tore the moss off the Bull Quartz vein and cut seventeen chip samples across the exposed width of the vein at approximately one-hundred-foot intervals, and then packed the hundred pounds of samples to our camp. In the course of sampling, Cliff in particular had observed several small patches of the silvery grains I had first noted.

"What is it?" he asked over dinner that night.

"I don't know yet, but let's give it a name," I replied. "We'll call it *Queerite!*"

We spent the next day on the tungsten slide at the crest of the mountain. We examined it under a groundsheet spread over our heads like a small mobile tent, since the ultraviolet lamp we used to examine the showing was effective only in the dark. I was generally disappointed with their tungsten showing, mainly because it was all "slide-rock" and nothing solid. I conveyed my disappointment to the brothers by my negative reply when they asked, "Should we stake more claims to cover it while we're here?"

"But," protested Cliff, "I got a seven-dollar gold assay in the stuff."

"No," I replied, frankly doubting Cliff's claim. "Let's wait first."

Two weeks later the assay results from the Bull Quartz vein became available and were sent to the Pioneer office in Vancouver. I received a telephone call from Howard James saying simply, "Come to Vancouver and bring your gear for a one-week trip."

When I arrived he gave me the sample plan I had drawn to scale and left for him and upon which he had inserted the assay results.

"It's unbelievable," said Howard. "A length of 1,720 feet, average width of 11.5 feet, and it all averages 0.24 ounces in gold and 11 ounces in silver. Ed Lovitt and I think you've been salted."

"Impossible," I exclaimed. "Cliff and Buster are absolutely honest and I never lost sight of the samples. I brought them as excess baggage by air from Prince George. I believe they're for real and I think I should now wire the Harrisons to start staking."

"No," replied Howard James. "You may wire them to say you are returning to Burns Lake to meet them. But you'll do the staking and get your option agreement in shape. We'll arrange a chartered aircraft for you to land at the Harrison cottage at Oosta Lake. Pick up the Harrisons and keep right on going into Lindquist to stake."

News of the strike attracted the immediate attention of the British Columbia Department of Mines authorities and several mining scouts who visited the scene. The British Columbia representative of a major New York-based mining company also arrived and prowled around studying our rock cairns carefully. These cairns contained details of our claim-staking written on paper and placed in cans. Since we were well above the timberline, wooden claim posts were unavailable. His study revealed that a small pie-shaped fraction had not been covered by our staking. Unobserved by us, he promptly staked that fraction. Our first clue about this was a communication to Pioneer from the New York-based president of the American company. They would assign this fraction to us for inclusion in our larger group in exchange for an equity in the entire property. To my dismay, the Pioneer directors reluctantly acquiesced to this proposed arrangement. Buster called it "a shotgun marriage."

After the war, Pioneer undertook re-sampling and diamond-drilling. To everyone's great disappointment, this extraordinarily imposing outcrop had very shallow roots. It offered little economic appeal, and Pioneer returned it to the Harrison brothers.

About fifteen years later, when I told this story to Joe Hirshhorn, the celebrated mining personality with whom I worked in the successful development of the uranium deposits on the north shore of Lake Huron, he was fascinated. "You want to tackle it again?" Joe asked.

"Yes," I said.

"Well," said Joe, "Let's give it another whirl! A crap game calls for more than one roll of the dice."

In 1958, with Hirshhorn financing, the Harrison brothers as associates, and a new name, we returned and tunnelled beneath the surface. The roots were exposed and little more. It was a fine dream with a rude awakening!

Nevertheless it taught me a hard but important lesson. The best outcrops do not necessarily produce the best ore bodies. Fortunately, as the years passed, I learned from personal experience that the converse could also be true: some indifferent outcrops, with faith and continuing effort on my part, yielded very important ore bodies. Among these were the Elliot Lake uranium deposits and our Pater copper-cobalt and Anglo-Rouyn copper-gold mines.

The "Capricious" Element in Geology

It is through personal participation in such unpredictables that one is lured to prospecting. Although mineral production is an industry, mineral search – prospecting – is a romantic adventure.

I had personal experience of this during the time I prospected for strategic minerals in the Burns Lake–Smithers area, when I became involved in a detailed study of the Cronin-Babine mine which earlier had produced lead and zinc. My study was concerned with the verification, if possible, that tin also occurred in or near these deposits.

This detailed research study became the subject of my Master's thesis with the encouragement of Professor Henry Gunning.

My research findings were well-regarded and received a good grade. But one of those participating in my oral examination, a brilliant UBC petrologist, Professor Swanson, criticized my use of a particular word in my thesis. "*Capricious,*" he said, in the midst of my oral examination, "is not a suitable scientific adjective to apply to the characteristics of volcanic rock forms."

I was convinced then and still am, that there is a capricious element in nature. Nature is not entirely predictable. If it were, there would be little romance in geology and prospecting. The manner in which rock formations form often suggests that random, or capricious, forces were at work in their creation. A less elegant synonym for capricious is probably *teaser* and the latter is probably one of the most used adjectives in the lexicon of many bush prospectors in pursuit of their mother lode.

In time, Professor Swanson came to share my view. A decade or more later, when he was semi-retired, he sent me a small autographed paper he had written dealing with the formulae proposed for the "averaging" of erratic gold assays present in the Box mine in Saskatchewan for which he had served as a consultant. Swanson's paper commenced with the words: "In mineral deposits where the ore metal is capriciously distributed. . . . " Doubtless, after long reflection he wished to assure me that he too recognized a certain bewitching charm in the randomness of nature.

Prospecting in Northern British Columbia

My search for strategic minerals led me to the Omineca district, the area centred around Fort St. James, east of Smithers and north of Prince George in north-central British Columbia. This area is markedly different and the topography gentler than the rain forests of the British Columbia coast and islands. In place of mountains there are hills with moderate timber coverings instead of rocks and rock slides. The rivers and numerous lakes are accessible by pontoon-equipped aircraft and canoe. It is, in part, "range country" with meadows and grasslands, all used for grazing. Pack horses were in general use in the early 1940s.

In the less-settled areas there was considerable "big game." Grizzly bear, mountain sheep, caribou, and deer were to be found at higher elevations. There were deer, bear, and wolf at middle to lower elevations, and moose, beaver, jack-rabbits, and many types of commercial fur-bearing animals in lower, wet areas. Partridge, grouse, and "fool-hen" (partridge) were seasonally abundant, and lake fish were plentiful. These circumstances had encouraged Indians in earlier times to establish settlements there, and later the fur-traders – principally the North West Company – to set up posts or forts.

The Omineca area is intersected by the east-west waterway of the Skeena River and its lakes. The famous Dewdney pack trail, built between the 1860s – from the Barkerville community of the Cariboo gold rush period – and the 1890s – to the Klondike goldfields in the Yukon – traverses this Omineca district. We frequently used abandoned portions of that celebrated trail.

Since Omineca, given its moderate climate and better developed infrastructure, was in general a far more hospitable terrain than the coast, I made Fort St. James my base for most of 1943. With Mary and our daughter Marion, then about three, we made our home in one of a colony of small attractive cottages at the edge of Fort St. James on the sandy shores of Stuart Lake with its flat hinterland of small pine, spruce, and poplar. Our neighbours were Karl Springer and Desmond "Cap" Kidd on one side, and Russ Baker, one of the local bush pilots, on the other.

Mary instantly became popular in Fort St. James with her home-cooking. Her generosity with freshly baked pies won her several life-long friends. Her cooking ability and hospitality were an important fringe benefit in keeping my prospecting crew intact and their morale high.

Our daughter Marion (identified as "Sugarplum" in the Pioneer Company's weekly staff journal, *The Office Keyhole*, for which I was the northern bush correspondent), also became widely known among the native majority of the village. Marion, a miniature of her lovely mother, was a blonde, doll-like figure, dressed in winter in an Indian-made parka of fox fur and usually clutching her very lively little white poodle to her breast. When Marion and her mother went shopping at the Bay Trading Post, or to pick up the mail at Soapy Smith's, Mary often pulled Marion on a small Indian-made sleigh.

The pair of them – more properly the trio, since there was much public interest in the poodle – were often followed by a single file of native women and children wherever they went, each trying to outdo the other with competitive bids. After weeks of effort, the bids had reached five marten pelts (or was it mink?) and were still being declined. It was only then that the Indian women realized that Mary was serious – Marion's poodle was not tradeable!

The large Indian and Métis population in and around Fort St. James during the Second World War may have developed, in part, as a result of the prosperity of the North West Company post established there in the nineteenth century. Fur, game, fish, and berries were abundant, and the waterways made travel relatively easy. The native people had adopted the white man's ways in considerable measure – including his work ethic.

When I moved to Fort St. James with my family in 1943, there were no public beer parlours in the town. In all likelihood, liquor could not be sold to Indians legally. I recall no liquor problems among them at that time, a situation that was to change grievously in subsequent years. During the year that we lived in Fort St. James we enjoyed our relations with the native people.

At the trading post at Christmas time, favourite items among Indian men were chewing tobacco and "chokemass" (cheese). The Indian women took particular interest in perfumed soap, which they insisted, to the despair of the trader, on unwrapping so that they might better evaluate and enjoy its delightful scent. When I spoke to a salesperson regarding this practice, I was told that the soap was rarely used for washing. Instead, it was carried in the women's "bloomers" to add to their personal fragrance.

Indians paid for their purchases more often with furs than cash. By exchanging goods rather than money, the Indians in that remote section of British Columbia were maintaining the barter system, a system vastly older than the paper money system which now operates so widely.

Of Bears and Wolves

One aspect of the native culture of particular interest is their ability to live in harmony with nature, avoiding direct conflict with animals. Knowing how to avoid confrontation with such animals as grizzly bears is and has been of long-standing interest to prospectors, including myself.

While I have never actually tangled with a grizzly, I did have one very tense eyeball-to-eyeball meeting with a huge bear. My companion on that particular prospecting trip in the Neilsp Mountain range near Fort St. James was a small but tough and wiry French Canadian, Alcide, or Sid, Robillard. Sid was a keen marksman and carried a rifle everywhere for food and protection. At that time, the Neilsp Mountains abounded in a variety of game, so we knew that bear could also be expected. At one point while we were prospecting, I picked up a brass shellcase dropped by some hunter and remarked to Sid as I slipped the case into my jacket pocket. "It will make a good whistle if we become separated."

As we plodded on, examining rock outcrops on our way, we came to a large burned-over section of land. The forest fire – probably ignited by lightning – had left behind a great charred and desolate expanse. Only a few blackened and bare trunks remained upright among the remains of fallen trees and burned stumps. As I looked across this desolate area from the vantage point of a small rock bluff eight or nine feet high, I decided that we must walk directly across it. I took off my loaded packboard for Sid to pass down to me from the bluff.

As I slid down, I noted, nearby, what appeared to be a large charred stump. When I stood upright at the bottom of the bluff to survey the burned-out expanse, the "stump" stirred, seemed to grow in size, and turned to face me. A startled bear stood only about a dozen or so feet away from me!

Slowly it rose on its hind feet, pawing the air and rolling its head as if it was having difficulty focusing on me. Upright, the bear probably stood seven or eight feet tall. The bear and I were hemmed in by the fallen tree trunks which formed a barrier around us. There was no escape route. We stood glowering at one another.

I could see Sid above on the bluff. He was semi-paralyzed with fear. His rifle was lashed to his packboard and it was obvious that he lacked the strength in his fingers to untie the knots. His eyes were fixed on the bear. Both of us remained utterly silent, afraid that a shout would only heighten the bear's alarm.

Slowly, I reached for my small, sharp, all-steel hatchet which I always carried in a leather scabbard at my side. Slowly I raised it in my right hand. I was under no illusion that my small hand-axe would either turn away a powerful bear or prove a match for him should he attack me, but if my life was to be taken it would be at some price – no matter how small.

How long we remained fixed in our positions I am not sure. It seemed an eternity but may have been only thirty seconds or less. As I stood, waiting for the bear to make the first move, my brain was churning over how I might escape safely. I remembered the brass shell cartridge. If I could blow a couple of sharp blasts perhaps that would distract and unsettle the bear.

Slowly, slowly, I shifted the hatchet to my left hand. With my right, I pulled the shell cartridge from my pocket. I forced myself to take a slow deep breath and sounded two sharp blasts. Instantly the bear dropped to all four feet and shuffled quickly around in a small erratic circle. I moved backwards perhaps six feet. My back was pressing against the base of the rock bluff; its solidity seemed to give me strength. I kept eyeing the bear.

Finding nothing in its small circle of exploration, it raised and shook its head. It seemed to be trying to clear its vision or to scent. It began ambling away from me over and under charred fallen trees. "Thank God," I thought, "it's leaving!" But my very thought seemed to trigger a change of mind in the bear, which abruptly turned around and headed back in my direction!

Now totally drained of strength I watched in desperation as the bear headed towards me. "This is it," I thought. "At least Sid knows the story." Miraculously, the bear halted, stared at the bluff and me through the charred stumps, as if sightless. Turning at a sharp angle, it noisily ambled away.

I helped a shaken Sid down the bank. Quickly he unfastened his rifle from his packboard and loaded it with shells. Carrying it at the ready, he followed me as I urged that we "get cracking and out of here, fast!" Prospecting could wait for a later day.

We picked our way across the burnt expanse and finally reached the edge of the forest where I set a brisker pace. Suddenly I was startled by a blast of rifle fire from behind. I looked back. Sid had shot without warning. "What now!" I wondered.

He had seen movement in a nearby shrub. We watched. Silence prevailed. Sid moved toward the shrub, rifle ready. He poked the rifle barrel into the shrub and hooked out a clump of fur. With a nervous laugh he threw it aside. He had killed a rabbit!

Again we set out, at an even faster pace. Finally I glimpsed the lake we had been heading for. Now we could stop for a breather. We slipped off our packsacks and sat down on a fallen moss-covered tree. It was wonderful to relax, even if briefly. After a few minutes both of us stirred to stand up – we couldn't! Our legs were like rubber. Shock from our encounter with the bear had set in, and it was probably fifteen minutes before we regained the strength to stand upright and walk again.

A week or so later, hardly recovered from our episode with the bear, Sid and I encountered wolves near Fort St. James. We were making a two-day traverse of a ridgetop on Nielsp Mountain. There was much evidence of caribou, deer, bear, and wolves. We passed several skulls, antlers, and partially eaten carcasses, and there were frequent fresh wolf tracks. Darkness was approaching, and, although the surroundings were not hospitable, there was a small stream for water and ample firewood, so we decided to camp for the night. We set up a canvas tarpaulin to serve as a roof in the event of rain, and spread out our ground sheet and sleeping bags on a rough mattress of juniper shrubbery plucked from nearby.

Sid started a fire for the tea pail and opened a can of bully beef and beans. I took my axe and went in search of some logs that would give us a fire that would last through the night. However, the small basin at the headwaters of the stream where we had set up camp was lined with thin spindly poplar trees hardly more than three inches in diameter; there were no spruce, pine, balsam, or birch logs. I had to drag over two or three large old stumps from a logged-over area.

We ate as the blackness of night crept up. A chilling breeze murmured through the poplars. I dragged one of the stumps over the fire pit embers as a token if not a source of warmth. Exhausted after a long day, we crawled into our sleeping bags and fell asleep.

Suddenly, a long, eerie, and seemingly anguished wail awakened us.

"Wolves," announced Sid, reaching for his rifle and releasing the safety catch. "I wonder how many?"

We both sat up in our woollen underwear, half out of our sleeping bags. The first long cry of the wolf leader continued.

"I can't see him," said Sid, "but maybe I can scare him." He fired two shots in the direction of the cry. There followed a few seconds of silence, but the long, quavering howl of the pack leader rose again. To our despair, this time it was echoed by the cries of several other wolves.

I unzipped my sleeping bag, pulled on my "tin pants" (stiffened three-ply heavy canvas with waterproof interlayers) and a heavy work shirt, and crawled out from under the tarpaulin cover. The sky was a black dome around me, save for a few stars and the dim outline of the surrounding poplars.

"I can't see a thing," I said, and struck the burning stump with the axe to enliven the campfire and provide more light. An eerie silence encircled us, but Sid was not deluded.

"I'll shake them up," he said. The words were hardly out of his mouth when he let go a volley of four or five shots in a circle around us. Immediately the howling began again, practically overlapping the last echoes of Sid's shooting, and seeming to come from every direction.

"I don't know if it's a small pack circling us or if they're all around us," said Sid.

"Well, quit firing," I said. "Save your shells until they close in. Let's get a real fire going. That may keep a distance between us. I think I see a small pack that keeps wheeling around us."

"You're crazy!"

"No," I replied. "Just keep staring down low and you'll see their eyes flashing between the poplar trunks."

After a pause, Sid exclaimed, "*Sacré Dieu*, you're right. Now I see them!"

There seemed to be little else to say or do. The eerie howling of the pack leader rose at intervals and was echoed by others in the pack. We knew we had to stall the creatures off until daylight, keep a good fire going, and if the wolves closed in, kill the leader. Sid and I passed a restless, disorganized night.

One of us tried to snatch a few minutes of sleep while the other sat, rifle in hand, stoking the campfire. The anguished wailing of the pack leader was occasionally picked up by the others. Always, when I peered about me, I could see the glint of flitting eyes.

Although supposedly on guard duty with rifle in my lap, I dozed off from exhaustion. The campfire was out when Sid shook me awake. It was daylight. I mumbled, "What a terrible dream!"

"No dream," said Sid, "It was for real, but not as bad as we thought. I checked over the ground. A pack of five or six only and they hung over there in a small circle. Them 'eyes' we saw everywhere were the stars between the swaying poplars. You're always like that, boss. Too good an imagination!"

Adventures in the Air

I shared my adventures in the air with some of Canada's most gifted aviation pioneers – the bush pilots – an appellation that gives no idea of the highly significant roles they played in the opening up of Canada's frontier for economic development. They created the art of bush flying and through the exercise of that art they helped Canadians overcome the seemingly invincible barriers of the trackless wilderness. They rolled up distances and brought remote places near. And they did it safely and with inspiration. The pilots with whom I flew knew how to bring their aircraft safely home through changing winds and sleet, fog and darkness, rising and falling water. They seemed as one with the birds!

By the late 1930s, when I lived in Tofino on Vancouver Island, aircraft were being used widely in mineral exploration. Over a decade earlier, in 1925, mine-maker Jack Hammell had learned, by flying supplies into the newly discovered Howey gold site at Red Lake in north-western Ontario, that in the winter an airplane could fly in an hour and a half the same distance a dog-team could travel in ten days. Hammell also learned that the versatility of bush aircraft stimulated the ingenuity of prospectors. Such aircraft could operate on wheels where rare strips were present, or with pontoons on waterways, or with skis on snow or ice. The advantages of aircraft in an industry in which it is essential "to get there first" were obvious.

In 1927, Hammell organized Northern Aerial Minerals Exploration (NAME) Limited, the world's first aerial prospecting company. Hammell's bold initiative of using aircraft in prospecting for minerals led others to do the same. I frequently used aircraft to visit mineral prospects.

The pilot with whom I flew most often on short trips along the west coast of Vancouver Island was Ginger Coote. Like many pioneer bush pilots, he was an owner-flyer. The bush aircraft of the 1930s were usually small, single-engine, propeller-driven monoplanes. At that time there were practically no airstrips along the west coast of Vancouver Island, let alone open level land areas, so pontoon-equipped aircraft were used. Since there are only a few large lakes along British Columbia's west coast and very few sections of rivers suitable for aircraft takeoff and landing (it is largely mountainous rain forest) the most appropriate access points for aircraft were the rare coastal beaches or river delta areas. Of all the bush flying I have done in my career, over many different terrains in many countries, some of the most frightening I have experienced was along the west coast of Vancouver Island.

In the late 1930s and early 1940s there was little meteorological data and no radar control. It was all visual flying, requiring a good memory for route references. When you became enveloped in cloud or fog you just flew by the "seat of your pants!" Literally – the pressure on either one rear-cheek or the other would tell you if you were banking left or right. The aircraft was operated by one individual who was weather forecaster, route navigator, pilot, and mechanic.

In the first small planes there were usually two double seats, room for four people, and some limited cargo space in the rear. I nearly always flew up front with Coote, even though that was traditionally the seat for the heaviest passenger on the flight. There were dual controls, each seat having a stick and pedals. Although I have never flown an aircraft I instinctively acquired most of the operating motions. On several occasions when we became engulfed in turbulent air, Ginger shouted to me, "Franc, help me with this one." Several times we decided, or were forced, to come down for unexpected landings until the weather or visibility improved.

In the late 1930s, I was assigned by Pioneer mines to do some prospecting in the Yukon, near Dawson. The prospecting challenge was to identify, if possible, the lode source of the rich gold placer deposits of Eldorado and Bonanza creeks. This project had been proposed to my boss, Dr. Howard James, by a colourful prospector of long experience in the Yukon, known locally as "Stampede John," who had developed some theories concerning the lode source. To fly to the Yukon I made arrangements with Yukon Southern Air Transport and met Grant McConachie, its creator.

Standing well over six feet, McConachie was a warm, friendly man with a broad engaging smile. He dressed in jeans and a lumberman's shirt, his casual informality blending encouragingly with his obvious efficiency as a pilot.

I had heard of McConachie's memorable mercy flight in 1932, when he was only twenty-three years old. McConachie and his partner and mechanic "Limey" Green had saved the lives of two severely burned trappers. Their own lives had been risked as McConachie skillfully piloted his critically damaged aircraft to Edmonton and essential hospital care for the wounded men.

For my flight to the Yukon, I went to Vancouver's Sea Island airport with my prospecting gear and met McConachie. The plane was on wheels, twin-engined, and had seats for twelve passengers – huge in my experience of bush flying to that time. There was to be only one other passenger (who failed to show up) since this was mainly a "cargo haul" of produce and mail to Watson Lake and Whitehorse. The return flight was primarily to bring mail and fresh lake fish to Vancouver. McConachie was interested to learn that I was a prospector who had done some bush flying. "Come up front after we're airborne and we can talk," he said.

Later I learned of the remarkable manner in which McConachie had acquired this and two other new Barkley-Grow twin-engined aircraft. His self-confidence, ambition, and demonstrated flying ability had enabled him to purchase these three fine aircraft from a liquidation in bankruptcy for a token $1 each and rental-purchase agreement to pay $1,000 per month out of earned income. Little wonder that McConachie later became an aviation industry pioneer of world stature!

My first Yukon-bound flight with Grant McConachie was memorable. The Barkley-Grow was loaded and fueled, McConachie revved up the engines and moved onto the runway, with freight crates strapped into position. Soon we were gathering momentum. I sat alone in the passenger area.

Suddenly the plane lurched to the left and veered off the black-topped runway into the high grass. Then the aircraft completed a half-left turn with that wing tip "mowing the grass." Instinctively, I feared an explosion or fire, but McConachie had quickly cut the engines. As soon as the plane ground to a stop I had the emergency door off and leapt to the ground. Complete calm prevailed when I looked back at the aircraft from perhaps fifty feet away. McConachie, half out of his pilot's exit, shouted, "Joubin – you're a fast man on your feet!"

The braking system on the left wheel had frozen, it would take until next morning to repair the damage. I told McConachie I did not wish to return home since the incident might upset my wife. He said, "Okay, but be ready for an early start."

The next morning we were airborne with two more passengers, both big-game hunters. When we came down for the regular stop at Watson Lake just north of the Yukon border, we unloaded freight and the two hunters left, but not before McConachie had made an indelible impression upon them and me. Two quarters of fresh moose meat were being loaded onto the aircraft. Seeing them, McConachie casually strolled over, drew a hunting knife from his belt sheath, cut off a slice of meat, and nonchalantly started chewing on it. Glancing up, he noticed one of the game hunters eyeing him. "Care for some anyone?" said McConachie, reaching for his knife again. "It's delicious! You, Franc?" Before I could refuse or escape, he thrust a strip toward me. I ate it but didn't enjoy it. It was unsightly and bland to the taste, a combination that did not impress me. Years later, in the Belgian Congo and Warsaw, Poland, I found raw meat rendered more palatable by a chef when served as steak tartare!

Like many other old-time bush pilots, Grant McConachie had a great sense of humour and a perfect rapport with his prospector, logger, and game-hunter passengers whom he regarded more as friends and co-adventurers in the wilderness than as clients.

McConachie and I shared several flights in the years immediately following that memorable first trip, then we went our separate ways. Overcoming a variety of problems, McConachie promoted the eventually successful Canadian Pacific Airlines with flights to many parts of the world. To him, and to the other bush pilots who always took me up and brought me down safely, I owe a debt of gratitude, not only for the skill with which they took me through the air but for the fund of rich memories they gave me.

Completion of My Master's Degree

During the winter months in Canada, most attractive "boot-and-pick" prospecting areas are covered with snow and ice and many prospectors engage in other activities such as trapping. Exploration becomes difficult or impossible, although advanced development of proven mineral deposits does continue. Since the life of a prospector in Canada is seasonal I worked in the late autumn, winter, and early spring of 1940 to 1942 on my Master's degree.

My fellow graduate students at UBC, while few in number, were able and dedicated. Several became noted explorers or professors of geology of national and international repute. Kenneth de Pencier Watson and Robert E. Thompson became outstanding professors, while Charles S. Ney and William R. Bacon became successful geologists. William H. Gross excelled both as a professor and as a professional economic geologist. All, save Bacon, have pre-deceased me.

I found post-graduate study stimulating and demanding. While I

was older than my classmates and lacked the momentum of continuity,
I had the advantages of considerable field experience and the self-
confidence it produces. Although at the time I had no fixed plan of
proceeding to a doctoral degree, which would have necessitated study
in another university since UBC did not then offer doctoral work, I
completed various extra elective credit courses such as scientific German, then a prerequisite for a Ph.D. degree. I maintained the lurking
thought that if I secured an average of 80 per cent or better on my
work at the Master's level, I would continue to the doctorate. I failed
that self-imposed standard by two points.

My family was of great help at this time. Thanks to Mary, my
home was my refuge, my relaxation, and my inspiration. Both Mary
and our daughter Marion took special care of me. One day, Marion,
then aged three, was found by a surprised neighbour waiting alone
at the bus stop where I usually got off, two or three blocks from our
home. When asked if she were lost she replied, "No, just waiting for
my Daddy to get home from school."

With the help of several excellent professors, I received my Master's degree in 1942. My thesis supervisor, Dr. Henry Gunning, and
my employer, Dr. Howard James, encouraged me to proceed to a
doctoral degree in eastern Canada, however, the uncertainty of the
war years, the needs of my family, and the illness of my mother, then
living alone in Victoria, all led me to delay and eventually abandon
that ambition. We remained in western Canada until the end of the
Second World War.

By the time I began my full-time professional career as a geologist
with Pioneer Mines I knew that a successful prospector and mineral
scout must keep accurate field notes. A good memory of where one
has been and what one has seen are invaluable. But memory must be
supplemented by written records. Good field notes help a prospector
make the most of his time and of what he has learned. Similarly, the
reading of geological reports, if any, and related materials on the
particular geographic location in which one is working or plans to
work is essential.

As a beneficiary of the writings of others I decided perhaps I could
also make a contribution to geological knowledge. My first technical
paper, published in a national scientific journal in 1942, described,
with forgiveable parental pride, my first-born mine. It was entitled
"Geology and Ore Deposits in the Musketeer–Buccaneer Area,
Vancouver Island, B.C." Subsequently, a considerable number of my

papers were published, some with the assistance of associates or bright protégés.

Most of my subsequent technical writing dealt with my professional activities as a geologist or related matters. My objective in writing has been to describe, for my peers and for lay persons, new phenomena which I had observed or to offer new concepts for the resolution of controversial geological problems.

When my family and I moved to eastern Canada, my immediate problem, however, was not of a scientific or technical nature. It was the highly practical challenge of becoming established with my family in a new location and deciding on the form of the next chapter in our life together.

VII

To Eastern Canada – and the Bay Street Jungle

Horace Greeley, the celebrated nineteenth-century American news-paperman, is widely remembered for his advice to young men of his day: "Go West, young man and grow up with the country!" That was probably good advice at that time. In 1946, however, I was about as far west as one could go in Canada, and at thirty-five years of age I was already wary of the infallibility of "conventional wisdom." So I headed east!

I took the train to Toronto a month ahead of my family. Soon after I arrived and began to work as the eastern Canada representative of Pioneer Mines I was invited to serve as a consultant to several leaders in the Canadian mining industry and to participate in joint ventures with various Bay Street "buccaneers." I chose carefully among the opportunities before me. During the next ten years, my first decade in the east, I enjoyed technical and financial success exceeding all my earlier goals. I also fulfilled the expectations of my closest collaborators, my mother Marthe, and my wife Mary.

Dr. Christopher Riley, responsible since 1939 for Pioneer's affairs in eastern Canada, including exploration activities in Manitoba and northern Ontario and Quebec, wished to return to British Columbia. Pioneer wanted to maintain an exploration contact in eastern Canada and I undertook to do that for them. The idea of exchanging jobs with Chris was attractive for two reasons. I was looking for a new challenge and I knew that Chris would leave a tidy ongoing operation for his successor.

Chris Riley had been born in England and brought to Canada early in life. Largely through his own efforts he completed his sec-ondary schooling in Summerland, British Columbia. Subsequently he enrolled in Brandon College in Manitoba, then a baptist college affiliated with McMaster University in Hamilton, and received his Bachelor of Arts degree in 1921. For several years he taught school in Alberta before, as I jokingly suggested to him, he "saw the light" and decided to study geology.

In 1929, Chris received the degree of Master of Science in Geology from the University of British Columbia, and in 1934, his doctorate in geology from the University of Chicago. He then joined the Geological Survey of Canada and completed a geological traverse by canoe and outboard motor from Lake Athabasca to Great Bear Lake and back, a distance of about two thousand miles. During his work with the Survey he became acquainted with many colourful characters, including the LaBines and the great bush pilots of those years, Grant McConachie, Wop May, and others.

Like my boss, Howard James, Chris was a person of strong social conscience, a truly helpful religious person. Occasionally, he quoted from the Scriptures. This rare talent was sometimes called upon in some of the remote corners of Canada when emotional or spiritual issues, sometimes a combination of both, appeared to require a degree of clerical formality. Chris was always ready to help. He told me of one occasion when he "was ready but not fast enough."

One of Chris's assignments when he was based in Yellowknife, at a time when that community was only a cluster of tents on the north arm of Great Slave Lake, took on an unusually eerie character. It was winter in that land of permafrost – the season of endless night.

A prospector had been found frozen to death on the tundra, an empty whisky bottle beside him. The deceased man's friends were troubled and came to Chris, who, in his semi-official capacity as Justice of the Peace, assured them he would be prepared to certify "death by natural causes" when the Mountie next appeared in camp. This was not sufficient, however, to satisfy the mourners. They felt their departed friend should be buried with all possible dignity. Chris agreed to help.

"First," said Chris, "we'll have to dig a grave."

"But we can't – the ground is frozen solid."

Chris thought about this. "Well, scratch as deep as you can. Collect a bunch of big loose rocks. Pile them around. We'll have to put them on top."

Several hours later, Chris was told that a shallow trench had been prepared. It had been difficult, but with the help of some powder it had been done. Now they were ready.

Seated beside his kerosene lamp, Chris had written out his notes for the burial service and had, undoubtedly, added some brief remarks laced with the Irish wit with which he was so gifted. During the quarter-mile trudge up the little hill to the grave site in the strange early-morning dimness of the sub-Arctic winter, Chris's nose told him that the mourners trailing behind him had already resorted in their grief to the usual "painkiller."

Soon they were at the grave site, huddled together. The deceased had been placed in his sleeping bag and rested in the shallow grave. Chris called for silence. And silence fell briefly.

As Chris bit his half-frozen lips to begin his remarks, a roar of husky male voices engulfed him – loud and clear – in the grey darkness and cold of that stark stony hill:

"Three cheers for good old Joe!" they roared. "Hip, hip – HURRAY! Hip, hip – HURRAY! Hip, hip – HURRAY! And a tiger!"

Then the whole gang of prospectors quietly turned their backs on good old Joe and "preacher Riley." The "top stones" could be rolled into place later. Back down the hill they shuffled and into a tent where some "painkiller" remained. Chris was left standing alone with the corpse at his feet. His thoughtfully prepared burial sermon, laced with gentle humour, remained undelivered in his hand. Knowing Chris, he probably folded it carefully and, tucking it into his parka pocket, muttered "Good for the next one!"

That event was long past when I met Chris as I began my work in Toronto.

To Toronto – Places and People

With Chris Riley, I went to Pioneer's offices in the Concourse Building, a block west of Bay Street on the north side of Adelaide in downtown Toronto. Although the Concourse was a handsome structure, it was regarded by some people as a "Bay Street" den of iniquity and intrigue.

As soon as I had become familiar with the details of the office, Chris and I went on a month's tour of Pioneer's activities in Manitoba, northern Ontario, and Quebec. In Manitoba we visited the Snow Lake gold rush area where Pioneer, along with other companies, was engaged in prospecting. Riley and I were well-received everywhere in Manitoba since he was regarded as a "native son." In northern Ontario it was the same – everyone knew Riley in communities and the bush camps alike. But it was in northern Quebec, in the frontier communities between Malartic, Cadillac, Val d'Or, and Bourlamaque, where Riley's natural exuberance and the extrovert nature of the northern Quebecois produced a "critical mass" that verged on self-combustion. In fact, that literally occurred late one night following a reunion party in the Bourlamaque Hotel – a fire alarm, luckily false. I felt a rare sense of embarrassment on that occasion because, among the excited hordes of hairy nude Frenchmen pouring into the hotel corridors, I was the "odd one" wearing pyjama bottoms.

Before his departure for Vancouver, Chris introduced me to various members of the geological and mining fraternity in Toronto. These introductions were invaluable because Chris was widely known and highly respected. Among his many eastern extra-curricular activities, Chris was a charter member of the Geological Discussion Club of Toronto. This informal group included a dozen or so of the senior names in Canadian mining and geology, including Bill James and his partner B. S. W. Buffam, Cyril Knight, Percy Hopkins, John Reid, Willett Ambrose, Charlie Houston, Dick Murphy, Neil Beaton, and others. Chris introduced me at a meeting of this club where I found, somewhat to my surprise, that several of them knew me through the articles I had written and published in the west. I joined the club, shared in the secretarial duties, and enjoyed it for many years as a most convivial and informative group.

After my month-long familiarization tour through the mining districts and the introductions he made for me in Toronto, Chris Riley departed for the west. Thanks to Chris and Carol Riley's thoughtful prior arrangement, Mary, Marion, and I, along with our spaniel Birdie, moved into their vacated apartment. (Birdie had replaced Fifi the poodle, who had contracted fatal pneumonia in northern B.C.)

Marion was six and had already done considerable travelling, most of it in the British Columbia mountains. On their trip east, the train had crossed the B.C. coast range, the interior mountain chain, and the Rockies, through mountain scenery, forests, and across cascading rivers. Then came the rolling Alberta prairie for a day or so, the flat expanse of Saskatchewan for another day and more, and the wide Manitoba prairie for yet another day. Marion showed increased restlessness as the long journey across the flat prairies continued. On the third night, as the train rolled on toward Ontario and Mary tucked Marion into her berth, she seized her mother's sleeve and asked in an anxious voice, "Mummie, do you think we'll come to the edge tonight?"

Mary and I greatly appreciated the help and generosity extended to us by our new-found friends in Toronto, but we were not impressed with the appearance of the centre of post-war Toronto. The wartime grime and neglect of public facilities not deemed essential to the war effort were apparent everywhere. We felt engulfed in a huge factory city.

Whenever we could during the next two years, we escaped to Montreal or to country towns or villages, such as Bancroft, to enjoy a more relaxed and cleaner weekend of gracious living. Undoubtedly we had been spoilt by the year-round natural beauty and social amenities we had enjoyed in British Columbia.

My place of work, the Pioneer offices in the Concourse Building in the centre of Toronto, was modest – "monkish" I remarked to Chris – in size and furnishings. The only embellishment was the odd commercial calendar. Every shelf and corner in the office, however, contained some oddity of nature observed and retrieved by Chris Riley – driftwood, tree trunk burls, oddly-formed boulders, and rock specimens amongst others. The space occupied by Pioneer Mines was divided into two offices with a store-like counter in the entrance area, behind which the secretary worked. When I took over, the staff included J. P. Dolan, the office manager, and a music student who worked as a secretary during her holidays.

J.P., like Chris, was well-known among the Bay Street fraternity. He was a mining accountant with promotional inclinations who had had considerable bush experience as a camp accountant, or time-keeper. He introduced me to the Bay Street promotional fraternity, which, as I recall it, he dryly described as being "as lively as the jungle!"

In Canada during the years 1947 to 1967, a unique group of entrepreneurs of the mining industry, celebrated as promoters or brokers and described as "buccaneers" by some American commentators, and "angels" by some of their beneficiaries, flourished in Toronto and Montreal. These were the money-finders for the highly speculative penny-stock companies that specialized in raising the money prospectors required to carry on their work. Without the money raised through the sale of shares in these penny-stock companies, those two remarkable decades of mine-finding in Canada would never have occurred.

The development of mines or oilfields involves three essential stages; search, development, and finally, after much elimination, production. The financial and technical risk is, of course, highest at the beginning and diminishes with successful investigation and development.

Booming Bay Street

When I arrived in the area, the mining promotion scene, both in Montreal and Toronto, was at a lively simmer but not yet "Boylen," as any punster who knew Jim Boylen, one of the primary "bucca-neers" in Canada's mining industry, might have observed.

In Toronto the leading mining promoters were clustered into three or four buildings in the core of the city's financial district, often simply called "Bay Street." This district was bounded by Richmond Street on the north, Wellington on the south, York on the west, and Victoria Street on the east. Bay Street runs north and south roughly in the centre of this district.

The Concourse Building was also the base of various well-known promoters. Sammy (later called "Sweetgrass") Ciglen, a lawyer and promoter; Sammy Zacks, a mining lawyer; Joe Hirshhorn, a stock-broker and promoter with whom I worked closely later; Bryan New-kirk and Dennyson Denny, both promoters, were among the more agile tenants in the Concourse Building when I came to Toronto. J. J. Byrne, a well-known prospector; Robert Bryce, a mining engineer; Harry Knight Sr., a broker; Gilbert and Charles LaBine, celebrated prospectors and self-promoters; and Jim Boylen, a prospector and developer, were only two blocks away. Thayer Lindsley, a highly successful mining engineer and developer of the Ventures-Falcon-bridge empire, and Arthur White, a broker and co-developer of the great Red Lake gold camp, were four blocks away. All were active promoters, and constructively so. On Pioneer's behalf, or later as an independent consultant, I met and worked with most of these men.

Why the designation "Bay Street promoters" was applied to the group is unclear to me since practically none had a Bay Street address. Perhaps the location of the Toronto Stock Exchange (TSE) and several unlisted brokerage houses on Bay Street gave it the name. The TSE, however, played practically no role in the unlisted penny-stock under-writing I describe.

The pattern of high-risk, high-return speculative financing of min-eral exploration during this period was relatively simple. It differed only in minor details in the provinces of Ontario, Quebec, and British Columbia. Of these three, Ontario was the primary focus of such financing in Canada and most familiar to me.

An individual prospector, or small private prospecting syndicate, would approach a promoter with a mining prospect. It could be a group of newly staked claims in a relatively unknown area, but with some factual or fanciful reason for believing it offered promise of success. Or it could be a "tie-on" group of claims adjoining a prospect enjoying developmental success.

The staking process usually starts with a prospector making a visual discovery of mineral in a rock outcrop, or an exploration corporation identifying a geophysical anomaly. Following the initial staking or claiming of such a discovery in the manner prescribed under governmental regulations, other licensed prospectors race in to stake next to the discovery, in anticipation that "more of the same" is present – which often is the case. Ore bodies are like bananas; where there is one, there may be a bunch. The claims staked later, on hope alone, are called "tie-on" claims. Ironically, "tie-on" claims quite often eventually prove of greater value than the original discovery claims.

A prospector might also approach a promoter concerning a prospect ("a showing") on which earlier development had been done and abandoned but for which there were new reasons why it should be re-activated. Among such reasons might be either an imaginative new geological theory, or improved economic conditions for the metal concerned which might enhance earlier evaluation of the worth of the prospect.

If the promoter was impressed by the prospector's enthusiasm and property description and "the fashion of the day" he might or might not enquire from a geological consultant as to its prospective merits. If the promoter was reassured he would usually have the same consultant prepare a descriptive prospectus of the property and exploratory objectives. The phrase, "fashion of the day" refers to the economics of the metal involved, the district involved (close to a proven orebody or mine nearby), and the success and reputation of the prospector and the consultant involved.

I frequently served as the technical and professional adviser in the preparation of such prospectuses. In preparing them I almost always visited the property with the prospector or promoter, to examine at least some of the claim posts and to validate the ownership and position of the claims. During such examinations I traversed some claim lines and studied carefully whatever geological information and/or evidence of mineral could be found or shown to me. In my report I summarized my evaluation of the property. Such an evaluation was necessarily vague and ranged from a cautious conclusion such as "deserves modest exploration" to the ultimate in professional commendation, "offers a reasonable probability of success." An important feature of the prospectus was the consultant's recommended work program and its related costs.

I do not recall ever totally condemning the potential of a prospect, since I have always been mindful of a certain black American youth's dictum, "God don't make no junk!" Experience has taught me that the bare analytical factors of appraisal, identified by my technical teachers, have their limitations. This practice of hesitating to describe any particular property as "junk" has served me generously. Several of my own exploration successes were made in the "junk" areas of professional colleagues.

If a promoter decided to develop interest in a property he would, with the assistance of a solicitor, acquire a charter for a public share company. Usually, during this time, such companies each had an authorized capitalization of three to five million common shares. Of this authorized total, a block of shares, known as the "vendor's block," of up to 25 per cent of the total could be retained by the promoter and would normally be divided between the prospector and himself. The prospector usually staked or optioned the property, the promoter assumed the responsibility of financial sponsorship, and underwriters sold the stock to the public.

Only 10 per cent of this vendor's stock was unrestricted and the remainder placed in escrow – the legal word for trust – to be released later for trading only upon the increasing value of the property through its development and with the approval of the Securities Commission. Such escrow stock could, however, be privately sold by the owners but at a considerable discount in value because it lacked immediate marketability.

Then the public corporation would be formed, the vendor's block of stock divided, and the terms of underwriting would all be approved subject to the strict rules and surveillance of the Securities Commission. The stage was then set for a legitimate exercise known as penny-stock promotion. For this stage, a prospectus, or geologist's report on the property, and a work program had to be outlined. Such "penny-stock" would be wholesaled to the underwriters under a formula of rising prices over time, with the initial wholesale price normally being 10¢, 15¢, or 25¢ a share, the public paying little more.

During the two decades immediately after the Second World War, a large section of the general public in Ontario purchased penny-stocks at one time or another. Practically all forms of lotteries or games of chance were then illegal, save for official racetrack wagering and modest church- or charity-sponsored fund-raising. The considerable inherent speculative instinct of the public responded enthusiastically to such penny-stock involvement. In many circles, discussion of various penny-stocks was often as common as discussion of the weather. Daily variations in the price of shares were accepted with philosophic despair or delight. Those who "followed" the market were always eager for "hot tips." When the stock they had purchased fell in price they would say laconically, "Ya can't win 'em all!" The value of such stocks fluctuated greatly, sometimes in the course of one day. Profits or losses could be evident or realized within hours. These fluctuations were based on reports or rumours of prospecting results from work being conducted on the particular company's claims – or nearby claims – plus the emphasis of public auctioning phobia.

Major differences between this high-risk, penny-stock exploration financing and outright gambling must be noted. Penny-stocks provided all the emotional excitement of buying a lottery ticket or "playing the horses" but there was a major difference. The shares were entirely different from lottery tickets, which in the overwhelming majority of cases are worthless after the lottery is over. Such shares were not simply betting tickets to be thrown away after a single race. They represented ownership in the corporate enterprise and carried shareholder voting-rights with the power to choose, retain, or dismiss the corporate officers at annual shareholder meetings, and the right, through mandatory audited reports, to know how corporate funds were spent and the work results achieved.

Shares in penny-stock companies often had a long life, repeatedly entitling the owner to recurrent, if diminishing, proprietary right in a succession of ventures through the same company or its re-capitalized variants. These shares also offered several ways to gain. A short-term gambler (or scalper) might be satisfied with a modest but certain profit and might complete his buy-and-sell transactions in a single day. A more optimistic and patient purchaser might retain his shares for a longer wait-and-see period in the hope of sharing eventually in a major successful project. To those who took the longer risk, and were fortunate, the rewards could be great. When I arrived on Bay Street it was engulfed with feverish excitement concerning shares in Quemont Mines which had risen like a rocket from a few cents a year before, to over $20 a share because of the discovery of a rich ore-body. Unquestionably many of the great mines of Canada emerged through the use of penny-share financing.

An added incentive to participate in the "penny-share" market was that during this period any value appreciation from casual transactions was viewed as "capital gains," and no applicable capital gains tax then existed in regard to the profits made.

The selling of publicly traded shares, including, of course, penny shares, was conducted under the general surveillance and continuing control of the Ontario Securities Commission. In addition to being watched by this agency, Bay Street was subject to the unrelenting gaze and rigorous study, during my early years in Toronto, of a "lone ranger" or "vigilante" figure. He served as a unique and voluntary protector of the rights of minority shareholders at annual and extraordinary shareholder meetings of both listed and unlisted companies. He was known in Bay Street circles as "One-Share Sweeney."

One-Share Sweeney

By becoming a registered shareholder through the purchase of very little stock in any company he wished to "analyse," Sweeney gained a certain degree of power which he knew how to use. As a registered shareholder he had the legal right, which he almost always exercised, of rising to his feet at shareholder meetings and literally cross-examining the corporate officers, particularly about the "grey areas" between corporate and personal affairs.

Sweeney undoubtedly selected for analysis those companies which were particularly vulnerable to public criticism. "He sure flushed the bush," Joe Hirshhorn once remarked to me in awe.

Quite often I saw One-Share Sweeney striding self-confidently through the Bay Street area, immaculately attired, with his well-groomed goatee and a flower in his lapel. To my regret I never saw him carry out his public cross-examination of corporate officials. I have often wondered why Sweeney had no successors. It still seems to me that his was the type of activity in which vigorous young lawyers of social conscience could provide a highly valuable and visible public service which offered, and offers, more than sufficient scope on which to base a career. And, in some manner, One-Share Sweeney appeared to profit materially through his vigilante role.

Sweeney's attention was naturally directed toward companies which he had reason to believe were in need of thorough "public laundering" before shareholders and the press. And the latter followed him everywhere! Fortunately none of the companies with which I was involved needed Sweeney's prying eye and tongue.

Assignment in French Guiana

While I was fascinated by the passing human and financial scene on Bay Street, my primary interest and activity was in the search for mineral deposits in Canada and occasionally overseas. My agreement with Pioneer Gold Mines during my Bay Street days was that I would devote up to one-half of my professional time under salary to overseeing their ongoing programs in eastern Canada, initiated earlier by Chris Riley. I could act independently during the other half of my time. When the extent of my non-committed time became known to others I soon received offers from various promoters and established exploration companies to work as a consultant or prospector-geologist for them. When I received an offer for a mission in French Guiana from the prestigious firm of James & Buffam, Consulting Geologists, I accepted it with enthusiasm.

This, my first major overseas assignment, was to undertake an evaluation of gold deposits in the interior jungle of French Guiana, at the headwaters of the Sinnamary River. The gold deposits were called *Saint Elie* and *Dieu Merci* and were the property of a French company named Société de Saint Elie. James & Buffam, and I as field operator, were to make an economic evaluation on behalf of the owner and the French government regarding the possibility of rehabilitating the mines through the attraction and careful development of Canadian and American capital. These gold deposits were known internationally, since they had produced gold for sixty years or more. But a first-hand, up-to-date analysis was now required.

The little I had read about French Guiana was limited to references about its role as a penal colony, "the dry guillotine" for the French Republic, to which were sent both habitual criminals from continental France and political dissidents of the French colonies. I had read, as well, of the trials of Alfred Dreyfus, which began in 1894 and ended in 1906, for his alleged treason to France; his exile to Devil's Island, off the country's coast; and his later vindication and winning of military honours in the First World War.

French Guiana had served as a penal colony for ninety years when that status was terminated in 1945. At that time approximately twenty thousand prisoners were released from the prison farms. They had to remain in the country and became known as *libérées*. Initially the *libérées* comprised over 70 per cent of the country's population. They were a polyglot group from the French pre-war colonies of Indo-China, North Africa, Madagascar, and other areas. Given French Guiana's unique nature and its remoteness from Europe, it is not surprising that it had been almost totally ignored during the years immediately preceding the Second World War, and had fallen into a tragic state of social and economic neglect.

My reading in preparation for the mission indicated only that French Guiana's total pre-war export economy consisted of copra (dried coconut) and rosewood oil. Both were produced on the huge plantations worked by the convict labour force, and both were exported exclusively to France.

Very little was known of the country's geology except by inference from its more thoroughly studied neighbours, Brazil and Dutch Guiana. A large portion of French Guiana was believed to be underlaid by pre-Cambrian-age rocks. Such rocks were known to be rich in minerals elsewhere in the Amazonian area. The gold deposits which I was to evaluate occurred in a shield-type formation and were the only mineral deposits of importance then known in the country. As these deposits were isolated in a vast jungle area and could be reached, at that time, only by river travel in dugout canoes and on foot, I was determined to exploit the opportunity of the long ground traverses to prospect as well for other possible mineral occurrences. This suggestion had met with my employer's ready approval.

I spent approximately four weeks on my mission in French Guiana. Every moment of that time seemed to provide new surprises, either of shock or delight.

When I arrived in Cayenne, the capital city, I went to meet the newly arrived governor, a tall, thin, handsome, seemingly very young French lieutenant who had served in De Gaulle's Free French forces. When I was presented to the governor, he was dressed in full ceremonial military regalia – right down to a sword at his belt and white gloves. De Gaulle would have approved.

The young governor stood on the marble flagstone patio of what had once been a most elegant small chateau, now half-smothered in uncontrolled vines and reeking of mildew. Two privates (known in military parlance as *poilus*, or hairy ones) stood a few feet away with rifles in hand and bayonets in their belts. After some pleasantries, the governor led me to a small table in the shade, set with white linen. He unbuckled his sword and placed it on a chair at his side. A servant appeared with wine glasses, a bottle of fine red wine, and a platter of crackers and pâté.

I handed the governor my credentials for examination including the required affidavit from Sheriff Connover of York County, Ontario, to the effect that I had "no known criminal record to that date." The governor's English was poor so he needed my help with the Sheriff's letter. When I translated the qualification "to that date" he allowed a weak smile to appear on his intense and serious face. He laid aside my letters of introduction.

"You realize this is a dangerous country," he said in French. "The 'types' everywhere are lawless, hardly human any more. It is a great tragedy!"

At precisely that point in our conversation, a coconut fell, striking the marble flagstones with the crack of a small cannonball. I had seen it fall, but neither the governor nor his guards had, since it fell behind them. The governor leapt to his feet and grasped his sword. The guards whirled around. No one smiled or said a word until the governor broke the silence to repeat, "It is dangerous here."

Weeks later, my bushwork completed, the governor and I became better acquainted. Fortunately, he was learning to relax. Before my return to Canada he officially offered me an option, on behalf of any principals I might interest, to lease the 10,000-tree coconut plantation of the vacated Saint-Laurent-du-Maroni prison, since there were no longer prisoners to operate it. I assured him seriously that I would investigate the economics of coconut export to Canada (I did. They were not good.)

In carrying out my mission in French Guiana I was determined that my work team would be small. I selected one mining company man, a native expediter and two *libérées*. One *libéré* was a former medical doctor and political dissenter of Thai origin. The other, his male assistant, was an all-round handyman. The doctor, I felt, could be medically useful, although I was cautioned that he was almost certainly addicted to drugs. Fortunately, we experienced no illness nor injury in the bush, although I did suffer briefly from a frightening intestinal disorder after leaving the country.

The doctor was a good companion. He introduced me to several surprising herbs in the jungle, including a small shrub called rotenone.

My bearers would crush the bark and throw it on the surface of streams to paralyse fish, which they then caught by hand for food.

To arrange food supplies for our expedition I had, with a mining company clerk, set out to see what we could find in the food stores still operating in Cayenne. Few supply ships had visited the colony during and after the war; it had literally become a forgotten colony. The stores were almost totally devoid of foodstuffs save for a tuber product called *manioc*, which resembles tapioca. Finally, we visited a wharf warehouse. Its shelves were also bare save for half a dozen small, faintly rusted cans of mutton packed in Algeria. I said I'd take them. I then noticed huge 100-kilogram burlap sacks in a pile and asked if they contained rice, corn, or copra. "No, peanuts," was the reply. I enjoy peanuts, shelled, nicely roasted and salted, so I said I would purchase one of the sacks. "Life in the jungle," I mused, "won't be all that bad!"

Finally my team left Cayenne by jeep over a long coastal dirt road. Soon we reached the delta of the Sinnamary River, baked hard in the dry season but almost impassable in the rainy season. Reaching that point was in itself an unusual experience: the coast road crossed several rivers emptying into the Caribbean. Some of the larger rivers were spanned by steel bridges decked with thick hardwood planks loosely laid crosswise and completely unattached to the steel girders. As our jeep rolled over the planks, they bounced up and down with a sound like machine-gun fire. At first I had the feeling they were collapsing under us. When I recovered after my first crossing and remarked on the grossly inadequate maintenance, I was told "On the contrary, this way the termites can never nest on the bridges."

Our jeep continued to the settlement of St. Laurent on the Maroni River, where the huge, recently vacated prison was situated. I gazed at the slow-moving, mud-laden water of the river and remarked aloud, "So this is the border between French and Dutch Guiana."

"Yes," was the answer, "but it's not an easy obstacle to cross, as many an escaping convict has learned. Watch!"

My companion cut a pole from a shrub with his machete and chopped it roughly into two-foot lengths. Then, approaching the water's edge, he slowly tossed the pieces of wood into the middle of the river. Soon the water was in turmoil. The pieces of wood bounced in the air as they were fought over and ripped apart by strange creatures in the water. I watched with much interest.

"Piranha," he said to me. "Flesh-eating fish – they've torn apart many an escapee trying to get across that forty metres of river!" After a reflective pause he added, "Also those who tried to save him."

The next day we were back at the mouth of the Sinnamary River, moving slowly upstream with a canoe in front of mine and two following. I sat in regal splendour on my sack of peanuts, my head covered with a huge reed hat for protection from the searing sun. The torpidity of the jungle gave me a feeling of relaxation and well-being. I opened my first can of Algerian mutton and began to eat from the can. The mutton was delicious, save for the irritation of having an unfortunate Algerian fly, entrapped in the canning process, in every second or third forkful. Finished, I casually tossed the empty can into the river. An ugly black snout quickly seized it.

"Oh, yes, keep your hands in the boat," my companion advised me casually. "Crocodiles."

An hour later, my mind was still on food. I decided to examine my sack of peanuts with greater care. I made a small hole in the corner of the bag and, to my dismay, I found the peanuts were still in the shell. When I shelled some and popped them into my mouth, I found to my greater dismay that they were unroasted. I had never experienced them in that state before and I quickly learned that raw peanuts taste not unlike raw potatoes. They were filling and curiously satisfying. Raw peanuts kept me in perfect health throughout that mission and I subsequently developed a lifetime affection for them in any form.

During my work in French Guiana I observed its flora and fauna carefully. Dense vegetation overhung the river banks. The jungle was silent, save for the raucous complaint of a macaw, usually unseen, in whose domain we were intruding. When seen, such birds were little more than brilliant splashes of crimson, orange, and green. A breathtaking variety of smaller, beautifully plumaged "birds of paradise" flitted through the foliage without a sound. Occasionally, butterflies with wingspans up to several inches would flutter above the water.

Finally a portage and narrow footpath were reached and we had to trek through the jungle on foot. We walked in single file with two bearers and scouts in front of me and the rest following. It was hot and terribly humid, and my group stripped to loin cloths. I wore only canvas and rubber "gym" shoes and undershorts, which were soon drenched with perspiration. On my head was my conical reed hat, and in my hand I had a staff cut from a bamboo stalk about five feet long. (Such "made-on-the-spot" staffs had served and continue to serve as my only aid and/or weapon in the bush.) Our group trudged on, one after the other.

Suddenly, a majestic figure emerged silently from the bush beside the trail and confronted us, arms akimbo in a posture of friendship and query. The figure was a statuesque and beautiful woman – light brown in colour. Later I learned she was the daughter of a mixed French-African mother and a giant Chinese father, a bush trader who probably exchanged cloth, tobacco, and trinkets for animal hides, bird plumage, butterfly wings, and possibly some gold. These first three items were used for feminine adornment in continental France.

This handsome, magnificently proportioned woman was perhaps six feet tall in sandals, with long straight black hair arranged in a large coil on her head. Perched on top of her head was a tuber root of some type which she had retrieved from the jungle. She wore a one-piece garment, resembling a large plain white sack with the corners removed for her arms with a generous V cut between her breasts. The garment dropped from shoulder to midway between hip and knee, not unlike the upper one-half of a Hawaiian muumuu.

She apparently knew and was known to all the others in my party, as evidenced by a short burst of humorous pidgin banter all around. Then, arms still akimbo and head and bosom upright, and with a majestic demeanour, she eyed me searchingly, starting at my feet and slowly progressing upward to the top of my head. Finally, in perfect French, she remarked aloud and with evident appreciation to the party assembled, *"Pas mal pour un blanc."* I was momentarily embarrassed by the compliment but dared not indicate that I understood French. She probably sensed my unspoken appreciation of her.

After further travel on foot we arrived, to my surprise, at a railroad line. It was narrow gauge, probably about twenty-four inches between rails, with flatcars of a size to match. The cars were propelled by human push-pull power regulated by a single "grunter" or "caller" who "set the pace." I rated a special car which carried me and the peanuts, with four men to propel it up steep grades. There was ample room for me on the platform going uphill but on a down-grade, all four pushers would climb aboard. One used a stick levered against a wheel as a brake. On the down-grades all four of my companions screeched with pleasure like excited five-year-olds on a circus midway loop-the-loop. Needless to say the train trip took hours.

Though I enjoyed the journey by daylight, I simply lapsed into shock when night fell and we continued alternately the slow grind uphill and then the spasms of hurtling downwards through the blackness. We jumped the tracks several times, and it was probably a combination of my wrestling experience which had taught me to "roll with the punches," and Celtic fatalism that spared me from a broken neck or fractured skull. The others around me appeared to be made of India rubber! If I have no fear of Hell it is because I travelled there and back several times on that trip in French Guiana.

After this long trek by jeep, canoe, foot, and finally this terrifying rail car, we arrived at the camp where they had mined gold for about sixty years. It was an interesting community of amazing contrasts.

The well-established and well-managed mining camp was situated at a relatively high altitude, thus the evenings were cool and pleasant. A strict colour line was maintained in the camp: there was no socializing between black and white in the residential area, but a reserved camaraderie existed between the white technical staff and the coloured foremen on the mine site, situated about a quarter of a mile from the residences.

The camp buildings were all made of bamboo and other dried reeds, with plank floors and steps. Those for white personnel were all built on stilts elevating them five or more feet above ground. The building I occupied was sparsely furnished with a bed enveloped in mosquito netting, a table, and two or three comfortable chairs, all of reed-work. There was no plumbing and a single light-bulb hung from the roof, which was fitted with a horizontal revolving fan.

The accommodation for whites comprised about a dozen buildings about fifty feet apart. All were set in a square of bare, hard-baked earth swept as clean as a courtyard by native women on their knees. The native people lived in a village about three hundred yards away. The white personnel all had duties which kept them occupied: the mine quarry operated six days a week while the milling plant operated day and night. On the other hand, the few white women remained in the compound and kept together. They read widely. There was a small organ and there was much letter-writing and frequent air travel to their families in France. One good radio transmitter in the manager's office was the only link with the outside world.

The half-dozen or so French personnel – two or three with their wives – were hospitable and friendly, a late dinner being the social event of the day. We relaxed together each evening in conversation over well-provisioned and well-cooked repasts, with fine wines and a carefully laid table. The men were all neatly dressed in white while the women wore attractive colours. The dining area was screened off, as were all the sleeping quarters, to prevent the many exotic flying insects attracted by the electric lights from sharing the food – or the blood of the diners.

My work was arduous but I quickly selected a group of three or four native employees of Afro-Asian blood, totally illiterate but highly intelligent, to help me. I explained what we would do, why, and how. They soon were working together as a totally devoted, hard-working team.

I had two primary objectives in my program of work in French Guiana. First I wished to determine how much of the mountainside, after sixty years of excavation by hand tools, still contained sufficient gold for continued profitable recovery. Second, I wished to establish how much gold remained in the few million tons of material mined and discarded earlier – the "tailings." I viewed the latter objective as the more important.

There were no suitable tools or equipment available to test the large surface areas of tailings surrounding the recovery plant site, so a simple procedure was developed. It consisted of securing a number of two-foot-long sections of two-inch-diameter pipe and driving this vertically into the tailings by heavy hand-held wooden mallets, and adding successive sections until the bottom of the tailings was reached at depths of six to twelve feet. After this the tailing-filled pipe was lifted carefully. I personally removed each two feet of tailings, placed it in a sample sack and identified precisely the depth from which it had come. After this the many samples were tested for recoverable gold content and with the volume ascertained, a total estimate of all remaining recoverable gold was determined.

The work environment in French Guiana was difficult and dangerous as far as I was concerned, since I was not familiar with the hazards. The area abounded in venomous snakes and scorpions. My work involved sampling rock, soil, and tailings, which necessarily meant disturbing or destroying the nests of these creatures. After sundown, malarial and other trouble-making insects lurked ominously in what were to me the more attractive cooler areas. Various vines and shrubs and much natural water were purveyors of disease. I quickly learned that if it were at all possible I should never take a step outdoors without an alert, knowledgeable, trustworthy native at my side. On this mission and others which followed, such guardians undoubtedly saved me from injury, debilitating disease, and even death.

In addition to my work on the St. Elie deposits, I was persuaded by the management to visit another area of known gold occurrences, some kilometres away, where no recent development had been undertaken. It was called *Isle de Dieu*, a name that totally belied its nature. My team and I set out early one morning on the day-long trip.

We had not gone far along a reasonably good foot trail before we came upon a fat, four-foot-long, deadly snake which my head boy beat to death. Severing its head with his machete he cut out its poison sacs and wrapped them in a leaf which he tucked into a fold in his loincloth. The sacs were to be given to the "ju ju," the tribal witch doctor, who would dry and pulverize them into dust. This would then be used as medicine by blowing it into the nostrils of victims of snake bite.

The snake's corpse was hooked with a stick and flung forcefully toward the deep jungle undergrowth. However, the body did not land where intended. It became hooked, and hung suspended over a low limb of a tree, to the loud laughter of the others in the party.

We moved on and eventually reached the gold area. It looked desolate. In contrast to its surroundings, this area was devoid of soil or vegetation, probably the result of repeated burning. The dome-like area was covered with slabby rusted rocks interspersed with red-orange sandy soil. Two of my group quickly approached the area. After some banging of their metal gold pans on the rocks to scare out snakes and scorpions, they scooped up some finer sand, returned to the trail where I stood, and started winnowing it; one person agitated the pan while another waved a tree bough to create air turbulence. Soon the pan residue was shown to me. It contained much jagged gold. In my enthusiasm I drew my prospecting pick from my belt and reached for the pan, determined to do my own testing. It was not to be and I soon saw why. Mortal danger lay beneath, among the surface boulders.

The men worked in pairs; each pair moved randomly over the scarred area, prying up rocks, batting at numerous scorpions, shouting excited warnings and killing another three or four snakes. Somehow, despite the constant danger, they kept gathering samples of sand, returning to my side, winnowing the material, and showing me the gold. This went on in a frenzy of fear, challenge, effort, and reward which intoxicated us all. Finally, I glanced at my watch and realized that we had to leave to get back to our base before dusk, when new perils would begin to emerge in the jungle. We started back on the trail at a jog.

At a shout from the lead man, I glanced around, startled. We were back at the point on the trail where we had earlier killed the fat snake. There it was, still hooked on the tree limb. But something strange had happened – it was fluttering like a paper ribbon in the light breeze. Before I could ask a question, two of my party were at work to answer the riddle. One was slashing a short path through the underbrush to get below the snake. Another was fashioning missiles of wooden sticks to throw at it in the hope of bringing it down. Finally, it was felled and brought to me on the trail.

The snake was held up vertically, headless end downwards, and shaken: a small pile of clean, white, tiny, fish-like bones fell out of it. The skin was turned inside out and given to me for examination: it was as dry and clean and as soft as brown wrapping paper. Then it was folded into an eight-inch-long and four-inch-wide package and offered to me as a gift. I studied its drab grey, brown, and black diamond pattern and saw no beauty there. I was thoroughly convinced that my womenfolk at home, though not normally squeamish, would probably faint at its sight. "But how could this happen in so short a time?" I asked.

I was beckoned by the man who had picked up the skin from the ground. I followed him back along his underbrush trail to the base of the tree from which the fat snake had hung, and he pointed to the trunk of the tree. A track, about half an inch deep and one inch wide, had recently been cut up the trunk. Sap was oozing into the cut.

"What did that?" I asked.

"Ants," he replied.

Not a bad job even for the industrious ant, I reflected. Probably eight to ten pounds of snake meat had been removed to the anthill in three hours. In my imagination, I saw the meat-eating ants surrounding me! "Let's get cracking," I said. It was the only English phrase I ever used in my team's presence, but they understood it perfectly. We resumed our jogging at once.

On a technical level I found mineral exploration in the tropics to be an exciting new world owing to the much-accelerated surface chemistry, both organic and inorganic, which flows from the intense equatorial solar energy. I was hooked on tropical zone exploration. If I viewed exploration as a romantic adventure, as I did in the northern latitudes of soft greens, greys, and browns, in the tropics that adventure is resplendent in a Technicolour drama of pink, crimson, orange, and emerald green!

My technical report on the French Guiana mission was prepared and delivered to my employers, who passed its conclusions along to potential investors. This report led me, indirectly, to various other mineral exploration missions for international private sector interests in several South and Central American countries and then to other sections of the world, including the Arctic.

After my return to Canada, Mary and I agreed that Toronto would be a good professional base for me and a good educational base for our daughter Marion, who was then about ready to start school. Accordingly, we bought a modest new house on what was then the northern edge of the city. Mary, a most remarkable homemaker, quickly transformed our new house into a comfortable and pretty home. Wherever I went on my various consulting assignments, I always looked forward eagerly to coming home to Mary and Marion.

Assignment in the Sub-Arctic

My next big mission was in stark contrast to French Guiana. Soon after my return to Toronto I was offered an attractive commission to serve as field project manager overseeing an exploration program in the eastern sub-Arctic. This involved some exploratory and developmental work on lead-zinc mineral deposits in the Richmond Gulf area of Hudson Bay, east of the Belcher Islands about nine hundred miles directly north of Toronto. The client was a Montreal- and Toronto-based company which was, reportedly, financed in part by the American Rockefeller interests. I looked forward to working among the Inuit and agreed to spend the summer of 1949 carrying out this project.

I recall, with some amusement, my first trip to the Richmond Gulf area. Our chartered aircraft was a single engine Norseman on pontoons. It was loaded in the usual manner for an exploration party, with pilot, mechanic, a geophysicist, a student assistant, and myself, with our personal dunnage, camping and electronic gear, and food supplies. Outside, a spare drum of aircraft fuel was lashed to one pontoon and a canoe to the other.

We made the trip from North Bay to our destination, the mouth of the Seal River, in several stages. First we flew to Moosonee, then to Rupert House, Great Whale, and finally our campsite at Little Whale. At each stop we stretched our legs, refueled, checked on weather ahead, and browsed through the Hudson Bay post for souvenirs.

At Rupert House we came down on the coastline of Hudson Bay and taxied to the muddy shoreline which, at that point, consists of twenty-foot-high clay bluffs. As we taxied in we caught glimpses of the white-painted wood structure of the Hudson Bay post and the nearby church. These buildings were quite picturesque, particularly when contrasted with the surrounding native shacks of unpainted wood, canvas and animal hides and a clutter of sleds and tethered howling sled-dogs.

At the top edge of the bluff the colourful figure of a male Indian appeared in leather trappings, his long braided hair tied with a red bandanna. Quickly, the student in our party dropped to one knee to snap what was probably a good silhouette picture. He then approached the still figure of the Indian, arms crossed, gazing down with fixed interest at our small debarking group. I heard snatches of the ensuing monologue as I slowly climbed the steep path to the bluff edge.

"Hi! You Indian? Maybe Chief?" The Indian's gaze remained fixed on the aircraft. "We come long way in Iron Bird. Five pale-faces. Travel North Bay to Seal. High, like Canada goose. We fly one sun."

The Indian remained silent, his gaze still fixed on the aircraft.

"We go Seal, find lead. Iron Bird leave us alone there. Iron Bird fly home fast, fast."

For the first time the Indian's gaze shifted from the aircraft to the student's face. He regarded him in stony silence for several seconds, then quietly asked, "What the Hell's your hurry?"

The speechless university student retreated in silence.

The landscape in this northern area was desolate. It consisted of great stretches of flat land relieved by sand dunes and a few sculptured ridges of rock, well named by French geologists as *roches moutonée*. Viewed from above they clearly resembled the backs of a flock of large sheep. These ridges rose fifty to a hundred feet above the sandy flat land.

The physical appearance of the area reflected the continuing impact of the powerful winds and the abrasive influence of wind-blown sand. The only vegetation was thin and matted moss and lichen. In summer, this tundra was alive with insects – mosquitos, blackflies, and spiders – some of which are consumed by the mice, lemmings, and Arctic birds.

Finally, at dusk we flew in over the campsite of tent-frames left in place by my predecessors from the season before. While we were still airborne, we spotted a small Inuit gathering of adults, children, and dogs around a cluster of skin tents on the beach. As we taxied to shore the group separated, the women and children going into, or behind, the tents while the men, about a half dozen, and the dogs moved toward the water's edge and the aircraft, halting about fifty feet away.

I advanced to meet them with the student, camera at the ready, on my heels. We stopped and exchanged smiles with the Inuit group. One of them stepped forward. He said he spoke some English and two others spoke some French. Then, pointing at his comrades one at a time, he introduced them. "Him, Tomluk. Him, Bobluk. Him, Billuk. Him, Jonluk. Me, Joeluk." They all seemed accounted for, and there were friendly grins on all faces.

Pointing a finger toward the student, I said, "Him, Badluk. Me, Goodluk." The joke appeared to be appreciated by all.

I learned, to my relief, that several of the Inuit were familiar with the work of the company which had retained me and that they wished to be employed again. I also learned with some surprise that several had worked for the previous manager in the operation of several diamond-drilling rigs. I remarked that the previous diamond-drill foreman, a French-Canadian, would join our party in another week. They remembered him and appeared delighted at the news.

The adult Inuit then helped us unload the aircraft and set up temporary accommodation. They assisted in the departure of the aircraft and showed me over the previous campsite and stored equipment. They were very well-organized, and I did little more than indicate what I wanted done. I left all of the "how" to them. Initially I had some misgivings but they were soon eliminated.

I indicated to the Inuit where I wished to locate the small pup tent which would serve as an office. The site I chose was within sight of the equipment storage area and also had a pleasant view of the water's edge. But the Inuit did not approve of that site. To save time

I compromised, saying that when the remainder of the party arrived a week later, we'd relocate the office. With evident reluctance they allowed me to have my way. Slowly the office went up.

It was a double-lined, totally contained tent. The inner lining was insect-proof mesh fabric with a separate entry slot, while the outer skin was made of a tough waterproof tarpaulin material for walls, sealed to a super heavy layer which formed the floor. There was a separate over-lapping entry flap. The tent was literally a sack within a sack. It was insulated for warmth, but, more particularly, for protection against the Arctic's summer plague of mosquitos and other stinging and biting insects.

The office was barely large enough for two to sleep side-by-side on twenty-four-inch-wide cots by night. By day, the cots were folded and put aside. A folding card table with legs cut to about eighteen-inch height became my desk; I worked upon my knees. To begin with, the two-way radio transmitter, which did not function well, was in the office. It was connected to a single aerial wire about sixty feet long, extending between two drill-rod masts about twenty feet above the ground. Some geophysical and survey equipment and first-aid supplies were stored, initially, in the office tent.

As I watched and assisted with the assembling of my new home, I was surprised at the methods the Inuit used to anchor it. There was no soil – only sand and rock – in which to hammer pegs for the side ropes of the tent, so my helpers practically surrounded the outside canvas edges with twenty-pound rocks side-by-side. They, of course, knew what they were doing even if I did not. I passed a tolerable first night of summer-season twilight in my dwelling and was up early next morning. The geophysicist had much experimental work to do. The Inuit went their way with the student. I went on a geological foot-traverse inland and across our mineral concession area with one Inuit companion.

Soon after we had set out we came to a thirty-foot-high vertical wall of fascinating columnar basalt. It instantly took my thoughts back to the Squamish River Valley of British Columbia and reminded me also of textbook photographs of the same volcanic phenomenon west of Ballycastle in Northern Ireland, where it is known as "The Giant's Causeway." Puzzled by the presence of this very young-looking formation within the ancient pre-Cambrian Shield area, I studied carefully a great heap of fallen columns and then decided to climb to the top of the wall with my companion.

The top of the volcanic sheet was most intriguing. It was almost a flat platform of black rock divided into geometrically precise units about one foot in diameter, almost like a designed and crafted flagstone patio. I took a few photographs and rock specimens and then looked at the surrounding area.

The vista surprised me. The topographic relief was slight and "well-worn" by glacial scour. It was devoid of vegetation, save for sparse, knee-high shrubs in some depressions. It looked totally arid. Remnants of earlier raised beaches and sand dunes could be identified. I had no desert experience at that time but the sight before me, in some directions, resembled photographs I had seen of desert terrain. I was puzzled by the appearance of the sand dunes, knowing little about the nature of their origin and never having read of the ferocity of Arctic winds. I was to learn quickly.

We continued to walk until about noon when my companion and I shared a can of bully beef and a can of baked beans. He seemed to prefer the meat to the beans but dutifully ate both. Then he took the empty beef can and lid and disappeared into a small depression, reappearing five minutes later with a can half-full of clear but brackish-tasting water. He indicated it was mine, so I drank it.

I took out my field notebook and made a few notes, oblivious to my companion's movements. When I closed my book and looked up, he was sitting beside me with a tiny stick in one hand and a grin on his face. With his stick he had drawn a checkerboard pattern on a patch of sand. On one side he had arranged some small pieces of the off-white coloured dolomite rock common to the area, on the other side were an equal number of pieces of a dark grey shale rock also arranged in order. I was uncertain as to the game he had in mind but assumed it was "checkers."

I made the first move and he the next. Soon I realized it would be checkers – accelerated too quickly for me, it seemed. He caught me exposed and took two of my markers in one move. I realized he was an expert, declared him the champion "to that point," and announced that we should "get cracking."

We walked for an hour or so before my companion pointed to a wispy cloud in the sky and indicated that we should return directly to the camp. Soon, the light, intermittent breeze sharpened to a gusty wind of unpredictable direction. We pressed on toward the camp, my companion the leader.

Before long, I was relieved to catch glimpses of the coast water, because the occasional gust of wind was of storm strength. I had to struggle to remain erect. Finally, my companion turned with a grin on his face and hand held up. I realized that we were practically "home."

We started to climb a gentle slope with a strong tail-wind pushing at us. I heard my companion shout and saw him break into a half-run. Looking beyond him, I saw an extraordinary sight – My entire office tent was hanging in the air, twelve to fifteen feet above the ground, resembling a soggy balloon, apparently still loaded with all our gear. It was being wildly buffeted by an almost vertically driven blast of wind. The two radio aerial masts attached to the tent were dragging on the ground, as was the aerial wire. I was greatly alarmed. Fighting the wind, I scrambled the last hundred yards toward the camp, hoping against hope that the aerial wire would not break and the tent be blown into the sea.

A great babble of shouting and barking arose as a dozen or more Inuit men, women, children, and dogs appeared on the scene. They grabbed the aerial line and masts trailing on the ground. With their body weight they slowly brought the tent and contents down to earth.

Someone, evidently, had gone to the tent for equipment, and, on leaving, had forgotten to close the double-flap entrance slots. The gusty wind had filled the tent, causing it to balloon upwards, carrying its contents of probably a hundred pounds or more while shedding the weight of boulders around the exterior perimeter.

Now I had learned about the violence of the Arctic wind. It became clear why the knowledgeable Inuit had not favoured the exposed site I had chosen for my tent, and why they had placed all those anchor stones – which had proved insufficient even though I had viewed them as superfluous – around it. In the following weeks and months, as the project proceeded, I witnessed many examples of the ingenuity, resourcefulness, and comprehensive intelligence of the Inuit, tempered with a strong sense of artistry and humour. The Inuit valued friendship. It was not without a catch in my throat and damp eyes on both sides that we finally parted company at Richmond Gulf when the job was done. For the trinkets I left behind, they presented me with small pieces of art in bone, walrus ivory, soapstone, and sewn pelts which I still admire and treasure.

The Inuit whom I met or saw, and those with whom I worked in the summer of 1949 were pleasant and smiling but hesitant in their relations with us. While I was there for several months and found that the Inuit men were uniformly agreeable and helpful they were at best shyly sociable, alone or in groups. I greatly enjoyed working with the Inuit and established excellent relationships with them. Still there was this persistent shyness. They ate hesitatingly with us but never invited us to eat with them.

The Inuit women and children lived together secluded from the areas where their menfolk worked with us. Since the women were more timid than the men, they hurried away together seeking to avoid observation whenever any of us who had flown in approached them. Despite this shyness and our cultural differences I developed the highest regard for these gentle and ingenious people.

I worked with the Inuit of north-eastern Hudson Bay and Ungava-Quebec many years ago and have often expressed a longing to visit them again, but friends who work among them now advise me not to do so.

"You would probably be heartbroken," they have told me. "During recent decades, North Americans, unintentionally, have done much to ruin the Inuit as a fine race. We have extended our hands to them in friendship. With our perverted sense of hospitality, one hand held a bottle of whisky and the other tobacco. These two have done much to destroy many of the Inuit physically and morally. The junk food and materialistic trappings of civilization are rapidly finishing the job. It is a profound tragedy."

My mission to French Guiana and my assignment in the sub-Arctic were only two of an increasing number of consulting projects in which I became involved as a professional geologist in the late 1940s. Originally I thought I might complete my doctorate at the University of Toronto while at the same time attending to Pioneer Mines' interests in eastern Canada. But my own consulting practice developed separately from my continuing work for Pioneer, and my earlier ideas of doctoral studies were overtaken by the professional opportunities which came to me. Dr. Howard James, who had aided me greatly in my move to Toronto as Pioneer's representative was always most encouraging. When the day came in May 1949 that I decided to become a fully independent prospector and consulting geologist, he supported me completely. Our friendship and professional relationships, which went back nearly a decade and a half to the time he had given me my first assignment with Pioneer, continued to the time of his tragic death in 1978.

As an independent professional I had to attract clients entirely on the basis of my own demonstrated ability. I took over, for my own consulting practice, the Pioneer offices in the Concourse Building. In addition, during 1948–49, I had opened a small walk-up office over a barber-shop in Sault Ste. Marie. I had a field camp and prospector employees in the Montreal River area north of Sault Ste. Marie. The Sault Ste. Marie and tent-camp offices served me and an associate, Arthur Stollery, a mining engineer, as bases for consulting related to various uranium discoveries then being made in that area.

In 1949 I was invited to write a paper on "Modern Methods of Mineral Exploration in Canada." It was chosen, among other papers, for presentation at the Fourth Empire Geological Congress held at Oxford University in England. Nineteen forty-nine was a busy and hectic year for my debut as a self-employed consulting geologist.

In retrospect, of course, perhaps the most significant event which occurred in 1949, as far as my professional career was concerned, was a chance encounter I had with Joe Hirshhorn.

VIII

Working with Joe Hirshhorn Among Bay Street Buccaneers

The word *buccaneer* evokes romantic images of adventurous men of the sea risking their lives in search of fabulous treasure. The courage and energy, the dramatic, sometimes ruthless, exploits of buccaneers – their fantastic successes, and their equally fantastic failures – have, over the years, in book and film, captured imaginations the world over.

Like most boys, I was fascinated by stories of swashbuckling buccaneers. In 1946, when I came to Toronto and became immersed in the Bay Street jungle of bears and bulls, I noted that the word *buccaneer* was applied to certain colourful mining promoters – aggressive individualists, adventurers who relished risk and public attention, a breed far different from the suave corporate captains of industry. On the whole, many played key roles in the process of hunting for Canada's vast treasure of natural resources, most often in remote wilderness areas.

One of the Bay Street buccaneers was Joe Hirshhorn.

We Are Introduced

I was at work in my office in the Concourse Building in Toronto sometime in mid-1949 when I had occasion to visit the washroom. The men's washrooms in the Concourse were large, high-ceilinged, and airy, with chrome fixtures and white tile. The urinals were commodious cubicles, separated by thick polished marble slabs, and about five-feet high to ensure maximum privacy.

This cool quiet sanctum seemed empty when I entered. Suddenly, a voice beside me barked out questions.

"Who're you? What's yer name? Yuh work here?"

Somewhat startled, I glanced in the direction of the voice. All I could see was the top two inches of a black-haired head in the adjoining cubicle. The voice repeated the questions.

"What's yer name? Yuh belong in this building?"

As I drew back from the urinal and moved toward the wash basins, I wondered, "Who is this bird?"

He was short – five foot, four inches – "like Napoleon and Nelson," he later would boast to me, dark-complexioned, broad-shouldered, with a good head of dark hair. I noted a well-tailored suit and highly polished shoes, an elegant shirt and tie, gold cuff links and watch. As we washed our hands he continued his questions.

"I'm Hirshhorn. Who're you?" he barked again.

We reached for towels, and he turned to face me. His face was large, his nose prominent, and his mouth firm and determined. His sharp dark eyes were arresting. Inquisitiveness, shrewd assessment, and calculation were all written on his face.

"I'm Franc Joubin. I'm a prospector-geologist," I replied. "I work out of the Pioneer office on this floor.

"Yuh don't say. Prospector, eh? I work with prospectors. Cumup. Cumup an' see me. Gimme a call. Maybe we can do some business." And with that he was gone.

It never occurred to me then, nor was there the slightest reason why it should, that Hirshhorn would later become my "angel," my high-risk grubstaker, and that we would work miracles together in the development of new mines, bringing Canada into the Nuclear Age and achieving personal financial success.

As I was more than busy with other clients I did not go up to see him as he had suggested. But I did ask around about him. I remember one of those early assessments: "Watch out – he's a ball of fire!"

Joe Hirshhorn – Before 1949

Joe Hirshhorn was born in 1900 in the village of Jukst in Latvia, and he came to the United States with his widowed mother and five brothers and sisters seven years later. Raised in a Brooklyn tenement amidst modest circumstances, Joe learned in his youth that to succeed in life he had to devote all his energy, thought, and time to that objective.

While in primary school he sold papers in the streets to help support his fatherless family. He left school at fifteen and began to work as a messenger boy for stockbrokers on Wall Street. The financial market soon became the focus of his life. He was fascinated by it and he began to make money. By the time he was twenty-nine, he reportedly had accumulated $4 million. Hirshhorn was a shrewd speculator, that was reflected dramatically in his decision to sell all his holdings in the stock market in August 1929, two months before the market collapsed.

His first wife, Jennie, wanted Hirshhorn to withdraw from the feverish financial world in order to pursue a formal education. Although he did give brief thought to attending Cornell University, he decided against it. Joe realized he was a trader and a speculator, a man of action, not a reflective intellectual. Gradually and cautiously, he returned to the stock market and began to take an interest in mining opportunities in Canada, making a three-week exploratory trip.

When President Roosevelt took the action in 1932 which resulted in a rise in the price of gold to $35 an ounce, Hirshhorn knew that Canada, as one of the world's leading gold producers, could be a good place for his activities. He had decided that beyond being a market speculator he would become a mine-maker. Thus in March 1933, Joe established an operational base in Toronto and opened an account in a Canadian bank with a deposit of $60,000 in the name of Joseph H. Hirshhorn Limited.

Hirshhorn's formal announcement that he had come to Canada to do business was typically exuberant. In a full-page advertisement (reproduced in part below) in the mining industry's weekly paper, the *Northern Miner*, on November 16, 1933, Joe Hirshhorn proclaimed:

"MY NAME IS OPPORTUNITY
AND I AM PAGING CANADA"

CANADA, your day has come.

The world is at your feet begging you to release your riches cramped in Mother Earth.

The world asks you to go to work, as you have never worked before, to prospect, to develop, to finance and to produce more gold.

All the mines in all the world since the beginning of time have failed to produce enough gold. The demand has been greater than the supply.

Canada, you have the Gold. Your record up to this time proves it.

Since Columbus discovered America in 1492 you have produced nearly one twenty-second of the world's gold output.

There is not any reason why you should not occupy first position. No one can stop you but yourself.

Go after greater gold production! Gain first place!

Think of being in a position to produce the most precious thing needed in the world right now.

Carry on until the pick strikes the hard firm yellow metal, until the cry of "Gold" resounds through the virgin forest.

Remember that Opportunity comes every day in the life of the individual and as the individual makes the nation, the future of Canada depends upon the efforts of each one of us.

And as for us, we believe in the future of this great Country to the extent that we have made investments in gold mining and shall continue to do so.

J. H. HIRSHHORN & CO.
Limited
Investment Bankers

TORONTO:
302 Bay Street
NEW YORK:
50 Broad Street

This rousing introduction and challenge, not unlike an evangelical tract, is still widely remembered and discussed. And, like a successful tract, it attracted the curious, the wonderers, and the serious.

Among those stimulated by Joe's proclamation were two prospectors, Fred MacLeod and Arthur Cockshutt, who were selling units in the Little Longlac Syndicate, which had been organized to develop a gold discovery near the town of Geraldton, Ontario. Hirshhorn is understood to have purchased 200 units in that syndicate for $2,000. His faith in the chosen prospectors was confirmed, and a mine resulted. His units were converted into public shares which he reportedly sold, in time, for about $500,000.

Hirshhorn was attracted also by the work of a Canadian mining engineer and developer, Robert A. Bryce. With American associates, Hirshhorn provided Bryce with much of the required financing to put the great Macassa mine into production in the Kirkland Lake mining camp of Ontario. This was not an easy task in the depression years of the 1930s, but Bryce, with Hirshhorn's financial help, did it, and both benefited as a result.

Many others flocked to Hirshhorn's open door. Prospectors, promoters, and geologists all came with their rock samples or theories. During my years in eastern Canada I hardly ever met a prospector or promoter active in those "gold-vintage" years of 1934-40 who had not received encouragement or assistance from "Little Joe" even if it was only a couple of hundred bucks. If, however, a prospector had been into the booze before he came to see him, Joe, a near teetotaller, would bark: "You stink – come back when you're sober!"

Among the many he helped, Hirshhorn picked some remarkable winners. One of these was mining engineer Doug Wright who brought to Joe's attention a Porcupine property near Timmins in northern Ontario. Wright, Hirshhorn, and Joe's lawyer, Bill Bouck, developed it into the Preston East Dome Mine which was highly successful despite the early scepticism of many "authorities."

When Joe began to promote the prospect he was ridiculed by some, as he was with most of his promotions. Much of the ridicule came from other promoters, all competing for the same reservoir of speculative funds. When Hirshhorn had raised the money for drilling the first three drill holes, he ordered Wright to start drilling at once. One of the three holes struck gold and was the key to the Pandora's Chest later exposed.

That mine elevated Hirshhorn's status from buccaneer to a corporate captain of industry (although he continued to remain shy of the latter role, largely delegating it to Bill Bouck). Later, Preston served as his principal source of capital for the founding of his crowning achievement, the multi-billion-dollar uranium field in the Blind River region of Ontario.

I never asked Hirshhorn how he picked his winners, but he volunteered the information many times. "Character," he would say. "I gotta see the man, look him in the eyes, listen to his pitch, see his hands, and figure if he's a worker or a bum. If I figure he's honest, maybe got a winner, and is a worker, he gets the moolah!"

Joe Hirshhorn's appearance in Canada in the early 1930s was a masterpiece of intuitive planning. He appeared at the right time and for the right purpose. It was obvious to thoughtful observers that Canada offered tremendous potential for increased gold production. The knowledge necessary to do this was available. Those who would find it, the prospectors and geologists, were ready and hungrily seeking a grubstake. And gold was the only metal which could, in that time of economic despair, "move quickly."

Joe made money as gold "moved" – not by impulsive action, but rather through considerable intuitive intelligence. He had a remarkably well-programmed organic computer. His gifts of natural intelligence and a sense of timing, combined with hard work and drive, provided the key to his success as a speculator. But Hirshhorn didn't just want to make money. His aim was to find and successfully develop mining properties of importance. He raised money only to finance specific objectives. These objectives were determined from the constant stream of proposals made to him by prospectors and exploration geologists and his shrewd assessment as to the credibility of the schemes presented together with the degree of the public's acceptance and financial willingness to pay the shot in testing the scheme.

Occasionally Hirshhorn spoke of the financing of mining ventures as "crap-shooting." He knew that such a reference was inaccurate, merely using it and others like it to add excitement or "pizazz" to a project. His constant aim was to find mines and become an empire builder. In the end, he succeeded.

Funds risked in mineral exploration differ from money spent on gambling in a highly significant sense. The major portion of money spent on exploration is applied to attempts to create new wealth for the nation and some reward for the risk-takers. It is high-risk funding for creative high-return objectives. The promoters must be constantly searching for winners or they lose their following.

The days and weeks that followed my first encounter with Joe Hirshhorn were filled with work for a variety of clients in the mining business. Then one day, two months or so later, my secretary said to me: "A Mr. Joe Hirshhorn is on the line. He says he knows you and that he's in the building. Will you take the call?"

Over the phone Hirshhorn's voice barked at me again, "Why haven't yuh bin around ta see me? Cumup right now. Got something on my mind. Cumup!" I went to see him. As soon as I entered Hirshhorn's office, he came to the point.

"Yuh know why yuh're here?" he asked. Not waiting for my reply he continued. "Uranium, that's why! I want ta get into the uranium business! Its got sex appeal! The time's right! I've talked it over with my friend Bill James. He says yuh're one of the two best uranium geologists in the business in eastern Canada! Mind yuh, he didn't say yuh were the best! Will yuh work for me?"

I replied that I could probably fit him in with my commitments to other clients on a part-time basis. And so began an intensive, rewarding, and successful chapter of six or seven years of my life centred on the search for mines and development of uranium and other metals.

My Interest In Uranium

My interest in uranium, and in the black naturally occurring form of uranium oxide called pitchblende, first began to develop during my high-school days when I learned that it was the source of radium. I knew that radium produces gamma rays which have the magic property of seeing inside organic bodies. I also discovered that these rays could destroy deadly cancer cells. Such miracles excited my imagination, and I read what I could on the subject.

Because of a certain pride in my French heritage, my interest grew further when I read that radium, the tiny fractional part of uranium that is the source of gamma radiation, had been discovered in pitchblende by the French scientists Becquerel and Pierre and Marie Curie in 1898. Three decades later, radium was discovered in Canada, making it, at the time, the second major world source after the Belgian Congo. Perhaps, subliminally, this made me think: "Why can't I find some radium too and become a hero?" After all, I had grown up with Horatio Alger's heroes!

In 1932, the lithium atom was split by John Cockcroft and Ernest Walton at the Cavendish Laboratory in the University of Cambridge. Ernest Rutherford, who had initiated the scientific study of the nucleus of the atom, and who became one of the founders of atomic science, described the possibility of vast amounts of energy being released from the atom as just so much "moonshine" – something that would just fade away. But it didn't. Atomic power became a dramatic reality. Its advent was widely compared to the discovery of fire – with all its benefits and dangers. When I first heard of this comparison I thought of all the benefits which came with fire; I thought that no one of sound mind would wish to ban fire, even though it can be highly dangerous. Mankind has learned how to benefit greatly from fire and how to control its dangerous and improper use. In so doing, mankind has demonstrated how social wisdom, the collective intelligence of the human race, can advance. I felt the same would be true of atomic power. The uniqueness of uranium, including its capacity for self-disintegration, intrigued me. Its ability to interact with all other elements, acids and alkalis, both organic and inorganic, amazed me. In time, I began to wonder whether radiation from a uranium source, possibly the sun, might not have been the original energy spark that kindled the chain of organic evolution and eventually life.

During the Second World War I had little time or opportunity to engage in any uranium-related activity. Uranium was omitted from our search for strategic war metals. Nor was any field equipment for its effective search then commercially produced or available to us. This total public and professional black-out of all reference to uranium struck me as odd at the time, yet my queries to equally involved professional explorationists produced no enlightenment.

The sudden and terrifying news of the detonation of "atomic bombs" over Hiroshima and Nagasaki offered the first inkling that they involved a uranium-based explosive. My personal reactions at the time were of mixed horror and despair. Despair because I realized that following that and Hitler's rocket-delivered "buzz-bombs" over London, and the British aerial bomb-firestorm that obliterated Hamburg (with, as few realize, a loss of life about equal to that in Hiroshima), modern war was no longer confined to military forces; civilian populations were now the pawns. This was a monumental new threshold of immorality.

During the period 1945-48, much post-war rehabilitation was commenced; this included the acceleration of mineral exploration here in Canada. My involvement at that time reverted to precious and base metal investigations. At the same time, although private sector industry was not yet permitted to be involved, I pondered the future of uranium and, characteristically, sought a brighter side to its apparent immoral use as a weapon.

In 1948, the government of Canada publicized its willingness to permit, and to subsidize through purchase contracts, the commencement of a private sector uranium production industry.

At the same time there was made available on the public market the first small flashlight-battery-powered Geiger-Muller counter that indicated abnormal radioactivity – from any source – by a ticking signal through an earphone attachment. I bought one of the first kits available, it would become part of my standard bush gear, as familiar to me as my spectacles.

About the same time, the media became more positive about nuclear research. In Canada our atomic energy agency had developed to operational level a nuclear reactor of unique design. It was powered with a lower-cost uranium fuel, and, to the growing number of anti-nuclear critics, it offered the improvement that its waste did not produce plutonium pure enough for bomb manufacture.

In the United States the political rhetoric and the press were becoming less strident. Even the spokesman for military research spoke openly of an accelerating shift toward the utilization of the atom in such things as aircraft-portable power-package units for almost instant generation of electricity for remote communities of from 5 to 10,000 persons. We heard encouraging words about the development of reactors for marine propulsion of vessels, ice-breakers, and submarines. At the same time the technical professions and public utilities were researching the feasibility of nuclear-generated electricity.

The dramatic research results in the fields of medical radio-isotope uses and food irradiation were attracting public attention. And I read more than the public comment on such matters. I was on various report distribution lists for unclassified research projects and could in most cases understand most of the contents because of my training in chemistry. I visited an early research exhibition of irradiated food-stuffs and two of the earliest operating power reactors.

Slowly I realized that, under controllable states, the atom could serve the human race advantageously. I accordingly included uranium in the category of minerals I would search for.

A decade later – in the mid 1960s – that assessment would change. The controlled atom had not failed, but its seemingly uncontrollable master had. And an even more terrifying and vicious successor had appeared. The earlier fission of uranium was supplanted by fusion, a physical phenomenon so violent that it remains uncontrollable to the present.

My Search for Uranium Begins

Between 1949 and 1955 I was particularly active in prospecting for uranium and developing uranium mines. The success my colleagues and I enjoyed in discovering uranium deposits in several areas of Canada during this time resulted in considerable discussion of our work in the media. As a result, I was frequently invited to speak on various aspects of uranium. The audiences, at first limited to technical and scientific circles, soon grew to include groups of economists, medical societies, social clubs, and societies with social and international concerns.

I welcomed such invitations as opportunities to serve in an educational capacity. Apart from addressing the specific interest of the groups concerned, my underlying theme remained the same: uranium and its usage, like fire and the manner in which it is used, are mixed blessings. The initial use of uranium for destructive purposes was a horrendous human tragedy that must never be allowed to be repeated. On the other hand, a vast number of peaceful and creative uses of nuclear fission can bring untold blessings to the human race.

My primary work, however, was as a prospector-geologist. To prospect for uranium successfully, of course, it was necessary to know where uranium might be found. When I first studied the scientific literature on the occurrences of uranium, only three areas of substantial quantities had been exploited – at Shinkolobwe in the Belgium Congo, in several of the south-western American states (along with vanadium), and in Joachimsthal, Czechoslovakia. There were numerous references to small indications of uranium in China, Cornwall, and South Africa among others. In addition to the discovery of pitchblende at McTavish (Echo) Bay, Great Bear Lake, in the Northwest Territories in 1930, occurrences of uranium in Canada had been reported at two points in Ontario – Bancroft, and north of Sault Ste. Marie on Lake Superior.

The reference to the "north of Sault Ste. Marie" occurrence had been published in Geological Survey of Canada reports several decades prior to its rediscovery and evaluation by a prospector, Bob Campbell, in September 1948. That was nearly one hundred years after Benjamin Stanard, the captain of a Lake Superior sailing ship who had an interest in minerology, had passed a rock specimen to Dr. John LeConte, an American geologist. This discovery was reported in the May 1847 issue of the *American Journal of Science and Arts*, through which it had become widely known to the prospecting fraternity.

Bob Campbell's find came to be known as the Camray deposit and it attracted much attention to the region. I was probably the first geologist to examine the Camray occurrence with care, as I had been retained in 1948 by Campbell's financial backers to prepare a prospectus toward the financing and development of the prospect. Campbell's efforts (and those of many other prospectors who followed in his footsteps) yielded about thirty other small and similar pitchblende occurrences spread over two hundred square miles of terrain bordering the eastern shore of Lake Superior. Eight of these discoveries were diamond-drilled. Three, including the original Camray, were explored underground. None, however, proved to be of economic value.

Despite these disappointing results, exploration for uranium was accelerated by the appearance of low-cost Geiger counters and spread rapidly east and north of the Camray district. I recommended prospecting over this wider range to all prospectors who came to my Camray field-camp for advice. I continued to hold the view that the region closer to Sudbury, possibly Cobalt, offered better potential for prospectors.

In 1949, a prospector named Karl Gunterman had come to my camp and asked me to look at a uranium discovery which he had made near the Agawa River. At that time, Arthur W. Stollery, an engineer with whom I had become acquainted in the Bridge River Valley of British Columbia, was working for me in the Camray district as a field assistant. I was pressed for time, so I asked Stollery to look at Gunterman's discovery. He did so and his report was negative.

Nevertheless, Gunterman later came back to my Camray field-camp to tell me that a specimen of rock he and Aimé Breton (his grubstaker, the proprietor of the Standard Hotel in Sault St. Marie) had Geigered in a local mineral collection was strongly radioactive. The source of the specimen was unknown to the collector but he believed it to be towards Sudbury and thought it had been given to him by an individual called Lang, since this name was vaguely recognizable on a tattered label attached to the rock.

Aimé Breton and Karl Gunterman were finally able to trace the source of the radioactive specimen to a series of old trenches blasted a half-century earlier in the Township of Long. The earlier prospectors had almost certainly been searching for gold. Breton and Gunterman then staked some claims to cover the old trenches. Gunterman had informed me earlier of this new type of radioactive rock which he and his grubstaker were trying to track down and stake, and although he had promised that I would be the first geological scout given an opportunity to examine it in place, he dallied. I only learned of its actual location when I visited the Soo and called in at Breton's hotel to find out how their search was progressing. Only Breton was there. To my surprise and dismay he bluntly announced that they had located the source, staked it, and had already offered it to others for option.

I asked who the others were. He proudly stated it was Thayer Lindsley's Ventures Group in Toronto. I knew T.L., as Lindsley was known, quite well.

I left Breton's hotel, went to a public telephone booth across the street, and called the Ventures office in Toronto. T.L. was not available but his executive assistant, Jack Cunningham-Dunlop, took my call. He listened to my story and said Ventures would not compete. He suggested that if I made a full examination of the prospect and considered it worth optioning they would like to have half the deal. I readily agreed. I returned to the Breton hotel and put Breton on the phone to Cunningham-Dunlop who confirmed the arrangement.

The next morning I was driven to the discovery site by Aimé Breton. It was extremely accessible – only a few miles east of Blind River on the north shore of Lake Huron and little more than one-quarter mile into the bush from the Trans Canada Highway and Canadian National Railway line. The exact location of the discovery was about one mile from the shore of Lake Huron and a few hundred yards from the easterly end of Lauzon Lake, a popular tourist area just east of Blind River.

The showings were exposed in three or four very old blasted trenches much overgrown with shrubbery and small trees. A bed of rusted and highly radioactive *breccia*, or conglomerate, was partially exposed. I took samples and climbed a small rocky knoll to examine a group of conspicuous claim posts. Breton followed. I made notes from the information on the posts in my field book. When I saw the names Fisher and Audette on some of the posts I asked Breton, "Are they your stakers?"

"No," he replied, "they're just a crazy pair of Americans, but I have a deal with them."

Later I learned that Fisher and Audette were two Americans who had come to Lauzon Lake to fish. "For fun" they had purchased a Geiger counter and used it as they tramped around. They had detected radioactivity in the old trenches and staked two claims over the trenches, prior to Breton and Gunterman staking.

That evening, back in Sault Ste. Marie, I learned that several other prospectors had already staked "tie-on" claims, over and along the north and south sides of Lauzon Lake and westerly from the Fisher-Audette-Breton-Gunterman claims. These stakers included several prospectors known to me who had been active in the Camray area "rush."

The next morning, Breton and I visited his lawyer's office. We prepared a simple exploration option agreement that allowed a thirty-day period for assay results to be received and considered, and for claim titles to be checked and placed in escrow. All this was to be done before the option became formally effective and cash payments and work obligations would be obligatory.

Unfortunately the results of the assays from my samples were disappointingly low. There was only a trace of uranium. But I stubbornly refused to accept these results as final. I asked Thayer Lindsley's office to have one of their staff resample the showings before giving up. And I invited several other major companies to do the same, including Algoma Steel and International Nickel. Two additional companies agreed to do so. One of the latter was Conwest, which sent in Richard Barrett, then a Professor of Mining at the University of Toronto, who served occasionally as a Conwest consultant. Those who came all had the same experience. They all found highly radioactive samples which assayed negligible uranium. On the assumption that the radioactivity must be due to thorium and/or potassium (both radioactive sources), the common conclusion, including my own, was that there was only a negligible and uneconomic content of uranium present. Shortly before the expiry of the thirty-day grace period, I wrote Breton's solicitor stating that my option would not be exercised and would therefore be allowed to lapse.

Fisher and Audette, with whom I never had direct contact, also allowed their claims to lapse soon after my examination. Breton and Gunterman retained their claims for an additional two years or so, then they, too, were allowed to lapse. What no one realized at the time, however, was that several years later these same old trenches, which had been the early centre of interest, would become the westerly end of the fabulous Peach-Pronto uranium ore body and the tip of the gigantic "Big Z" structure. But all this lay in the future as I began my association with Joe Hirshhorn.

Technical Mine Consultants

Between 1949 and 1952 I handled special assignments on a part-time basis for Hirshhorn and his Technical Mine Consultants (TMC) group.

This was a company which Joe had created in 1936 or 1937 to handle the technical aspects of his mining activities. Between 1952 and 1955 I became its full-time general manager.

When I had agreed to act as part-time consultant for Joe Hirshhorn, he had told me that I would be working with Mike Young who headed the TMC group. Young had several men assisting him whom I knew. They were either consultants or permanent staff members. Two of these were Dr. Garnet MacCartney and Dr. William Gross, who were held in particularly high regard as geologists; I felt reassured by their involvement. We were to work as a team to prepare the documentation for an international corporation to finance uranium exploration in the Beaverlodge area of Saskatchewan. My involvement in this work was limited to the complicated task of completing a prospectus and submitting it to the Securities Exchange Commission in Washington, D.C., for approval, since shares in the company for which the prospectus was being prepared were to be sold in the United States.

Hirshhorn, who rarely served on the board of any company he incorporated or controlled, had persuaded Paul V. McNutt, a former governor of Indiana and former United States ambassador to the Philippines, to serve as the president of the company, American-Canadian Uranium Company Limited. The vice-president of this company was to be Josiah Marvel, Jr., who had been the United States ambassador to Denmark. I would soon learn that Joe always enjoyed an impressive choir behind his pulpit!

I did not enjoy rewriting documents and reports which had been submitted earlier and returned for revision. Attendance at briefings with officials of the Securities Commission in Washington, D.C., I found to be quite boring. A point was reached, however, when field evaluation of the Canadian mining claims involved was required. I asked, and it was agreed, that I be given responsibility for this field work. The two weeks I spent tramping over the Goldfields-Beaverlodge area of northern Saskatchewan to view the Hirshhorn-controlled uranium discoveries, and a visit to the federal government's Eldorado (Beaverlodge) Mine was an exhilarating period for me.

This was in 1948, after the government of Canada had finally lifted the tight wartime security that had surrounded all uranium exploration and nuclear research. During this period of secrecy a tremendous government-sponsored exploration program had been mounted and richly rewarded with the discovery of the very important Beaverlodge uranium deposits for which a large production plant was approaching completion at the time of my visit.

The Hirshhorn holdings that I appraised and reported on were situated in several mineral concessions which had been granted by the government of Saskatchewan to Norb Millar and William, "Wild Bill," Richardson before assignment to Hirshhorn. Both had approached Hirshhorn at his Toronto office. Richardson was a suave, young, handsome promoter who had the foresight to incorporate a company named Goldfields Uranium. "It's a name that can't lose," Joe said to me excitedly. Hirshhorn, who was convinced that certain names had captivating mystical values, wanted that corporate vehicle at any cost.

After Hirshhorn acquired control of this company from Richardson, it had a checkered career. Following considerable field study and prospecting, I had reported that certain of those concessions had been "found wanting." However, Hirshhorn disposed of them to another promoter, Hoskings, for a large quantity of stock in his company, Hosco. The Hosco block of stock went into the Goldfields portfolio controlled by Hirshhorn. What happened later as far as these companies were concerned had nothing to do with my activities for Hirshhorn. But it gives an interesting glimpse into what sometimes happens with penny financial prospecting companies, many of which enjoy several re-incarnations.

Goldfields became a dormant corporation. Subsequently it was passed on to the Rio Tinto organization of London, England, with other of Hirshhorn's lesser companies – his "cats and dogs" – when Joe eventually sold his interests to Rio. The Goldfields corporate shell, with Hosco shares in its portfolio, was then purchased from the Rio group for a trivial sum by a highly gifted developer-promoter, Norman Keevil, Sr.

Keevil, an extremely able geophysicist, was aware, as were only a few others, that the revitalized Hosco Company was exploring well-placed land in close proximity to an important new discovery, Noranda-Mattagami, in north-western Quebec. Keevil was astute enough to learn of the large quantity of Hosco stock held by Goldfields. His purchase of Goldfields, solely for its long-forgotten interest in Hosco, rapidly returned his investment probably a hundredfold.

Hirshhorn had been right. Goldfields had a name "that couldn't lose" but it had required time; from Richardson to Hirshhorn to Hoskings to the Rio organization then to Keevil, before, as Joe would describe it, "the payday."

My work for Hirshhorn with Wild Bill Richardson and his Gold-fields Uranium did not lead to a uranium discovery. But my work with Norb Millar, "the flying prospector" did. I had met Norb Millar earlier and respected him as a hard-working and dependable prospector. He was also a stimulating intellectual and a conversationalist who was always good company on a bush trip.

More fortunate, or perhaps more discerning than Richardson, Millar secured a concession with better potential from the Saskatchewan government. Like all other lands in the Beaverlodge, Martin Lake, and Nicholson Bay areas, Millar's concession had been systematically and exclusively prospected for uranium, under conditions of stringent secrecy, by federal government geologists and prospectors during the years after the Second World War. That systematic effort had resulted in the important Eldorado-Beaverlodge Ace and Fay uranium mine developments.

Norb Millar had secured copies of the newly released maps of the previous surveys and had re-examined carefully several of the showings reported earlier. Among these was one he felt would be a winner. When I was led into the bush and shown it, I agreed. Apart from its identification by number on a survey traverse line, I was delighted to find that the prospect had a personality. My careful scratching of a pitch-clotted blaze on a small nearby pine tree had revealed the single name, "Smitty." Despite this, Norb Millar insisted that the mine-to-be should be called The Rix, and so it was.

The Rix "Baby"

With funds provided by Joe Hirshhorn we developed the Rix into a small but rich and profitable producer of uranium. The capable development team that placed the Rix in production by the fall of 1952 included Paul Young, chief engineer; R. H. (Harry) Buckles, engineer and field manager; and Walter F. Atkins, mine manager. Another group, J. R. (Ran) MacDonald, Gordon Moore, Howard Hall, M. (Dit) Holt, and a remarkable woman accountant and radio operator, Monty Montgomery, supported by university part-time students, were engaged in the large-scale regional prospecting program we undertook simultaneously, but without significant results.

Little did we realize it then, but the modest Rix operation would, as is so often the case in exploration, provide a significant key to greater things to follow; in this case, to the treasure of Elliot Lake.

Norb Millar, who had introduced us to the Rix prospect, was a flying prospector, operating his own tiny, pontoon-equipped, two-seater Gypsy Moth, which he handled with the same ease as others would a canoe. I made several trips with him in the Moth to visit widely scattered prospects he or his associates had staked. One stands out in my memory.

Norb wished to show me some oxidized cliffs in the Werner Lake area of north-central Ontario. Since there were no nearby lakes or rivers on which we could land, we had to view and assess the cliffs from the aircraft in flight. This meant approaching the cliffs as closely as we dared. We probably spent twenty minutes in this nerve-racking exercise. Then we headed for home.

On the way back to our base Millar decided to visit a trapper friend. In due course we arrived above the trapper's cabin beside a small lake. Millar made a low circle over the cabin but there was no smoking chimney, no yelping dog, and apparently no one in the cabin. After a final low dive over the cabin, Millar's aircraft climbed, and then sped for our base.

The plane was equipped with a coiled forty-foot antenna which Millar usually unreeled as soon as he was aloft. Using his short-range radio, he could then establish communication with airplane bases or other pilots. It was necessary, of course, for the antenna to be rewound before landing the aircraft.

As we approached our base on this particular flight, Norb attended properly to all landing procedures, including winding in his antenna. As we taxied in toward the dock, however, he exclaimed, "Something's wrong. Probably rudders." Careful handling, with the help of a breeze, brought us to the float, and Norb and I climbed out. I quickly set about mooring the plane.

Norb examined his pontoon rudders. He reached into the water and yanked up a copper cable. Soon a chinaware insulator appeared, but the cable seemed to have no end. He kept pulling. Finally, the end of the cable appeared. Attached to it was another insulator and a small splinter of wood. I watched without a word. Norb answered my unasked question. "Guess we took away the trapper's aerial on our last dive!" he said. "Too bad!"

The Rix became the first private-sector producer of uranium in Canada since Eldorado–Great Bear in the late 1930s. The modest success we had with the Rix was exploited to the hilt by Joe Hirshhorn as he encouraged the public to share in our good fortune. His rallying cry to Bay Street traders thereafter became, "Watch us!" And they did!

During these years I was engaged in a variety of challenging activities in addition to my work for Hirshhorn's Technical Mine Consultants. As a totally committed prospector, my objectives were broadly based and my explorations in effect were aimed at identifying any mineral of economic value, whether it be base or precious or an industrial mineral. For this reason it was essential that I be knowledgeable concerning new technical developments in my field. Thus I took a particular interest in the new types of electronic and technical devices being developed to assist geologists and prospectors in their work.

Tracking Ore Bodies with Technical "Doodlebugs"

For generations, prospectors used magnetic compasses in their search for iron ore. With the development, production, and sale of portable Geiger counters after the Second World War, a new instrument became available with which prospectors could detect radioactive materials. Another highly significant device, which began to influence the work of geologists and prospectors about the same time, was the magnetometer. The development and use of such magnetic, electric, or radiometric equipment required specialists known as geophysicists.

The magnetometer is designed to measure the strength of a magnetic field on or beneath the Earth's surface. This instrument may be used on the ground, in the air, or beneath the sea, from a mobile base, either surface vehicle, aircraft, or ship. It was developed during the war to detect submarines and mines from aircraft in flight. Many base-metal ore bodies contain iron minerals that are magnetic so the exploration fraternity soon adapted these instruments for use by hand on land or for aerial surveys.

Since aircraft can fly over areas to which access on the ground can be gained only with difficulty, the cost and time advantages of using this method for preliminary prospecting or screening are obvious. The airborne surveys produced maps upon which the uniquely magnetic features ("anomalies") were shown. It was then necessary for a geologist to investigate such anomalies on the ground to confirm their presence, form, casual features, and geological environment, all in order to determine if the anomaly indicated the presence of an associated mineral deposit. If the evidence was encouraging, then additional instrument surveying of much greater precision was performed.

Given the huge areas of often low-lying water, clay, or swamp-covered Precambrian rock which constitute the Canadian Shield and contain its mineral potential, the advantages of using the most sophisticated prospecting devices were obvious. Accordingly, in 1950, I formed a team with Ross Toms, a remarkably able northern frontier prospector, his partner, Olie Bones, and a very able geophysicist, Carl T. Bischoff, to perform, on a contractual basis, ground magnetometric surveys. My primary role was to find clients for the service and to act as the geological interpreter of the geophysical data secured.

Among our clients for such surveys were some prominent companies headed by Thayer Lindsley, Karl Springer, and Randy Mills, among others. Our team worked primarily in the Chibougamau region of northern Quebec. I remember with special pride work undertaken in the dormant Opemiska Lake area for clients with land holdings surrounding Lindsley's Venture's Opemiska Lake prospect.

The Opemiska copper-gold discovery had been made in August 1929 by the Springer brothers. That discovery attracted prospectors from all parts of Canada. Some underground development of the rich copper-ore bodies was done but a combination of the Great Depression, low copper prices, the remoteness of the area, and geological problems in "following the ore" because of fault displacement, all forced a closure of the operations in 1936.

In 1950 Randy Mills and Karl Springer, both acting for companies that held land adjoining the Opemiska prospect, decided to have magnetometer surveys performed on their holdings to determine if any of the rich Opemiska ore extended onto their own properties. For the most efficient survey I felt we should mount our instrument over the known Opemiska ore body and calibrate it. Then we would proceed to track its course to determine if and where it entered the land holdings of our clients.

I approached T. L. Lindsley and sought permission for my experiment on his property. After some hesitation he agreed, provided he was informed of results secured from the study.

To my team's surprise and delight the experiment worked well, but with astonishing consequences. The Opemiska ore body proved exceptionally well-adapted to tracking with a magnetometer since the ore body was adjoined by a layer of highly magnetic rock, "a basic dyke." Not only could we determine the direction and amount of several fault dislocations in the ore body which had contributed to much earlier despair, we eventually tracked the Opemiska ore structure with confidence for about one mile. The ore structure persistently remained on the Opemiska property – to the amazement and delight of T.L., his manager Cunningham-Dunlop, and financial broker Sandy Richardson, to whom I personally reported our findings. On the other hand, our clients, who owned the adjoining lands and who had paid all the bills for the experiment, were in no mood to rejoice.

The following year Ventures resumed development of the Opemiska, which was placed into production in 1953. It developed into a large and very profitable mine over the two decades which followed.

The Ungava-Quebec (Chubb) Crater

My involvement in the development of the Chibougamau mining camp was only one of a number of interesting activities which directed my attention to the Province of Quebec. Another had resulted from an earlier visit made to my office by two fellow prospectors.

In February 1949 Fred W. Chubb and Norb Millar had come to me for professional advice. They were excited about a discovery they had made. Upon my assurance of total confidentiality Chubb produced, dramatically, two or three aerial photographs about one foot square and asked: "Could that circular structure be a diamond-bearing kimberlite plug?" This is the type of rock formation in which diamonds are found in South Africa and elsewhere.

I examined the photographs carefully. These photographs, which were of excellent quality, were vertical exposures of strip photography taken by the Royal Canadian Air Force in the course of its national program of photographing Canada from the air. The circular structure to which Chubb directed my attention was strikingly apparent. Norb Millar's attention had been seized by it when he was examining photographs in the RCAF photo-library in Ottawa.

After examining the photographs and reflecting on them I observed cautiously, "No, I don't believe it's a kimberlite, nor, in that terrain, a volcanic crater. It may be a meteoritic impact crater. In any event, it should be examined in the field. Will you tell me where it is?"

"In Ungava, Quebec. The sub-Arctic," replied Chubb.

"That's too far away and too costly for me to persuade a client to put up the funds for a charter aircraft on pontoons to fly us in there for an examination," I replied. Chubb appeared crestfallen.

"Look," I said, "why don't you ask Pierre Berton at *The Toronto Star* to finance a trip up there. I'd go along for the ride if they wanted. Berton might see a good feature story in such an expedition."

Chubb seemed to perk up and said, "I'll try him." While he did not succeed in interesting the *Star*, he later secured the co-operation of Dr. D. V. Meen of the Royal Ontario Museum and the *Canadian Geographic Journal*, and an expedition to examine the site was arranged.

The crater proved to be 11,136 feet in diameter and 1,203 feet in depth, with a rim 333 feet above ground level. It contains a lake holding some meagre fish and is surrounded by a considerable number of smaller circular lakes.

While fused silica has not been discovered nearby, the huge dimensions of the crater suggest that it was caused by some type of implosion, such as the impact of a meteor.

I read with great interest the *Canadian Geographic's* description of the crater. I was pleased that due credit was accorded to Chubb and Millar for their perception and technical curiosity concerning it and even more delighted to learn that it was officially given Chubb's name. That experience with Chubb and Millar and the record of what they later found helps to explain why I regard prospecting as a "romantic adventure."

The professional life of a prospector usually reaches a high point when he or she discovers a prospect that turns out to be a mine. Occasionally geologists share in such adventure. That was the case with my involvement in the identification and development of the Rexspar deposit.

Sam Ciglen and the Rexspar

In the early 1950s, while still doing odd jobs for Joe Hirshhorn before my full-time association with him, I received one of his usual curt directives: "Get Sam Ciglen off my back! He's driving me crazy with phone calls!" I went to see him.

Ciglen told me that he was the legal counsel for a westerner in Kamloops, B.C., who had an option on a property that was "radio-active" and who possessed a certificate from "a government geologist" that indicated a uranium content. I asked if he had a copy of the certificate. "No," he said, "but I have a box full of the uranium rock here." With a sly wink he added, "I keep the stuff under my secretary's desk."

He led the way to his receptionist's desk. Sure enough, there was a sturdy wooden box, originally used for shipping dynamite but now filled with about fifty pounds of mineralized rock. I selected a piece, Geigered it, and later had it analysed. The presence of uranium was confirmed. I flew west to Kamloops to examine the prospect for Hirshhorn's account.

The property in Kamloops was an older, known prospect of several rock exposures that had been trenched and blasted because of the presence of lead, iron pyrites ("fool's gold"), and a pink mineral called fluorspar. A recent re-examination of the deposit by Dr. A. H. Lang, a uranium deposit expert of the Geological Survey of Canada, had established that it was highly radioactive. His analyses had indicated the presence of uranium and several "rare earth" minerals in abnormal quantity. I knew Dr. Lang from earlier associations over the preceding fifteen years and greatly respected his ability.

Following my report and recommendation to Joe Hirshhorn, we took an option on the Rexspar. We promptly set to work trenching, diamond-drilling, sampling, and adit-tunnelling the prospect. Over a period of about three years we developed a potential of about two million tons of uranium ore. While it was low-grade, it was also a low-cost open-pit operation. Long-term advantages of the Rexspar included the potential production of fluorite and celestite for use in the metal-smelting industry and various rare earth minerals for small-market but high-value use in colour transmission in TV and other illuminations.

The mineralogy of the Kamloops deposit for metal extraction was complex. For help in this regard I turned to a friend and former professor, Dr. Frank Forward, head of the Metallurgy Department at the University of British Columbia. Dr. Forward was a brilliant, internationally recognized authority on "leach" metallurgy. This involved dissolving the mineral being sought through the use of a carefully selected liquid and recovering the desired mineral from that liquid.

Forward had contributed in a very significant way to the development of the complicated alkali leach treatment required for the Eldorado-Beaverlodge uranium ore. His research for our Rexspar project was conducted in the Department of Mines laboratories in Ottawa, with the ore from the mine property. Later he did similar research on ore from the Pronto mine we developed near Blind River. He was the first to demonstrate the practicability of uranium recovery from such ores by his novel auto-oxidation process. He converted, with high-pressure steam, the iron sulphide (pyrite), also present in these ores, into sulphuric acid, which then served as the solvent for the uranium and other metal elements.

The team I directed on the Rexspar development included chief engineer Paul Young, Harry Buckles, Walt Atkins, J. W. Scott and Stanley Leeming. Donald H. James, the son of my early employer and lifetime friend Howard T. James, Managing Director of Pioneer Gold Mines, also provided important geological help in this and subsequent projects. It was a great blow to all of us who knew Donald as a fine person and brilliant exploration geologist when he died some years later at the height of his career.

Our Rexspar development team concluded that we should place the prospect into production given its potential for uranium and other relatively rare and economically important by-products. We completed our planning for a satisfactory rate of production and were reasonably close to securing a substantial contract with the federal government when the Blind River (Elliot Lake) development took off in 1953. Our work in the Blind River area, with its enormous potential, required all of our time during the following two years, thus Rexspar was shelved. Eventually it was assigned to the Rio Algom group, who in turn, assigned it to others.

Our involvement in the Rexspar property brought us face-to-face with the opportunity to be among the first in Canada to exploit the porphyry copper deposits of the Kamloops area, about eighty miles to the south. That opportunity was thrust at us at least three times by my good friend and co-prospector of earlier years, Spud Huestis, the eventual developer of Bethlehem Copper in southern British Columbia and the pathfinder of all other activity in that area. Hirshhorn and I had provided, indirectly, some of Huestis' first staking funds for the lands that later became the highly successful Bethlehem mine.

With Spud Huestis in New Brunswick and British Columbia

Late one autumn day when we were developing the Rexspar, I was passing through Vancouver and unexpectedly met Spud on the street. He was working temporarily as a part-time streetcar conductor until spring, when he could hit the hills again as a prospector. He expressed curiosity about The Rexspar, so I suggested to him that he spend the approaching weekend as my guest at that camp.

Two days later we stood on the rock dump of an adit drift being driven through one of the Rexspar ore bodies. Spud examined a chunk of the mineralized rock carefully and listened to the buzz of my Geiger. With complete conviction he announced that he knew where a similar deposit could be found. "When I was a kid in New Brunswick about thirty years ago, I used to sit on the outcrop while fishing in the nearby river."

Only my considerable trust in Spud's honesty, and profound respect for his "prospector's nose" prevented me from treating his statement as a joke. I told him that if he'd go back to his New Brunswick outcrop and check it out for radioactivity, I would ask Joe Hirshhorn to grubstake the trip. And if there actually was any uranium in the deposit we'd make a deal. Spud was soon on his way.

Characteristically, nothing was heard from him for two or three weeks. Then, late in the evening of the twenty-second of December, the telephone rang in my Toronto home. It was Spud from Saint John, New Brunswick. "It's all okay. It's hot. I've done a lot of prospecting and have two outcrops a mile apart. You've got to come, fast!"

I turned to Mary and Marion – then about eleven years old – who both knew Spud well, and said simply, "Spud wants me in Saint John, New Brunswick. Want to spend Christmas there?"

Mary's answer was fast and clear. "Spud and you are both crazy, but Marion and I will go with you."

Between Christmas festivities, and with brooms to remove the thin layer of snow, Spud and I examined the showings. There was indeed radioactivity and the characteristic orange-red stain of uranium exposed to weather was also present in the outcrops, in a rock-type quite similar in appearance to The Rexspar. Spud's discovery was staked over the following two weeks and he returned to Vancouver.

Joe Hirshhorn quickly arranged for the incorporation and financ-

1   The Joubin family in 1915; my parents
    Auguste and Marthe, my little brother
    Gerald (whom I called Tibby) and
    myself.

2   Tibby and I in 1919, proudly showing
    off our first tailor-made suits.

3   Victoria, B.C., 1924: I am wearing my
    public school cadet uniform.

4

5

4 A portrait taken while I was a student
   at Victoria High School.

5 In 1932 I pose as a member of the
   YMCA wrestling club.

6 I was the lessee of this gold mine at
   Greenwood, B.C., in 1937.

6

7

8a

8b

7   Mary and I were married in December
    1937.

8   Both these pictures were taken in
    1939. *Above*, a companion and I
    underground at the Musketeer Mine,
    and *below*, prospecting on Adams
    Plateau in British Columbia.

9

9 Stampede John and I, taken in 1940 when we were prospecting for Pioneer Mines.

10 The Pioneer Mine plant in 1938.

10

11

12

13

14

11 Taken in the airplane carrying me to a prospecting base at Fort St. James, B.C., in the early 1940s.

12 Marion filling my shoes.

13 Karl Springer, myself, and "Cap" Desmond Kidd talking shop near Fort St. James in 1946.

14 Surveying the Hudson Bay scenery at Little Whale River in 1948.

15 Joe Hirshhorn at his "piano."

15

16

17

17 These anonymous prospectors in a camp I visited in Athabaska, Saskatchewan, in 1950 are included to illustrate what a "semi-permanent" prospecting camp looked like.

16 My job with Hirshhorn included listening to prospectors' poetic descriptions of their discoveries. This one is near Bancroft, Ontario, and I'm standing on the left.

19

20

18 I examine our "Queerite" discovery at Whitesail Lake, B.C., in 1952.

19 Standing beside a newly erected claim post near Sudbury in 1953.

20 During the construction of the Quirke Mine at Elliot Lake in 1955. Left to right; myself, Dean Acheson with Joe Hirshhorn's daughters and wife in front of us, Joe, Marion, Mrs. Hart, Mary, and Bob Hart.

18

21

21 Sam Harris and I at the Nordic Mine in Elliot Lake about 1957.

22 Joe Hirshhorn, Paul Young, myself, and Bill Bouck enjoy a happy reunion at the railroad station in Blind River in 1954.

22

23 Mary and I at the party given on my retirement from Joe Hirshhorn's TMC Group.

24 An aerial view of Franmar, our farm at Kettleby, northwest of Toronto. Mary delighted in our life at Franmar.

23

24

25 Mary and Michael Eschli, our farm manager's son, install some ducklings in their new home.

26 The "Pullman Coach" on which I perched atop my sack of peanuts for a hair-raising journey to the St. Elie Mine in French Guiana.

27 I'm holding the orphaned jaguar cub that found my lap so inviting on a trip to Mexico.

28   29

30

28 A drill exploration group in Kenya.
    I'm third from the right in the striped
    shirt.

29 Marion and I during a family trip to
    Mexico.

30 Some years later, in 1961, Mary and I
    stood proudly beside Marion on her
    wedding day.

31 I stand among a group of pygmies in
    Brazil during my United Nations
    assignment to that country in 1968.

31

33

32

32 Taken during a visit with one of the
    men who have influenced my life,
    Dr. Norman McKenzie, the retired
    president of the University of British
    Columbia.

33 John Black Aird and I hold a gold
    brick, among the first produced after
    we bought the Pioneer Mine.

34

35

36

34 My grandson David and I on a visit to the Pioneer Mine in 1986.

35 In 1983 I received the Order of Canada from Governor General Edward Schreyer.

36 Lieutenant-Governor Lincoln Alexander presents me with the Order of Ontario in 1987.

37 In 1987, at a function of the Churchill Society, I stand with Viola MacMillan, known as the Queen Bee of Canadian prospectors, Dr. McCormack Smyth, and Lady Soames, Sir Winston Churchill's daughter.

38 Taken in 1987, when I visited the X-Cal gold prospect at Fort St. James as an advisor.

37

38

39 In 1988, I enjoyed a visit to my
    granddaughter Marea in Paris.

ing of a new company, New Brunswick Uranium and Metals, which purchased the claims from Spud for some cash and a block of escrowed stock. Spud did not like receiving escrowed stock and asked Hirshhorn to purchase half of it from him for cash, which Hirshhorn promptly did. On handing Spud his two cheques, Hirshhorn asked him teasingly what he would do with the money. Spud did not reply. Later, he said to me, "I'm going to finish staking the old Snowstorm prospect in Kamloops." Casually I replied, "Keep me in touch with what you find." Subsequently, these claims became the Bethlehem Copper Mine, the first identified and successfully developed copper porphyry deposit in Canada.

Spud kept his word. When he had a large enough block of ground staked, he employed a bulldozer to trench the topsoil from above and around the old Snowstorm workings of twenty years before. Several times he phoned long-distance to Toronto urging me to come west and visit his new showings.

I took Spud seriously and asked my Rexspar manager and geologist at Kamloops to examine his copper showings. Their report that it was "either the biggest thing in the country or nothing at all" satisfied neither Spud nor myself. Spud persisted. I explained that my intense preoccupation with Blind River developments would not permit a personal examination but asked if he would agreed to have Howard James either make the examination or select a colleague to do so. Spud admired Dr. James and agreed to accept his decision as final. A consultant acceptable to Spud was found by our friend Howard James, but his verdict was "far too low-grade – no hope at all." Finally, Spud optioned the property to a major American company. After considerable work they lost interest. Spud persevered. With the professional support of an imaginative geologist, Dr. William White, a few faithful colleagues, and Japanese financing, he eventually succeeded. By the early 1970s Bethlehem had paid all its debts and $17 million in dividends! Hirshhorn would describe it as "Spud's payday."

Spud's gains from the success of The Snowstorm (Bethlehem) property were not the only return he enjoyed from his association with Joe Hirshhorn and myself. His New Brunswick uranium prospect had not measured up to critical drill testing. Its claims were dropped and the company lay dormant with some unspent funds in its treasury. Hirshhorn disposed of the company with other "cats and dogs" when he sold all his mining assets to Rio Tinto. Some years later the corporate shell was sold once again, this time by Rio Tinto to an energetic and successful promoter who renamed his newly acquired vehicle "NBU Mines." Like many other penny-stock companies it quickly became successful in its exploration operations under new direction. All the escrowed stock was freed for public trading at a time when it was worth several dollars a share.

It was only at this point, almost twenty years later, that the transfer company involved brought me abreast of all that had transpired during the interval, and sought my assistance in locating Spud. Spud could not be found in Vancouver. I eventually tracked him to California and wrote to tell him that his trip to New Brunswick that Christmas in the early 1950s had finally produced, albeit very indirectly, a nice dividend of probably a quarter of a million dollars, which could be realized by identifying himself to the transfer company.

Bancroft Uranium and B.C. Lead, Zinc, and Gold

On a weekend holiday trip to Bancroft, Ontario, with Mary and Marion and our spaniel Birdy, I was recognized and approached by a stranger who had attended one of my lectures on uranium exploration at the Prospector and Developer's Convention. This was Art Shore, a prospector who had just made a radioactive discovery in nearby Faraday Township which he asked me to examine.

When I accompanied Shore to his first trenching, I found that it was indeed highly radioactive. I took some rock samples and advised him to do additional work. He did so and sent me additional favourable data on his progress. I passed this information on to Joe Hirshhorn's Preston East Dome company, only to be told by its consultant, Dr. G. B. Langford, that "uranium ore bodies are not found in pegmatite dykes." In mid June 1951, I introduced Shore's agent, Ernie Wood, to the Bryant Newkirk group, which optioned the prospect and over a three-year period developed the deposit into the Faraday Mine with an initial production contract approaching $30 million.

At about this same time, I had come upon references in an old British Columbia Department of Mines report about long-known lead-zinc mineralization in carbonate rocks near Howser on Duncan Lake, about seventy miles north of Nelson, B.C. The mineralized area appeared large, but only one patented claim was indicated on the map accompanying the report. I liked the general geology so I asked Ross Toms to leave from Ontario to join Spud Huestis in British Columbia to stake it.

After the claims were staked, Toms, Huestis, myself, and a few others in our syndicate were persuaded to option them to a company headed by Karl Springer, which in turn optioned them to an American company. A breakdown of communication between the latter two companies resulted in a failure to record assessment work, the lapsing of the claims, and the immediate restaking of them by and for Consolidated Mining and Smelting Company (Cominco). This deposit ultimately became the immensely important Duncan Lake lead-zinc deposit developed by Cominco. Such is the luck of the prospector.

My colleagues and I did not share in the financial benefits which flowed from Cominco's exploration of their Duncan Lake property, but we shared the satisfaction of knowing that we had been there first, and that we had been on the right track. In the drive to discover mineral deposits, the big ones that get away are often as memorable as those that bring the big payday and reach the dinner platter.

In 1951, I secured a new option from the Harrison brothers, of Burns Lake, B.C., on their gold-silver-telluride deposit which we had found during the war years and which had been drilled and relinquished by Pioneer Mines. I interested Joe Hirshhorn in the prospect and he formed and financed the Deerhorn Mines Company which undertook some adit underground development below the earlier drilling. That work confirmed the grade and volume of our earlier drilling but did not add to the modest reserves. For that reason and because the price of gold was still low, the property was returned by us to the Harrison brothers.

Serendipity, a Flophouse, and a Lac La Ronge Copper Mine

From June through September 1951 I was in the Beaverlodge area evaluating the drilling of several uranium and separate nickel and copper showings found on Hirshhorn's concessions. Since I was based in the relatively comfortable old gold-mining town of Goldfields, Mary and Marion stayed part of that time with me in the splendour of a modern dwelling which had served earlier as the RCMP staff house.

It was an exciting time for eleven-year-old Marion. Occasionally she was invited to fly to various prospecting camps as "co-pilot" to Lefty, the commercial bush pilot who used his pontoon aircraft to provide air service for the region. Toward the end of this period in Beaverlodge I "stumbled upon" the La Ronge copper-gold deposit that later became our successful Anglo-Rouyn Mine.

In late September 1951, I flew with Lefty from Prince Albert to Goldfields to assess the progress being made at our Rix uranium mine. When the weather "closed in" over the community of La Ronge, Lefty decided to land there and stay until the weather improved.

As I sat alone late that afternoon, waiting for a meal in the only boarding house in the community, a stranger appeared. I invited him to sit at my table and he told me his name was Hansen and that he fished commercially from Lac La Ronge. I told him I was a prospector-geologist.

About twenty years earlier, Hansen told me, he had had a contract with a company to freight in goods and mail to a diamond-drilling camp at Waden Bay on the west side of the lake, about twenty miles north of La Ronge. However, he had never visited nor seen the mine where the diamond-drilling was underway, about a half mile from the lake. On several occasions the young engineer in charge had told him with conviction, over coffee and pie in the cook-tent: "Some day there will be a copper mine here," but within three months the camp closed down and the young engineer left. Twenty years of total in-activity had followed, but the memory remained with Hansen.

"Could you find that trail again, into the old camp?" I asked.

He said, "I think so."

I reached for my wallet, drew out two twenties and a ten, and placed them on the table before Hansen. "I'll make a deal with you," I said. "If you can travel on the lake this afternoon, head for Waden Bay and find that trail – this money will pay for your trouble. If you have time, try to follow the trail into the old camp site and blaze the route. In any event, mark where the trail leaves the lakeshore. We'll fly north and low, along the west shore of the lake as early as the weather clears tomorrow. Have a fire going at the lakeshore and send up plenty of smoke when you hear our aircraft. We'll come down. If you've located the trail to the camp, we'll go in together. If I like what I see, we'll help you stake it and buy the claims from you."

"How much?" he asked.

As a digression to give me time, I asked, "What would you do with the money?"

"Well," he said, "I need a better fishing boat and I know where I can buy a cabin cruiser only four years old for about $6,500. But I'd fetch Hell from the old lady if I spent that much on a boat."

"Why?" I asked.

"Well," said Hansen, "she wants a better shack. The old one is a mess."

"Well," I said, "how does $25,000 cash strike you, for any claims we stake? Or," I added, "if you are a gambler, we could give you stock in any company involved – probably 200,000 or 300,000 shares of stock. If the property makes a mine, the stock could go to $1 a share – perhaps even $5." (Stock in Anglo-Rouyn, the company that ultimately developed the property, rose to $4 a share.)

"No stock," Hansen said. "I just want plain honest money." With that he rose, picked up the $50, shook hands, slipped a bottle of beer in his parka pocket, muttered, "see you in the morning," and left.

Rain squalls and a low cloud ceiling kept us stranded in La Ronge much of the following morning. Shortly before noon Lefty and I took off. Soon we saw the smoke signal and came down. Hansen was waiting, soaked but happy. He had located the abandoned camp site and a piece of the old drilling equipment.

I hustled through the wet bush with him to the site. I spotted a ridge of rock outcrop, walked to it, and climbed on top, followed by Hansen. It was bare and slightly oxidized over a width of about twenty-five feet. There were two old blasted rock trenches across the rusty zone.

I could see little in the trenches but rusty iron stains and a few green specks that could indicate weathered copper. I was disappointed by its appearance, but took heart in the assumption that the oxidation could spell surface leaching. I knocked off a chip sample across the width of the zone along the edge of the trench. I said to Hansen, "Let's prospect."

We walked along the top of the ridge. The weakly oxidized zone continued for approximately six to seven hundred feet of the ridge exposure without apparent change in its appearance. When we returned to the old trench, I noticed a few lensy quartz stringers erratically oriented in cracks of the rock. I knocked off some random chips of quartz from several of these stringers, even though they seemed to lack mineralization, and put them in a sample sack. Before leaving, I promised Hansen I would be in touch again if the assays were interesting.

A week later I received the results of the assays. The copper zone sample assayed, as expected, only 0.2 per cent. The quartz sample, however, was a surprise. It assayed 1 ounce of gold. I asked Harry Buckles, a senior member of our staff in Beaverlodge, to go with two others to Lac La Ronge, pick up Hansen, and start staking the property at Waden Bay to which Hansen had taken me. Buckles was also to prepare a written agreement with Hansen along the lines of the verbal agreement Hansen and I had made. He was to receive a cheque for $25,000 only if two drill holes assayed satisfactorily.

Drilling started shortly after the staking was completed. Three weeks later the assays were received. The two holes, drilled 230 feet apart, averaged a satisfactory 2.4 per cent copper over an eighteen-foot width, but with only a trace of gold. Years later, in the summer of 1957, again under the direction of Harry Buckles, we drill-developed 2.5 million tons of ore to a depth of 500 feet. The grade averaged 2.2 per cent copper, but with only a trace of gold. However, six hundred pounds of split core samples sent to the mineral dressing laboratories in Ottawa reported .08 ounces of gold in the mill testing.

Production did not commence until 1966. By that time the property was under the management of Rio Tinto. It had been necessary to wait for electric power and a road to smelter facilities in Flin Flon. The ore body was exhausted by 1971. From the more than two million tons treated, recovery was 2.1 per cent copper, .05 ounces of gold and .2 of silver, and gross production from the mine was in the order of $40 million. Regrettably, we did not wait to benefit from the greatly increased prices for gold and silver of the 1970s. If we had, an additional $6 million a year would have been realized.

What happened to Hansen, the fisherman who had had such faith in "the nice young engineer" who, twenty years earlier, was so certain the property could make a mine? Unfortunately none of us would know. As our drilling of the property proceeded, I had asked Harry Buckles how Hansen had made out and was simply told "Okay. He was offered stock in the company but would take only cash, so it was paid him."

Some years later I learned that a local prospector-promoter, Eric Partridge, and his two stakers, had beaten Hansen and Harry Buckles' crew to staking all of the ore body. Thus Hirshhorn not only had to pay Hansen, but also purchase some necessary claims from the staking competitors.

Our First Uranium Sales Contract

In September 1951, Joe Hirshhorn's Technical Mine Consultants, made its first approach to Eldorado Mining and Refining, which, since 1948, had been the government of Canada's sole agent, and the agent in Canada for the United States government, for the purchase of uranium. The purpose of the meeting with Eldorado's President, William J. Bennett, was to discuss our first uranium sales contract for the small Rix Mine. There was, at that time, only an inkling of the several huge Blind River contracts which we would sign later, and which, in my time, involved over $700 million. This first negotiation was to secure an agreement for the treatment and purchase by Eldorado of the crude ore mined from the Rix, which we were to deliver to the nearby Eldorado-Beaverlodge treatment complex near Uranium City. We also had an exploratory discussion regarding the Rexspar deposit.

In addition to myself, the negotiating party included John Black Aird, then a young lawyer of the firm of Edison, Aird & Berlis, and Paul Young, TMC's chief engineer. Joe Hirshhorn dealt with several law firms both in Canada and the U.S.A. but his primary legal adviser and colleague in Canada, throughout my period with him, was Bill Bouck. Joe highly respected John Edison and was attracted to John Aird as "a comer." Joe's character judgements proved correct, as was so often the case. Indeed, it came as little surprise to us who knew and worked with John Aird that he reached the peak of national and provincial acclaim as a member of the Canadian Senate, Lieutenant-Governor of Ontario, and a corporation officer. Occasionally, our negotiating group included other technical specialists such as Harry Buckles, mining engineer, or Reini Ehrlich who later became our chief metallurgist. Our negotiating team always did its work well and was essentially the same team that Hirshhorn, Bouck, and I retained for practically all subsequent major contract negotiations concerning most of our Blind River operations.

The Junta, Snakes, and Copper in Venezuela

At the time of our first negotiations with Eldorado on behalf of the modest Rix Mine, Joe Hirshhorn was still only one of my clients. In December 1951, I agreed to examine several mining properties in Venezuela for my long-time patron and friend, Dr. Howard James of Pioneer Mines. This technical work turned out to be most interesting, involving the examination of nickel, gold, and copper deposits and a huge pre-World War I copper and smelting enterprise suddenly abandoned as a result of political upheaval following a military coup many years earlier.

At that time in Venezuela, an earlier coup had resulted in a junta of three governing "colonels" seizing power. Only one remained at the time I was there. While I did not meet him, I did have a run-in with one of his cruising goon squads.

I had a three-day wait in Caracas for my guides from the interior, and I enjoyed it walking about the city. I was somewhat puzzled, however, when I received three or four calls at my hotel room from sultry-voiced damsels speaking English, using such lines as "It's Rosita. Remember me? Never mind – come and join me in the Lo Mismo bar for a drink. Your friend John told me you'd be here. I'm in red and I'll be sitting in a corner."

My first reaction was that these were simply local *filles de joie*. When I jokingly asked an English-speaking waiter in the dining room about them, he whispered "Steer clear of them. Most are political agents wanting to learn your business in this country." I followed his advice. But then things took a rather unpleasant turn.

I was out for an early afternoon stroll, and because it was warm I took off my jacket, put it over my arm, and entered a small park with some shady trees. I walked along a path to a large statue of Simón Bolívar, national hero and liberator, and, seeing an empty bench, sat down. Suddenly I was seized from behind by two men in civilian dress. My arms were grabbed firmly, twisted behind me, and I was shoved through the park to a plain four-door car waiting at the curb. As we approached, a rear door was flung open. I was thrust into the back seat by my two custodians, one of whom was handed a heavy-duty revolver by a man in the front seat.

The car sped through the busy city traffic to a quieter suburb and drew up beside an ordinary-looking office building. I was hustled into a ground-floor office and directed to a chair facing a senior officer wearing a simple uniform. My custodians sat in chairs on either side of me.

The senior man started questioning me in Spanish. Answering in English and French, I told him I did not understand Spanish. Then I asked, *"Policia?"* to which he nodded. I removed all my identification cards and related papers from my wallet, jacket, and trouser pockets and showed these to the senior official. Clearly, my documents – all in English – were not understood by my interrogators. To my alarm, everything I had produced was placed on a sheet of paper and taken by one of the junior men to an adjoining office. Things were getting uncomfortable.

Finally, another man, younger and with an even more official uniform, entered the room and deposited my documents before me. In a low calm voice he said in English, "Your offence is forgiven. You shall be taken to your hotel."

The use of the word *offence* particularly irritated me. "What offence have I committed?" I asked the English-speaking officer bluntly.

He paused for a moment. Then, with a half-smile on his lips, he said, "You passed before the statue of The Liberator, Bolívar, improperly dressed. That was a gross indignity to our nation. The car will take you now to your hotel. No more questions please."

As it turned out, the police were the least of my hazards in Venezuela. My guide, interpreter, and co-promoter of the mining prospect to be evaluated was a Canadian named Freddy Schultz. (I had known his father Paul Schultz, the mill superintendent of the Pioneer Gold Mine in British Columbia, for years.) During our jeep trip to the interior Freddy and I got lost as we crossed a wide parched plain. It was tremendously hot; we also became extremely thirsty. To our relief, we sighted a cluster of trees. Quickly we drove in that direction in the hope of finding water. Among the trees we found a single, tiny clay and wood cottage, almost completely enveloped by huge vines of bougainvillaea blooming in several different colours. It was a ravishingly beautiful sight.

There was a deep well in front of the cottage, with a simple twine-and-wooden-bucket device to raise the water. A half-dozen gentle and curious occupants soon emerged from the cottage and stood in a small group beside the well to look over the strange intruders. We parked the roofless jeep in the shade of a large tree and hurried toward the well. Freddy explained to the occupants in Spanish that we were both thirsty. A few minutes later, our directions confirmed and our thirsts quenched, we said, "*Hasta luego,*" and returned to our jeep.

Freddy had started into the jeep before I had. As I started to climb in, he suddenly reached over and shoved me sprawling onto the roadside. I sprang to my feet quickly. "What's up?" I half-shouted.

Freddy's face showed his alarm. He pointed his finger toward the depression in the horsehair-filled seat cushion on my side of the jeep. "Look!" he shouted. "A coral viper. Touch it and you're dead!" Turning, he shouted in Spanish, "Give me a machete!" I peered cautiously at the deadly but beautiful viper. It was, without question, one of the loveliest living creatures I have ever seen. Less than a foot long, the coral viper was elegantly tapered and coiled neatly like a priceless string of pink, white, and green beads reposing in a jewel box. Freddy quickly disposed of it.

"Where could it have come from?" I asked Freddy.

"Dropped from the tree," he said. "Vipers climb, and like other sources of trouble for humans, they fall from trees. There's always a temptation to park under a shady tree in the tropics, but often it can mean trouble. Double trouble, so remember!" He started to laugh.

"What's so funny now?" I asked.

"Oh, nothing really. I was just seeing in my mind's eye the newspaper headlines back home if a viper had finished you. 'Franc R. Joubin, prominent Canadian geologist, dies from fatal snakebite to his backside by poisonous viper!' "

To this day, be it a dining-room chair in a grand hotel, a seat at the opera or in a Concorde jet, a prospector's stool or a rock outcrop, I always examine the site with care before I sit!

Despite my encounters with the police and the viper, I completed my assignment in Venezuela successfully and submitted my report to Pioneer Mines. I summarized my findings on the mineral deposits and the smelting operation I had examined and concluded that Pioneer should not invest money there. At that time the officers of Pioneer Gold Mines, having ceased exploration in eastern Canada because it had been largely unsuccessful, were tentatively considering the policy of foreign exploration. All of its senior geologists had left, as I had, to work on their own as consulting geologists, occasionally undertaking special assignments for Pioneer similar to the one I had completed in Venezuela. In this way we kept in touch with the company and particularly with Dr. James, who maintained a continuing interest in all of his former colleagues both as individuals and as professional geologists.

Given the uncertain future of Pioneer it had been, in retrospect, a wise decision on my part to come to eastern Canada and then to become an independent consulting geologist. Similarly, my decision to work on a consulting basis with Joe Hirshhorn had proven to be mutually advantageous. I knew even before Hirshhorn became one of my clients that he was a winner. He was a natural treasure hunter. I knew also that while few men have the ability to raise really big money for speculative mining ventures, Joe was one of those few.

Just how gifted Hirshhorn was in finding high-risk money, and how exhilarating (and sometimes exhausting) it was to work with him I learned, with a vengeance, as we teamed up with Bill Bouck and other colleagues to bring in our Blind River mines and create the community now known as Elliot Lake, Ontario.

IX

The $30 Billion Discovery: Staking the Big Z

In June 1952, when I accepted Joe Hirshhorn's proposal to join him as a full-time partner in his mining enterprises, I did so because I knew that he worked hard and had an amazing intuitive sense regarding both mines and money. As well, I was ready and eager to move forward to the next stage in my career. I had shared in a variety of mineral discoveries and had gained the experience needed to develop a discovery into an operating mine.

I was forty-one years of age and certain that more and bigger discoveries lay ahead. My mother reminded me, every five years or so, of our visit to the clairvoyant when I was a boy and of the good fortune that had been predicted for me and that was to come after age forty. Each time she spoke of this I smiled inwardly. I knew that in the vast majority of cases good fortune comes because the person to whom it comes recognizes opportunity when it arrives. Individuals make their own good fortune – and in many cases their own misfortune.

As Joe Hirshhorn and I began to work together on a daily basis, I kept to the routine I had followed throughout my professional career: in any new undertaking I always stood and looked before I walked, walked before I ran, and ran before I leaped. I always considered my specific objectives carefully and proceeded to their realization cautiously and persistently. This pattern of steady professional progress had brought me satisfying results and a certain reputation. I had become known to the mining fraternity in Toronto's Bay Street jungle as an able, hustling field geologist and prospector.

In proposing that I work with him full-time, Joe agreed that I would have an option to participate as a partner with an interest up to 10 per cent in all or any of his mining ventures. This agreement was supplementary to a conventional employment contract. When our agreement was set out in writing it covered one-half of a sheet of Joe's personal stationery.

This option agreement was not offered to me gratuitously by Joe Hirshhorn. Joe did not work that way. My agreement with him was bargained for. It was based on an understanding that my salary would be less than that paid to other staff at Technical Mine Consultants.

Our agreement benefited both of us directly and many others indirectly. Our key venture, the development of the uranium deposits we would discover on the north shore of Lake Huron, required, at the outset, $35,000 in seed money. After five and a half years Joe and I divided a paper profit of $35 million for that project alone. It was on that occasion that Joe told the news media, "Blue chips are alright for Momma. I like a thousand-for-one payday!"

During the years I worked full-time with Joe, we were involved in a variety of unusual projects. Beginning with the Rix-Athabasca mine in the Beaverlodge district of Saskatchewan, I directed a small group of geologists, engineers, and metallurgists. That group, which varied in number from half a dozen to a couple of dozen or more, depending on the season and the projects underway, was highly successful. Its members discovered and developed, to the stage of actual production decision-making, eight uranium mines across Canada (in British Columbia, Saskatchewan, and Ontario), a copper-gold mine in Saskatchewan, a copper-cobalt mine in Ontario, and an iron-ore deposit in Labrador. Our principal achievement, of course, was the discovery and definition of the large Blind River–Algoma uranium mining region, and our development of seven of the eventual ten mines in that area of Ontario. Through our efforts Canada became one of the world's leaders in uranium production.

The thousands of individuals who subsequently gained employment as the uranium deposits we had found were developed and brought into production were among the direct beneficiaries of that discovery. Canadians generally were beneficiaries also. In the early 1980s it was estimated by a knowledgeable analyst that our discoveries had added about $30 billion to the Canadian economy to that date.

These achievements required, in Joe's words, "time, brains, guts, and moolah." The entire team at TMC was highly motivated, and all worked hard. We shared a constant sense of excitement and accomplishment. Initially, as always, there were sceptics among the Bay Street outsiders, but Joe never faltered when he or our undertakings were criticized. Fundamentally defiant, he seemed to enjoy criticism. Although he scorned his voluntary critics, he never tried to outsmart his trusted staff team. He constantly asked us searching questions and was satisfied only by reasonable and understandable answers.

Hirshhorn's primary role, of course, was to provide the money for our ventures, which for our Blind River project alone would approach $250 million. He jokingly continued to call himself a crap-shooter. In reality, he was extremely cautious. My role was to evaluate the potential of the prospects brought to our attention, initiate new ones, and be responsible for all technical aspects of their development.

Basic policy was initially determined by Hirshhorn and me, with occasional assistance from Bill Bouck. When the enormity of the Blind River–Elliot Lake venture became clear, Bouck became a full-time member to form our basic "troika."

Joe was the emotional, or physical, member of our threesome. When he was enthused, Joe would shout, gesticulate, prance about, and wave the cigar, lit or unlit which was always near at hand. I was the contemplative realist, concentrating on Joe's "machine-gun" delivery. Bill, who had a brilliantly analytical legal mind, spoke only rarely. He was our conscience, our guide and director. If Joe and I were discussing some financial manoeuvre or a negotiating stance of which Bill disapproved, a frown would first appear on his brow, then his mouth would break into a pout, and finally he would look upwards toward heaven, calling, it seemed, for Divine help to save us from being swept over the brink of propriety.

Joe, for instance, might ask: "Why does the Ontario Securities Commission need to know that this property was prospected earlier by others? What they don't know won't hurt them!" Or Joe might say of someone who had dealings with us: "He's a jerk. A weirdo! He's sick, or crazy, or both!" Bill would roll his eyes. Joe and I always knew from Bill's demeanour if we were going too far. We were always governed by his considered judgement.

As our projects began to roll, Joe's optimism grew. His pleasure, his joy, and his skill were in the raising of the thousands and later millions of dollars we needed for the development of our projects. While he was admittedly one of the giants in the promotion of speculative mining ventures in Canada from the 1930s onwards, I used to wonder how Joe would fare in the milieu of international world bankers where the need was for tens of millions of dollars. But my doubts were soon dispelled. Over the course of my association with him he readily attracted some of the finest American, British, and French financiers to counsel and eventually to participate with us.

To ensure that we could communicate readily, Joe insisted that we have adjoining offices with wide connecting twin doors, usually opened, between us. He seemed to take pleasure in shouting to me through this doorway any exhilarating news he received by mail or telephone. There was a second, smaller office down the hall where my secretary worked and where I could work when I wished to avoid interruptions.

This second office served, in addition, as the official "security room" where certain files were kept under lock and key. At that time and later, much technical information relating to uranium production and processing was carefully controlled by Canadian and American government authorities. Only persons cleared individually by government authorities were authorized to have access to such classified information.

In the TMC offices access to classified information was limited initially to myself, Paul Young, Reini Ehrlich, and my secretary, Mary Kumomoto. Joe Hirshhorn did not qualify and his only voluntary reference to his non-qualification (made to me privately) was simply "one of our family tangled with the McCarthy crowd." Joe did not appear unduly slighted by the official denial of security clearance to him.

Lack of access to the technical information concerning uranium production and processing had no influence on my day-by-day relations with Joe. I respected the limitations placed on me, and Joe never asked me about it.

Joe's Daily Working Routine

The Blind River–Elliot Lake discovery and its development resulted from the coming together of a variety of elements, abilities, and circumstances which made it all happen. One of the key elements which transformed our find into profitable uranium mines was Joe Hirshhorn's working routine.

Hirshhorn had installed on his desk an exceptionally extensive telephone network. It consisted of two hand-held telephones (sometimes in simultaneous use) and about twenty or more push-buttons to connect him directly to his banker, traders, and brokerage officers in a score of cities. He called this is "piano." It was his pride and joy, as well as his most effective professional tool.

Joe insisted that a clean new blotter be placed on top of his large desk pad each morning before he arrived. Throughout the day as he made, and received, an unending stream of telephone calls, and as he cajoled and coaxed and persuaded those with whom he spoke to participate in his mining and other deals, Joe scribbled on the blotter. As the day neared its end, the blotter became covered with notes and numbers, each of which had a special meaning to him. Before he left his office at the end of each day, Joe removed the blotter from his desk, folded it carefully, and put it in his briefcase. Each night, somewhere, alone, he carefully reviewed the day's events from what he had scribbled on that blotter. Where necessary, the information was transformed into permanent records.

Joe Hirshhorn was primarily an intuitive, vocal person. Eighty to ninety per cent of his business was transacted over the telephone. When not in a meeting, Joe was almost continually at work on his telephone "piano." He was the centre of a widespread and highly efficient financial and mining communications network.

The Mad Money Syndicate

In my contract with Joe Hirshhorn it was agreed that he would maintain a sum of money ($15,000) in an account that I could spend entirely at my own discretion. It was also agreed that any and all the profits arising from the use of this fund would be shared by the two of us on the basis we had established. Our success resulted in part from Joe's willingness to establish this account, which we called the "Mad Money Syndicate."

During 1952, I drew from the Mad Money account three times. The first was for an attempt (which failed) to stake the property north of Lake Superior which subsequently become the Manitouwadge mine area. This was another big fish that got away. The second was for an effort to persuade Joey Smallwood, the irrepressible premier of Newfoundland, to grant us permits for both on-shore and off-shore oil and gas exploration rights in the Straits of Belle Isle region. While I had high hopes for this second project they were also not realized. The third time was for the re-staking by TMC of the original Breton-Gunterman showing north of Lake Huron, not far from Blind River.

In May 1949, as described earlier, I had examined the property on the north shore of Lake Huron which had been staked by Karl Gunterman and Aimé Breton. From the time Breton had first taken me to the site near Blind River, where the old highly oxidized trenches were located, I had been impressed by the radioactivity but frustrated and puzzled, as were others, by the absence of uranium in all surface samples taken. Now, three years later, my interest in the area was rekindled by a newly published Geological Survey of Canada bulletin by A. H. Lang, entitled *Canadian Deposits of Uranium and Thorium.* It was a remarkable compilation of data for practically all known radioactive deposits in Canada. (I noted with interest that I was quoted as the source of information concerning several occurrences.) Lang's article referred to a rock specimen reported from a "Location X," which had been sent for analysis to the government of Canada's laboratory in Ottawa. That specimen had assayed encouragingly in terms of uranium content. As soon as I read this I became determined to find out where "Location X" was.

On making enquiries I learned that Location X was an actual geographic point on the shoreline of Lake Huron, probably within two miles of the site Breton and Gunterman had staked earlier. The north shore of Lake Huron, including Location X, was one of rough beauty. Much of the shoreline was rock, sculpted by the strong winds and storms that swept across northern Lake Huron. The sandy cove nearest to Location X was at Bootleggers Bay, about three miles to the west, an open expanse where boats could shelter. The rocky shoreline was covered with picturesque, short, twisted trees, mainly pines, and undergrowth shrubbery, primarily green juniper. Inland from the craggy rock and gnarled tree fringe, the vegetation consisted largely of small poplar and lesser birch. Occasionally very old and rotted or burnt pine tree stumps were present in the shrubbery, indicating that loggers and forest fires had swept sections of the shoreline, perhaps a century earlier.

Despite a remaining snow cover, I directed two of my staff prospectors to visit Location X in the spring of 1952 to take samples of any radioactive material they found there, and to determine the status of the Breton-Gunterman claims. Their telephone report to me was that Location X was on land owned by some individual or organization, and that the mineral exposure of iron oxide was unimpressive and only weakly radioactive. However, they also reported that only three or four claims of the earlier Breton-Gunterman property remained staked. No assessment work had been done, and the claims would accordingly lapse in two or three days. I told them to re-stake the same area for our account. They staked thirty-six claims on May 18, 1952, all of which were recorded. Funds from the Mad Money Syndicate were used to pay for this staking.

Later, when I mentioned this activity to Joe Hirshhorn in the course of my routine reporting to him on our Beaverlodge activities, his reaction was immediate and decisive. "Another uranium prospect? Okay. What will you call it? The Uranium King? That stinks! If you think the prospect is any good, we gotta have a decent name. Why not Peach?" I wilted but agreed. Joe was superstitious about names. If at all possible he preferred names starting with the letter P. So Peach Uranium and Metal Mining Limited was incorporated as a small public company in 1952. I was its president and general manager.

Nonetheless my earlier quandary of 1949 remained. How was I to resolve the puzzle of high radioactivity and low surface assays? In retrospect I realize that my urge to re-stake this area was largely intuitive. My response was probably motivated by my "organic computer," which by that time had been "programmed" with much data on scores of uranium prospects across Canada. Nonetheless, I was at a loss to know when or how I would proceed with the testing of the prospect. The answer did not come until the eleventh hour or, more precisely, the eleventh month after the staking when I met Dr. Charles Davidson, then chief geologist to the British atomic energy establishment, in London where he provided me with the clue that enabled me to solve the puzzle.

I travelled to London in March 1953 to try to secure funds for the development of a concentrating mill for our Rix uranium mine in Athabasca. Meeting one of Britain's most knowledgeable experts on uranium who gave me the key to the enigmatic Breton-Gunterman showing happened by sheer chance. But before that fortuitous encounter, I was the unwitting butt of a rather curious embarrassment.

On my arrival at the airport I was met by a uniformed chauffeur and limousine sent by my banker hosts and driven to the Savoy Hotel. Soon after I had registered I was rushed off to a luncheon with a dozen English businessmen.

After the luncheon, which went well, the guests and several members of the press adjourned to the commodious suite reserved for me. I was there relieved to find that my luggage had "caught up" with me. But to my surprise, everything had been unpacked and hung up neatly by a uniformed individual introduced to me as my valet.

Suddenly the loud and commanding voice of one of the guests issued from the bathroom doorway to those assembled, "Come and see this!" Several of the group, myself included, moved toward him to peer into the bathroom. It was a palatial room, all in marble, with enamel and gold-plated fixtures, and with two telephones perched on a shelf between the eight- or nine-foot-long bathtub and the throne-like bidet.

The focus of interest, however, was a small marble-topped table on castors, presumably intended to transport madame or monsieur's cosmetic supplies and implements about the room. My valet appeared to have been confused by the lack of a separate toilet case in my luggage, containing all the usual accoutrements and supplies of a city gentleman. Daringly, he had done his best to rectify the situation. Out of a tattletale-grey canvas sample sack – my "B.S." bag for every bush emergency, which I had automatically included in my packing – he had removed and placed upon the towel on that table: a small pair of rusted scissors in a leather protector, a large pair of tweezers, a scalpel, a small brown glass water-tight bottle containing wood-stem matches, several short ends of wax candles to start a camp fire in wet weather, an Indian bead and leather wampum pouch of sewing needles and assorted fishhooks, and a small Finnish hunting knife in a scabbard. As well, he had set out small assorted coils of fishing line and fine wire for animal snares, several small semi-rusted tins of medical salves and one of heavy glue, a small magnetic compass, a spare hand-lens, a coil of "catgut" to repair snowshoes, a small honing stone for my axe and knives, a carton of Band-Aids and a tube of zinc ointment, three or four sturdy elastic bands, a plastic eye patch to protect any eye injury, and various other items – everything, in fact, that a well-equipped prospector might require for survival in the Canadian bush!

A reporter who was present declared she had never seen anything like the bizarre contents of my bush kit since she had interviewed Mahatma Gandhi. Later on, to my great embarrassment, *The News of the World*, a London tabloid that often allows free rein to sensationalism at the expense of accuracy, published an article about me that was almost pure fiction. It purported to describe my activities in northern Canada. Apparently I encountered either grizzly bears or ravenous wolf packs almost every other day as I canoed or snowshoed my lonely way through the wilderness. I certainly couldn't recognize myself from that article, nor indeed could I remember ever giving any interview. I concluded that the piece had been the product of a viewing of the contents of my bush kit. I still wonder what on Earth went through the mind of the Savoy Hotel valet that day – perhaps the meticulous laying out of my bush kit was simply a demonstration of dry English humour?

Dr. Charles Davidson

During the time I was in London I made a point of visiting the British Museum to examine an exhibition of mineral specimens from many parts of the world and, in particular, a uranium minerals collection. When I enquired at the Museum about information concerning uranium I was referred to Dr. Charles Davidson. My first meeting with him was one of the most insightful experiences I have ever had. He was a brilliant geologist in every respect. Our wide-ranging discussion would provide me with much food for thought as well as the key to the "mystery" of the Breton-Gunterman Long Township showing.

Charles Davidson had gone to South Africa in the early 1940s with Dr. G. W. Bain, a professor at Amherst College, on behalf of the Anglo-American Combined Development Agency in connection with its world-wide search for uranium deposits. The existence of uranium in the Witwatersrand gold-bearing ores in north-eastern South Africa had been known from the late 1920s. However, the quantity of uranium ore present, particularly in the huge tailing piles resulting from decades of gold recovery, was unknown, as were the desirable manner and economic feasibility of its recovery. Davidson and his American colleague had made a considerable contribution to the resolution of those problems.

Davidson and I found that we had a variety of shared interests and hence much to discuss. He kindly suggested that we continue our conversation over luncheon at his club. As we shared reminiscences of our professional adventures, he spoke of a particular problem he and Bain had had with the Witwatersrand tailing piles, and which he and another colleague had also experienced with some old mine waste dumps in Portugal. The essence of the problem was that although strong radioactivity was present in both cases, the near-surface content of uranium was depleted by leaching of the uranium. He explained this critical paradox to me.

When uranium mineralization is accompanied by an iron sulphide and this combination is exposed to rain, the water can trickle down and gradually decompose the iron mineral. In so doing it releases sulphur from the iron which can combine with the water to form an acidic solution. This in turn can dissolve the uranium mineral and leach it, thereby removing it from its original location to another, usually deeper, location in the ground. Given Davidson's outstanding international reputation as a scientist, I had to take his ideas seriously.

It was only after my return to Canada following my meeting with Charles Davidson that the full implications of this surface-leach theory in regard to the Peach claims occurred to me. The question in my mind, of course, was whether this theory would prove to be correct when applied to our properties on the north shore of Lake Huron. I was eager to make the test. To do this, it was necessary that we diamond-drill the property below the zone of surface oxidation and, of course, well below my earlier sampling and the shallow trenching and sampling of Breton and Gunterman. To proceed I had to persuade Joe Hirshhorn to provide $35,000. That required time.

While he might call himself a "crap-shooter" Joe Hirshhorn was, in fact, highly cautious when it came to actually putting money on the table. It took a month of persistent pleading to persuade him. He repeatedly said, "Sure, get the driller to work, I'll find the money later." A drill at work on a property would facilitate his securing the working funds from others as opposed to risking his own money.

At last, with only a month or so before our claims were to run out, Joe "found" the $35,000 and I thereupon signed the diamond-drilling contract. Paul Young, TMC's chief engineer, Don Smith as project engineer, and "Dit" Holt as his assistant all set to work immediately. On April 6, 1953, diamond-drilling began on our Blind River prospect.

A Fiery Introduction to Peach

During the second week of April 1953, the first drill-core samples from the Peach deposits were sent for chemical analysis to the University of British Columbia. Problems and surprises followed.

It was relatively simple to send the samples air-freight daily from Sault Ste. Marie to Vancouver. My reason for sending them to Vancouver was to be absolutely certain that the analysis was of the highest technical quality. I was convinced that this was obtainable at the UBC laboratories of Professor Frank Forward, whom I knew well, and who had served the Eldorado-Beaverlodge uranium complex as a metallurgical consultant.

Yet even this simple plan was not without problems. Although the core was radioactive when tested at the drill site, we were acutely aware of the presence of radioactive thorium in the samples. This element is a next-of-kin to uranium. Both have quite similar characteristics and thorium, like uranium, undergoes self-destruction and emits energy in the form of radiation. Our radiation detection instruments, however, could not distinguish between radiation from uranium and radiation from thorium. Since uranium was of economic value and thorium was not, this created major problems for the prospector in the field and even in analytical laboratories.

When the assay reports on the Peach deposit samples were not forthcoming from Professor Forward's laboratory, we became increasingly anxious. After almost a month of drilling and the dispatch of fifty-six core samples, my patience was exhausted. I telephoned Vancouver for an explanation.

There had indeed been a problem. Two weeks earlier, the laboratory had been destroyed by fire! Fortunately, all our samples were safe in another building. Work on rebuilding the laboratory had proceeded day and night since the fire, and it was to be operational again in a day or two. Could we wait a little longer? Relieved that nothing had happened to our samples, I said yes.

A week later, on May 2, 1953, a single small envelope arrived with all the results from our fifty-six Peach samples (taken from a score of drill holes, spaced about a hundred feet apart). I called Paul Young, our chief engineer. Together we co-ordinated the assay results with the drill logs. An hour or so later, Paul and I went to Joe Hirshhorn's office and told him that we had a big, but low-grade ore body.

Joe asked, "How does it compare with our other baby, the Rix?"

"Only one-third of the Rix grade, but we're right on the railroad tracks, and it's big." I replied.

Charles Davidson's theory had been proven correct in regard to our problem. I wrote to him soon after the results of our successful drilling had been confirmed to share the technical details and to thank him for his major contribution to the success of our undertaking. In his graceful reply, Dr. Davidson mused, "Just call me the camp's midwife."

That evening Bill Bouck and I joined Hirshhorn for our regular business dinner in his suite at the King Edward Hotel in Toronto. During that meeting I reviewed for their benefit the entire history of the Peach deposit: my first encounter with Gunterman in 1948, the examination of the showing for my own account and Thayer Lindsley, the dismal surface-sampling results, and finally the joint abandonment of the project. I also noted that in each ton of ore from the Rix mine in Saskatchewan we had recovered ten pounds of uranium. In the Peach ore there would only be three pounds of recoverable uranium. However, because of the much larger quantity of Peach ore and its excellent location in respect to all infrastructural facilities, our production costs would be much lower than for the smaller Rix deposit.

When I mentioned Thayer Lindsley's name, Joe immediately said, "I'd like to work with T.L. on this. I'll call him tomorrow. Will you take him to the property if he's interested?"

"Sure," I replied, "I'd love to."

Thus, a couple of days later, Thayer Lindsley and I spent an afternoon together at the Peach site. He carried a geologist's pick, and had draped his lanky frame in an old well-worn, canvas bird-hunting jacket with several large pockets. We examined the drill core but he appeared much more fascinated with the oxidized trenches that marked the original discovery site. There, despite my repeated remarks that I and several others could not secure uranium assays of significance, T.L. – the "old Master" – carefully selected several specimens of oxidized conglomerate and placed one in each of his several pockets. (He later told me he had assayed them for gold content with one positive result.) During the afternoon we spent together, Thayer told me that he would welcome an opportunity to work with Hirshhorn. He suggested that they form a syndicate to prospect along the easterly trend of the conglomerate belt toward Sudbury, which we had not done to that point.

Lindsley concluded that the Peach had a future. His conclusion, of course, was based on the good assay results we had received. We arranged for one of his senior staff geologists, Dr. Dan Bateman, to make a more thorough examination of the property. Bateman concluded, however, that since the Peach ore-zone dipped toward the Murray fault system, of which we were aware, it would have little depth projection and therefore would be, at best, a small mine. Given the evident limitations of the size of the Peach deposit, for that reason he recommended against Lindsley's participation.

Technical Mine Consultants group was well aware of the presence of the Murray fault system as mapped by the Geological Survey of Canada and the Ontario Department of Mines. Geologists use the word *fault* to describe a break or fracture in the continuity of a rock formation. From 1948, I had grown to respect the Murray fault system as a very important mineralized structure ("juicy plumbing" was the geologist-prospector's description of this structure) extending centrally through the Sudbury copper-nickel basin practically to the shoreline of Lake Superior, with numerous small mineral deposits spread randomly along it, several of which I had examined. But here, passing within one-half mile or so of the Peach uranium ore-body, it was a mixed blessing because it would probably limit the depth of that ore body. Had I invited a geological opinion from Bill Bouck on the problem, he would likely have said that it was "sent to try us." Hirshhorn's aggressiveness suited me better. Characteristically, he announced, "Where did Peachie's ore come from? Where does it go? We gotta find out, Frankie boy!"

As it turned out, two years later our group caused the Murray fault structure to yield its treasure to us in the form of the profitable Pater Mine copper-cobalt ore body. But it had certainly caused initial uncertainties as we sought funds for the development of our Peach prospect.

When we had confirmation from Professor Forward that the samples from the Peach deposit contained uranium we not only had to secure money to finance its development, we also had to find an out-of-print geological map of the region. All of this had to be done in a hurry. (In the meantime Joe agreed, without argument, to change the name from Peach to Pronto which, of course, starts with a P and is the Spanish word for "hurry.")

While we searched everywhere for a copy of the rare old geological map of the region, we explored the rock outcrops in which the Pronto deposit was located for miles to the east and west. In the west only local and weak radioactivity was found. However, to the east, we detected radioactivity and staked for the Plum Syndicate, another of Hirshhorn's ventures which I directed, the precursor to the Agnew Lake field. We also explored the Blind River community and detected radioactivity beneath its garbage dump to the west. Harry Buckles and I felt it would be demeaning for us to stake any claims at such a site! Our initial probes about ten miles to the north of the discovery revealed hills of obviously barren granite.

After sustained, vigorous searching it was Harry Buckles who finally found a copy of the thirty-year old geological map known as Collin's "Blind River Sheet" in a second-hand bookstore in Toronto. Almost at the same time, our ally, Bob Hart, Exploration Manager of Preston Mines, which Hirshhorn controlled, obtained one in Timmins. This map, which provided detailed information on the area in which we were working, had been prepared in 1914–16 and 1922 by W. H. Collins and P. Eskola. (Collins later became Director General of the Geological Survey of Canada and Eskola became an internationally known geologist.) This map proved to be of critical importance in our tracking, staking, and subsequent development of what became known as the $30-billion uranium field.

Staking the Big Z

Drilling the Pronto deposit had provided the geological key to the location of the ore zone which was the basal conglomerate bed overlying the archean granite. This contact was, to "knowing eyes," the most easily identifiable geological feature of the landscape, provided it was not soil- or water-covered. The position of the contact had been carefully indicated on the Collins map. Now, with the map in our hands, we could see at a glance why we had had earlier problems. The contact takes the form of a great sweeping Z-shaped geological formation, quickly dubbed the "Big Z." Appropriately, the course of the northernmost section of the Z is defined by the Serpent River. The form of the Big Z, which has an overall length of about ninety miles, is outlined by large lakes and rivers.

The entire area is one of very ancient rocks – crustal archean and sediments of proterozoic age – all folded into the Big Z configuration. As well, it had been well-sculpted by erosion during the long period of geological time, including the latest Glacial Period. In the intervening area there are well-rounded hills, and between the rounded edges there are swamps, streams, and lakes that also strikingly delineate the Big Z pattern. In the past, this area supported an important soft-wood logging industry and during our early prospecting period of the 1950s, appreciable logging of birch and maple for the production of veneers continued. The region was also an important fur-trapping area, since beaver still abound, and is beautiful, particularly in the autumn and winter.

Huddled over the Collins map in our Toronto office, we quickly realized with some awe the enormous scale of the challenge that loomed ahead of us. It was far bigger than anyone had expected. I reeled off orders for immediate action.

"Pair off. Get Geigers. Charter a couple of pontoon-equipped aircraft. Drop in on those lakes at points where the contact location is shown on the map. Look for oxidation, rust-covered rock – from the air and on the ground. Test for 'radac' (radioactivity) in the air and on the ground. Do it all in one day, if possible, and report back."

The next day, Harry Buckles, TMC's chief field-man, reported to me that he and Don Smith had found the outcropping oxidized conglomerate, or radioactive zones, covered with a relatively thin layer of soil at several points along several miles of the middle section and eastern edge of the northern section of the Big Z. Bob Hart, Preston's exploration geologist, and his assistants, Firth and Johnson, had found radioactivity conglomerate along several miles of the northern section. Our original discovery was, it appeared, the rattle of the tail of "the serpent."

Clearly we had to stake quickly if we were to exploit our new knowledge. But obstacles appeared. Remains of another group's prospecting camp and some gear had been left at a location on the middle section of the Big Z. This equipment had been used only shortly before, by Teck Mines, directed by geologist Fred Jowsey who had been searching the area for copper and found none. We decided to await the dismantling and complete removal of the Jowsey group's field gear before we showed our hand. To do otherwise would have been to risk strong competition.

Not far from this camp, Buckles, Smith, and Hart had walked to a low cliff where their Geigers had "gone crazy." This site later became the Buckles mine, which proved to be the only surface ore-grade outcrop along the entire ninety-mile length of the Big Z. When Harry Buckles saw, in the same vicinity, some relatively old claim posts bearing the name "Metivier" he probably smiled. Joe Metivier was a French-Canadian conductor on the train that ran between Sudbury and Blind River. Not long before, Buckles had become acquainted with Metivier who had told him that his brother Charles had a copper prospect at Lake Nordic about twenty miles or so north-east of Blind River which he wished to sell. His copper claims soon became Buckles's uranium claims and Buckles brightened the life of the Metiviers with, if I remember correctly, a cheque for $25,000 and some mining stock.

A month of intensive planning followed. The Teck Mines equipment was removed by them. We stopped drilling and withdrew all our equipment from the Pronto claims so that any "watchers" would think we had given up in despair. Our senior staff of Young, Buckles, Smith, and Holt, with Bob Hart and a few others from the Preston Mines staff, including Bill Hutchinson, its general manager, were making independent staking plans which I co-ordinated in keeping with an agreement which Hirshhorn, Bouck, and I had made.

We had reached that agreement by spreading out one of our two prized vintage copies of the Collins map on the coffee table in Hirshhorn's suite at the King Edward Hotel in Toronto. By this time the map was covered with pencilled notations made by my staff and myself. We had just finished our usual dinner of shrimp cocktail, roast beef and horseradish, and baked potato, and were having our coffee.

As we looked at the copy of the Collins map and traced the path of the Big Z, we realized once more the enormity of the staking task and the short time we had in which to accomplish it. We all knew the regulations governing the staking of mining claims in Ontario.

For administrative convenience, the Province of Ontario was then divided into about a score of mining divisions, each with its Mining Recorder's office. Any individual, eighteen years of age or older, could purchase a mining licence at nominal cost, renewable annually. In the 1950s this allowed the licensed individual to stake only nine claims of his choice per year in each mining division, restricted, of course, to Crown Land, about 80 per cent of Ontario at that time.

To stake a mining claim, a licensed prospector, working in the area of his choice, had to cut a four-foot high post or fell a small tree four feet from the ground. At each corner of the desired claim the prospector had to cut and point the top of each of the posts or the tree stumps into four flat faces on which he was to write his name, the time of day and the date, and affix a small metal tag with a serial number and post number provided by the Mining Recorder. Each claim had to measure about one-quarter of a mile on each side and a post was to be placed at each corner. The claim boundaries were to be oriented on approximately north-south and east-west directions. Between each post a straight boundary line is marked. Usually, if there are trees this is done by "blazing," cutting chips of bark from a line of trees to leave a visible track. If no trees are present, which is rare, lines are indicated at intervals with coloured ribbon or spray paint.

Within a short space of time, depending on the remoteness of the claims from the Mining Recorder's office, the staking had to be recorded in a registry open to public scrutiny in the Mining Recorder's office. A nominal registration fee had to be paid for each claim and a sketch map with all particulars of location, staker identity, and time of staking had to be presented to the Recorder. All staking, of course, had to be on "open land," an area not yet staked by another person. Such a staked claim remained the "property" of the staker for one year, and for each successive year that the staker performed a minimum amount of trenching and blasting and exploration on the claim. If the staker revealed mineralization of apparent value on the claim, he might survey the land and acquire a lease for mining purposes.

Reflecting on the technical and legal details which had to be carefully followed, I observed, "Boy, this staking is going to be a big job! We'd like over a thousand claims of approximately forty acres each, but, of course, I can't be sure what we'll get. We'll need at least fifty trustworthy stakers. Each and every claim must be registered in the Recording Office within thirty days of staking. Registration of the first claims staked by us will immediately become public knowledge. It will alert competing prospectors who watch the Recording Offices carefully. Fortunately for us, the Big Z straddles two different mining districts so our stakers can use their staking licences twice, once in each district, to stake eighteen claims each. For secrecy, we'll keep all stakers in the bush until we are completely finished. There'll be a lot of paper work for filing at the recording offices, Bill, so we'll need a few bright young lawyers who'll work closely with the prospecting and staking teams from our bush camps. When the work of staking is done each day, they'll prepare the appropriate forms.

"Hutchinson and Hart say they can provide a lot of the stakers from the Preston staff since the mine is still on strike. They'll also provide the air support, the gear, and grub from South Porcupine, in the north, since it's quiet up there and the air charter service is reliable. We aim to start staking by June 1 and we'll have only *one month* to do the whole job."

I explained that the whole exercise would cost a "bundle," probably somewhere between thirty and seventy-five thousand dollars, depending on how far we could go without competition. Continuing my explanation, I said, "I should know now, Joe, how you want to divide the region between Pronto, any new deals, and Preston, so I can work things out with Bob Hart."

Since Joe Hirshhorn controlled Preston East Dome and since he needed cash quickly to pay for the staking of the Big Z and all the related costs, he used Preston as banker as well as a principal partner. The expenses advanced by Preston for the staking of claims for other Hirshhorn companies would be repaid to Preston in cash or share equity. For Preston, of course, this involved no sacrifice. The Preston money used to finance the staking of the Big Z made it a more profitable company for Hirshhorn and its other shareholders. Since Bouck was president of Preston, I handed him the pencil and said, "Bill, we are spending your company's money. Mark off the area where it should go. We'll find others to take the rest."

Neither Hirshhorn nor Bouck responded immediately. Then the silence was broken by Hirshhorn: "Franc, you tell us how to split it up."

"No, I want Bill to decide," I replied.

Bouck declined my offer of a ballpoint pen and drew a stubby lead pencil from his vest pocket, made a point approximately in the centre of the map and paused. "Should I go up and down or sideways?" he asked.

"Sideways," I suggested. Bill drew an east-west line on the map. "Okay," I said, "I'll pass this on to Hart and we'll get cracking on the staking."

Little did we appreciate then that Bouck's stubby pencil stroke on May 23, 1953, divided a mineral treasure that in 1982 would be valued at $30 billion, of which almost $1 billion was produced during its six-year infancy and $7.4 billion by 1987. I still have that original map, mounted and framed with all its creases, its pencilled notations and even some sweat blotches! It was faithfully returned to me after that frantic and glorious month in the bush in the late spring and early summer of 1953, during which Harry Buckles carried it in his jacket pocket as he played his key role of field co-ordinator in what was later described as the "back-door staking bee."

Regrettably, W. H. Collins, who had prepared the map, that so simplified our task was long since deceased. Nonetheless, we later paid tribute to his life and work by inviting his widow to formally open the W. H. Collins Hall, which Joe and I subsequently donated to the community of Elliot Lake. It became the community social centre for the citizens of Elliot Lake who proudly call their town "The Uranium Capital of the World."

The Staking Campaign

After Bill Bouck drew the east-west line on the Collins map, dividing the Big Z into two parts, it was agreed that Preston East Dome would be responsible for the staking of the northern and central sections and Technical Mine Consultants would be responsible for staking the southern section. Bill Hutchinson and Bob Hart were asked to assemble a crew of seventy-five or so experienced and completely trustworthy stakers. They agreed they could recruit such a group, equip them, charter aeroplanes, and find pilots who wouldn't talk about the work they contracted to do for Preston. Hutchinson and Hart were to fly their group of stakers and provisions to the Big Z through the "back door" from South Porcupine to ensure that potential competitors in the towns along the north shore of Lake Huron, between Sudbury and Sault Ste. Marie, would not become aware of the massive staking that would soon be underway.

While some of those recruited as stakers came from Toronto, the majority were from Porcupine, where the Preston mine is located. It was used as a headquarters for the staking operation since we reasoned that hardly anyone would expect such staking to be carried on from a base over two-hundred miles to the north. This, of course, was the rationale for the "back-door staking." Our key objective was to stake as many of the promising areas as possible on the Big Z before the rest of the mining industry became aware of what was underway and sent in competing stakers. Similarly, arrangements were made for the staking of the southern section of the Big Z by the TMC group headed by Harry Buckles and his colleagues, Don Smith, Dit Holt, Roy Pountney, and Manfred Johnson.

The staking crews for both sections were given precise directions. When all the supplies and equipment were ready, and the directions were clearly understood, the crews climbed into pontoon aircraft and took off for the various lakes along the Big Z. This string of lakes is drained by the Serpent River, which rises in Ten Mile Lake, with an elevation of 1,304 feet, and meanders through the region to its outlet on Lake Huron with its elevation of 581 feet.

The terrain in which the stakers went to work was not easily traversed. It was covered with a rather dense growth of small pine, spruce, maples, and poplar mixed with patches of deciduous hardwoods. As they began work on the Big Z, the stakers were greeted, as they had known they would be, by hordes of insects, which compounded the difficulties encountered in the rough terrain.

Staking began on May 27, 1953, as Dit Holt and Allan Graham, working under the direction of Don Smith, led their respective prospecting and staking crews into the field near Magog and Pistol lakes.

The same day Bob Hart sent crews to stake in the western end of Elliot Lake. Other crews staked along the north belt.

Many accounts of our staking of the Big Z give the impression that all of our stakers and all of our supplies were flown in from Porcupine in the north. In large measure they were, but it was also necessary to bring in material and supplies from the south. Don Smith arranged for these to be purchased from merchants in Blind River and other towns on the north shore of Lake Huron and transported along with numerous stakers by Carl Mattaini's pontoon air service based in Algoma Mills, just east of Blind River. During a considerable portion of the thirty-day staking period there were regular morning and evening service and communication flights to as many of our staking parties as possible. In this way we kept in touch with the entire group of stakers, more than one hundred individuals at the height of the staking.

To ensure that the required documents were completed correctly, two young lawyers worked closely with the staking parties. As the staking proceeded these lawyers drew up claim form applications, usually around the evening campfire, so that the necessary legal documents would be ready upon our emergence from the bush.

Our entire group of about a hundred staked a total of almost fifteen hundred claims, covering an area of about fifty-six thousand acres during the six weeks of high pressure staking from May 27 to July 9, 1953. This protected almost the entire length of the Big Z as intended and to varying distances – save for one critical section, acquired by a rival group and later conveyed to Denison Mines. For a single group of stakers this Big Z operation was of a magnitude unprecedented in the history of Canadian mineral exploration to that time. Dit Holt, who, in 1979 and 1980, served as president of the Canadian Prospectors and Developers Association, would observe many years after that exhilarating event: "I have never seen so much ground staked and brought into production in so little time."

The record of how a group of fewer than a dozen geologists, engineers, and experienced prospectors co-ordinated the highly effective and discreet efforts of a team of nearly one hundred stakers, drawn from many sources, is a truly remarkable story. It is even more remarkable when one considers that in 1953 it was still necessary to rely on the skill and trust of individual workers, using only manual tools. This was well before the "hi-tech" era of helicopters, chain saws, spray paint, and ribbons. Each quarter-square-mile claim had to be blazed by axe along its four sides and each corner required an inscribed claim post.

Throughout the exercise, Joe Hirshhorn served as the dynamic "field marshal," constantly shouting to me through the open door of our adjoining offices in Toronto: "What's the news? What's the news?"

When he wasn't acting like an expectant father, Joe was playing away on his "piano," but he was playing cautiously. Amazingly, he was telling the few intimate clients to whom he had sold Peach stock for drilling money: "Don't sell! Don't sell! Hold for a big roll!" And roll it did!

When drilling started on the Peach deposit, shares were sold privately for $1 each. After the Big Z staking became known and the Peach drilling results were announced, Peach shares rose to $135 per share. And Joe knew that if the Big Z proved to be as "juicy" as the Peach, he would have to play his "piano" as never before.

Bill Bouck kept his usual cool but was tremendously busy. He was in constant touch with the two young lawyers, Bill Regan and Don Mills, who travelled between the bush camps compiling and collecting the bundles of documentation required to record our claims on "filing day."

With Paul Young at my side, I worked primarily from our headquarters in Toronto. I kept in close touch with Bill Hutchison of Preston, who co-ordinated all logistics from his base in Porcupine. The field managers, Harry Buckles or Bob Hart, would send me progress reports – they sent couriers out of the bush at night to call me long-distance from public telephone booths. The pace was hectic, yet there was no frenzy. We had our plans and everyone knew what he or she had to do. Yes, a number of women who could not resist the temptation were involved in the excitement of the staking. Several were wives of members of our group, including Ruth Buckles, Muriel Smith, and my secretary, Mary Kumomoto. They were provided with miners' licences and axe-men, whom they followed through the bush or in canoes along lakeshores to inscribe their names upon "their" claim posts.

A most extraordinary aspect of our gigantic staking operation was the total absence of subsequent litigation, or any challenges by others, questioning the accuracy of our staking or our compliance with all conventional rules and regulations then existing. Later problems did arise regarding two locations which presented us with unexpected complications. Both were in the underwater area of Quirke Lake, midway along the northern limb of the Big Z. We would suffer seriously from one of these complications and profit modestly from the other.

As mentioned, our objective of staking all the claims planned along the Big Z was not fully attained. One of the unresolved mysteries of our staking program was how and why Art Stollery, whom I had employed earlier when I was a consultant operating from a Sault Ste. Marie base, suddenly appeared on the scene as some of the Preston stakers were on the site of what later became our Quirke Mine. At that time Stollery was in partnership with Fred Jowsey and Jim Kenmay, both active exploration geologists. It is reported that he arrived on an aircraft owned by Carl Mattaini, and piloted by George Smith. Stollery may merely have had a hunch that something was underway. Or serendipity may have brought him in. Certainly Fred Jowsey had been directing the drilling of a copper prospect for Teck Exploration in the central sector of the Big Z, just before our own entry into that area. But although Jowsey knew the area well, he was totally unaware of any radioactive deposits there, since, as he noted later, the Teck Exploration manager had not included Geiger counters in his field gear.

Earlier, after our successful drilling of the Peach property and our first examination of the Collins map, I had asked Harry Buckles and Don Smith to make an aerial reconnaissance of the entire area. They had employed the services of Lau-Goma Airways operated by Carl Mattaini. Both he and George Smith flew pontoon-equipped planes in which they took sportsmen, timber cruisers, prospectors, and others, to the many isolated lakes and rivers of the Algoma region, which they knew well. Since Lau-Goma offered a public commercial service there were no restraints save the judgement of the pilots as to what clients they wished to serve or where they were taken. While Mattaini and George Smith knew of our whereabouts and general activity, we did not attempt (and knew we had no right to try) to have Lau-Goma Airways divert curious clients away from any specific part of the huge tract of Crown Land which included the Big Z.

However he found out, Stollery moved in; he and his associates staked a total of eighty-eight mineral claims, mainly under the waters of Quirke Lake and about mid-way along the north limb of the Big Z. Eight months later, the Stollery-Kenmay-Jowsey claims were sold to Stephen Roman's organization. As it turned out, after the critical correction of certain staking irregularities, Roman's company, Consolidated Denison, ultimately developed about 40 per cent of the total uranium ore reserves of the region on those lands. This was a large portion of the potential of the Big Z. When the eventual eight mines of our Hirshhorn–Rio Tinto group were developed, they accounted for 60 per cent of the area's total reserves.

Just as Art Stollery came upon some of Preston's stakers and bluffed them about what ground he had already staked, so they would ignore it and he could acquire it, our crews also contended with other, but friendly intruders. One of these was Paul Westerfield from Cincinnati, Ohio, a tall genial banker and natural philosopher, with a soft, mid-American drawl.

The Westerfields and Blueberry Pie

Westerfield and his family were in the habit of spending their summers enjoying the glorious outdoor life they had discovered at a quiet cove where the Serpent River joins Quirke Lake. Westerfield's son, and various banking colleagues, would fly their small pontoon-equipped planes to and from this haven of tranquillity and fine fishing to which the Westerfields had come for many years before our Big Z crew appeared on the scene.

On a sandy point of the bay, Westerfield and his family had built a small but attractive and comfortable log cabin. Despite the isolation of their hideaway, the Westerfields were highly sociable and always greeted rare passers-by warmly.

I was introduced by one of our group (probably Bob Hart) to Paul Westerfield, his wife Betty, and son Paul, Junior, in early June 1953 just after we launched the Big Z staking. We were promptly invited into their cabin. Fresh coffee and fresh blueberry pie were placed before us. We told them in general terms that we were prospecting. They probably sensed our optimism and excitement.

The questions which Paul Westerfield put to us indicated clearly that he was itching to find out more, but he did not press us. Their uncomplicated acceptance of us, and their constant hospitality, made a memorable impression on all of the members of our staking crew who passed by their cabin on foot or by canoe.

It came as no surprise to me then, that as the deadline for registration of our claims and public knowledge of our activity drew near, Harry Buckles, Bob Hart, Dit Holt, and Don Smith jointly asked me: "Where does Paul Westerfield fit into the scheme of things?"

My reply, as they probably expected was, "Give Paul the story, the whole story, on the day before we file our claims. If he's interested and wants advice, give it to him. He'll have a jump on the outsiders. He's earned it." That is what we did. And Paul Westerfield acted upon our suggestion.

He called his small group of associates The Spanish-American Syndicate. Later he turned to us for advice about the exploration of his claims. With Hirshhorn's approval, I allowed him to draw on the expertise of two of our growing resident staff, Dr. E. L. Evans and Dr. Stanley Holmes.

Westerfield's drilling, under our direction, eventually proved successful, and his syndicate became Spanish-American Mine Ltd., a public corporation financed largely by Hirshhorn. It was brought into production by TMC. Later, control of the Spanish-American passed from our hands to our successor, Rio Algom, controlled by Rio Tinto of England.

Finally, on Saturday, July 11, 1953, after six weeks of carefully planned but hectic work, our staking and registration of claims on the Big Z was complete. While many people knew of our earlier work on the Peach deposit, little information about our massive staking of the Big Z had leaked out. But as soon as word spread that we had registered about fifteen hundred claims, one of Canada's largest staking rushes began. Prospectors flooded in. Within a few months the entire region had been staked. About eight thousand claims were registered.

With our own staking done, our next task was to program and commence our development. An unparalleled period of diamond-drilling commenced. Never before had so many diamond-drills been at work in Canada in an area of comparable size and for a single client. The combined TMC-Preston group, co-ordinated under my general direction, operated about twenty drilling machines day and night. A phenomenal amount of energy was expended as the rush to develop the new uranium reserves got underway.

We popularized the drilling of deeper holes in Canada and, in so doing, improved that technology. Perhaps 80 per cent of all holes drilled at that time for mineral exploration were only to depths of 100 to 500 feet, 18 per cent were from 500 to 1,500 feet and 2 per cent from 1,500 to 2,000 feet. Drill holes to a 3,000-foot depth became commonplace with us. We also popularized branch deflectional drilling. If a deep hole brought encouraging results, we used the same hole to drill two or more deflected branches from near the bottom, resembling the root structure of a tree, to provide more than one sample section. The mining industry soon followed our lead.

At that time there were no roads or trails over which drilling and other equipment could be brought into the region. Air services were required to an unprecedented extent. Carl Mattaini and his Lau-Goma Airways were at the centre of this activity. Mattaini recalled later that on one day alone, he piloted over forty flights to various lakeside bases. In each of 1953 and 1954, Lau-Goma Airways logged in excess of 250,000 miles. They flew on pontoons between the "break-up" in the spring and "freeze-up" in the late autumn, and on skis when the lakes and rivers were frozen. We prospectors and drill crews not only "walked upon the waters" (when frozen!) but also worked and drilled on and through the ice surfaces to determine the extent of the uranium ore body in the rock beneath. One of our mines, Panel, was completely developed and became productive beneath a large lake.

The result of all this development activity was that twelve mines were brought into production within the incredibly short span of five years. The base was established for the development of several mines which have now been operating since 1957. And adequate ore reserves have been identified which could support continuing operation of the mines well into the twenty-first century.

After we finished staking the Big Z we were joined by neighbours who, although they were our competitors, shared with us a general feeling of camaraderie which was expressed in many practical ways. While a number of companies were active in the early years, two major companies emerged. One included the various mines Joe Hirshhorn and I and our colleagues developed which came to be known as Algom Uranium Group and later as Rio Algom Group, after our mines were purchased by Rio Tinto of London. The other major player was Consolidated Denison Mines, controlled by Roman Corporation and the Stephen Roman family.

Algom Uranium and Consolidated Denison each had their own land and plant and were involved in the same type of search for the same type of treasure. Joe Hirshhorn's observation was: "We're all in the same crap game."

We also had neighbours of another kind whose territory – land, water, and air – we had invaded: the local wildlife. Happily, however, the prospecting fraternity had long ago learned to adapt to and co-exist with all forms of flora and fauna. The Algoma district, with its many lakes and rivers and glacier-sculptured hills largely covered with mixed "second-growth" forests of evergreen and hardwood trees, provided a fine habitat for moose, deer, brown bear, and smaller animals. Some, like the beaver, wolf, and marten, were of considerable value for their pelts. Usually there was abundant fish in the lakes, and fowl included geese, ducks, and grouse.

In the early autumn there were low-bush blueberries which were large, plentiful, and luscious. If the patch was large enough you could quickly fill your harvest basket, as my wife Mary often did with a small band of women friends and, occasionally, a poodle for "protection" in case of berry-picking bears.

By accident, or by design of the Creator (or perhaps my biased taste,) the finest blueberry patches seemed to me to be closer to the more radioactive rock outcrops. Years later, when Mary mentioned such blueberry patches to acquaintances or friends one of her listeners occasionally would recoil in horror and exclaim, "But what about nuclear radioactivity?" which would be my cue to awe the alarmist by asking, "Have you never heard of irradiation, the modern form of 'cold sterilization'?" and continue on in expert form: "Intensive research has already determined that it is more effective than pasteurization, which the world now accepts, in reducing food decay, since the latter requires the application of heat that commonly destroys useful vitamins. Besides, irradiation is no more than the cautious extension of the same solar radiation of the sun that, through photosynthesis, created and sustains all life on this planet including the blueberries we are talking about!"

For lovers of exotic food, who arrived in the early days of the development of the town of Elliot Lake, frogs were among the natural gourmet delights of the area. Found particularly in the marshy (irradiated!) zone where the Serpent River approached Quirke Lake, these frogs were huge and numerous. A couple of times, when we had to ford the marsh area on foot, I thought a visiting geologist beside me had stumbled and fallen into a mudhole or quicksand, only to discover he had wilfully knelt to grab at the huge frogs, stuffing them into his many-pocketed jacket for later consumption.

It was only on rare occasions that I was able to enjoy the delightful world of nature surrounding Elliot Lake. Once our staking of the Big

Z and formalities relating to it were complete we had to get on with the herculean financial, scientific, and technical tasks involved in developing and placing the discoveries into production.

Development of the Big Z

The most productive of our Elliot Lake mines were those on the central and northern sections of the Big Z, fifteen miles or more north of Lake Huron. The first mines we brought into production in that area, however, were those on the southern section, the Peach (later known as the Pronto) and the Pater, both of which were quite near Lake Huron.

Because it was our first operating mine in that area, Joe Hirshhorn and I frequently referred to the Pronto as our "baby." To this day, I remain more attached sentimentally to the Pronto Uranium Mine, and its curious twin brother the Pater copper-cobalt mine nearby, than to any of the other larger mines on the Big Z.

The Pronto and the Pater were marked by alternating hope and despair. But the Pronto and the Pater were our prototypes. While their eventual success was relatively modest, they pointed the way to much greater treasure. If Hirshhorn were still alive, and we were "nattering" about the good old days, I would probably suggest to him that our "baby" could just as well have been called "Pathfinder" as "Pronto." I am sure he would have agreed and not only because "Pathfinder" starts with a P.

Paul Young, TMC's chief engineer, with Bill Hutchison of Preston, and Don Smith, the development engineer, laid out and directed the development and construction of the Pronto Mine. Key support staff included the plant manager Eric Holt – Dit Holt's father – geologist Ralph Benner from Cobalt, and Dr. Stan Holmes from Tennessee.

But no plant could be built without metallurgical research to develop the uranium-recovery procedure. The research required was of major concern to us. The first mineralogical study I had requested revealed that the Blind River uranium occurred in the form of a rare and complex mineral called *brannerite* which, to our knowledge, had never before been commercially exploited. The young metallurgist to whom we turned for help with this problem was Reini Ehrlich, a 1946 graduate of the University of Toronto. At that time Ehrlich was employed at a remote silver mine. When I recommended Ehrlich to Hirshhorn, and added that in addition to holding a metallurgical degree he was a hard worker, young, ambitious, and did not scare easily, Hirshhorn's comment was, "And I know his old man Gus. The kid's got to be alright!"

Our trust in Ehrlich was not misplaced. With his colleagues Ron Ennis and Ken Hester, and the enthusiastic co-operation of technical experts headed by John Convey of the federal government's mineral research laboratories in Ottawa, Ehrlich soon had the problem solved, not only for ourselves and our six subsequent mills but also for all those competitors who followed.

If possible, we wanted to use a "leaching approach" by finding a liquid solvent that would dissolve the uranium; we could then precipitate the solution and filter it, leaving a uranium concentrate. We took the empirical approach of trial and error. Having some knowledge of chemistry, I had said to Ehrlich, "Try a series of a half-dozen of the different acids. If that fails, try some alkaline solutions. Start with the cheapest and most easily available solvents." Ehrlich set to work and within a month was on course. All aspects of our uranium recovery method were "classified" by Canadian and American authorities at that time.

Our metallurgical research, with slight modification, also provided an extremely efficient and low-cost patented method for the recovery of high-quality thorium, a plentiful accessory metal in the Blind River uranium deposits. (The large-scale usage and economic value of thorium, however, are yet to materialize.)

Production at Pronto mine commenced in August 1955, about twenty-five months after we had begun diamond-drilling. The total cost of bringing Pronto into production was about $6 million. (Today it probably could not be done for less than $25 million.) Despite the many new and unpredictable aspects of the operation, this record of cost, speed, and efficiency was regarded, at that time, as phenomenal.

The production capacity of Pronto was fifteen hundred tons per day. Subsequent mills at the Nordic, Quirke, Spanish, Panel, and Milliken mines each started at twice this rate. As the years passed and the number of mills was reduced, for reasons of economy and market contraction, those remaining grew in size and efficiency, but they all owed their beginnings to the Pronto.

The weeks and months following our initial drilling of the Pronto prospect were packed with surprises, dismay, delight, alarm, and intense planning. Later, after our mammoth staking operation, a crew of writers and photographers from *Life* magazine arrived to prepare an article on the Big Z rush for the August 1, 1955, issue.

Jesse Lasky of Jesse L. Lasky Productions of Hollywood flew to Toronto to try to convince me to let him use the story of my life in a film on the future peaceful uses of atomic power. I told him that I was too busy, but the whole truth was that I dreaded the glare of the limelight already focusing upon us. I received hundreds of letters from all over America congratulating me, asking for work or for donations to charities. Some people sent cheques for me to invest in mining stocks; all were politely returned.

Break-in at the Pronto

One of the unpublished events that followed our discovery and staking of the Big Z was an attempted break-in at our core storage barn midway through the drilling program. Our drilling operation was conducted only a quarter-mile from the Sudbury-Sault Ste. Marie highway and the CN railroad. We had rented the vacant premises of a small farm beside the highway as our base for this drilling, using the barn for core storage and sampling. Don Smith, our project manager, had installed core racks, a sampling bench, and a sturdy locked door. Our staff of four, including a cook-watchman, lived in the farmhouse.

The "fresh" drill core had to be closely guarded to prevent illegal trespass and possible criminal misuse. It offered a tempting target for stock tipsters, "scouts" searching for information that could be exploited – upwards or downwards – on the volatile "penny speculative" markets of 1950s Bay Street. Even worse, our fresh core was a tempting target for criminal tipsters who could "salt" the core by sprinkling it with well known high-grade ore from other sources to "make a market" they could then exploit. Appraisal of uranium-bearing core can be done easily by simply passing a small pocket-size Geiger counter near or over the boxes containing it.

One morning in April 1953, Don Smith and the drillers were at work at the drill site. Only the cook remained at the campsite. A pick-up truck, apparently making a routine business call, turned off the highway, drove up the lane, and parked in front of the storage barn. Two burly men got out of the truck and walked to the barn. By this time the cook had become aware of their presence and went out to ask what they wanted. He half-felt he recognized the driver of the vehicle as a lodge operator based in Sault Ste Marie who dabbled in prospector grub-staking and as an assessment work contractor. The other man whose voice was slurred, as if he had been drinking, replied, "I'm the local mining claims inspector. I have a right to see the core."

The cook suggested that they return during the lunch hour when the manager would be there. The pair ignored the suggestion and started tugging at the padlocked barn door. When the "mines inspector" turned toward the cook and demanded the key, the cook reached for his "clanger" instead – an eighteen-inch-long, one-inch-thick piece of drilling steel – and started loudly ringing his steel triangle. Its purpose was to signal work crews to meals or to indicate an emergency. Two or three minutes of tugging and swearing made no impression on the barn door lock, so the men scrambled into their truck and fled, passing Don Smith's incoming vehicle at the intersection of the farm lane and the highway. Although neither car stopped, Smith had a good view of both men and later identified them.

We decided neither to press charges nor to publicize the incident. The individual who had said he was a government claims inspector had lied. The truth was that he was an experienced bushman and casual part-time employee of the government inspector. If this man and his accomplice had gained access to the core and passed a Geiger over it, the radioactivity would have been apparent. Had they had the intelligence and the money to act upon such information by purchasing units of the Peach Syndicate then trading at about $1.50 each, they could have made a handsome profit.

A Widow Invests in the Peach Syndicate

Although I kept my wife Mary generally informed of my activities, she never pried into my day-to-day professional affairs. She trusted my judgement and was satisfied with what I told her. As the initial drilling proceeded I could not contain my enthusiasm. I said to Mary one day, "Our Peach shares will have a lively market and pay for a month of family holidays in Mexico this winter." Mary decided, entirely on her own, to use that information in a less selfish manner.

Among the friends we had made in eastern Canada was a widow, a trained nurse, who supported her two children, a boy and a girl about twelve or thirteen years old. This friend was determined to secure the best possible education for her two children, and, knowing this, Mary quietly told her about the Peach Syndicate and its potential risks and benefits: she could lose everything she invested in the Peach or she could make some money. I knew absolutely nothing about Mary's talk with our friend. At that time, as managing director of TMC, I was totally immersed in the mounting challenge of the Big Z staking, which had to be completed before any publicity could be given to the successful drill results of our Peach/Pronto property.

Several days before we were to "lift the lid," as Joe Hirshhorn put it, on our momentous accomplishments of the preceding six weeks, Bill Bouck and I met with Hirshhorn for our weekly dinner in his King Edward Hotel suite. Before we commenced our serious discussions that evening, Joe remarked casually, "A crazy thing happened today in the Peach marketing. Al White who handles the stock trading called to ask me if there's any real news yet. He knows we're drilling, of course, but doesn't know the values we've been getting. Al said he had a funny buy order and I asked him why it was funny."

Joe then told us that a nice woman, who had preferred not to leave her name, had walked into White's office with about $1,000 in her purse and simply said she'd like to buy all the Peach she could.

Joe continued: "Al asked if she traded in stocks often and she said she had never bought any stock before. Never in her whole life! Al seemed really worried that she could lose her money. I said, 'Al, she's a pro. She's from some other broker's office trying to learn what we have.'

"Al replied, 'No, I'm sure she's legitimate, but is it safe for her?' I told him, 'Al, sell it to her.' Funny, eh! She's probably been listening to a teacup reader."

The pieces fell into place for me about ten years later. Our friend's son graduated from medical school and I learned that my wonderful Mary had acted as her friend's silent angel.

The Spectacular Quirke

During the early diamond-drilling on the Quirke ore-body, our first discovery on the northern section of the Big Z, we had probably three drills at work under the general direction of Bob Hart, geologist from Preston East Dome Mines. Given the general similarities between the Blind River uranium-bearing conglomerates and those of the uranium gold-bearing deposits of the South African Witwatersrand deposits, we had decided to assay regularly for gold content as well as uranium.

After the core samples from the Quirke were first assayed for uranium by a specialist analyst, some of the reject, from the same samples, was sent to the well-equipped assay laboratory at the Preston East Dome Mines. There it was re-analysed for gold content by Preston's experienced laboratory personnel. At the time perhaps a hundred or more samples from our drilling had been assayed. Traces of gold were found to be common but not one economically-significant assay had yet been indicated from much widely spaced drilling. Then, with dramatic suddenness the picture changed.

In mid-December 1953 I received a telephone call from Hart, trying, unsuccessfully, to suppress his excitement. As was our custom, he had driven several miles to a public pay phone on the highway for greater privacy. We thus avoided the possibility of public eavesdropping, to which we were exposed with our two-way bush radio-phone system. My secretary and I always knew that we were about to receive highly confidential news when the opening words included, '. . . calling from a pay phone."

Hart's message was brief. "We are into gold values at Quirke and nothing low – high-grade! Not one but several samples. I've asked the lab at Preston to check all their equipment for salting. Sometimes we have a run of v.g. [coarse visible gold] from the Preston ore that hangs up in the crusher or pulverizers. But they tell me they've had no recent mine-run of that kind. I've prepared the assay logs for three different Quirke holes. All are high-grade, in the ounces. I've also gone over the split core with Manfred Johnson [his senior prospector and discoverer of the Quirke outcrop] but he can't see any v.g. It must be very fine grained. I'll call you back in three hours when I get a report from Preston that they've checked all their equipment and reassayed the same samples."

Three hours later Hart called again: "No possibility of salting at Preston. Careful checking of the assay confirms earlier values. But the whole situation still looks fishy."

My immediate reply was, "Put all boxes of split core into one of our vehicles and deliver it as quickly as possible to Toronto, I'll 'tee up' Dr. Langford [a long-time director of Preston and at that time also head of the Department of Geological Sciences at the University of Toronto] and have him arrange for microscopic examination of the core and probably more analyses. I'll tell Joe and Bill Bouck the story, but there must be no publicity until we are sure, sure, sure!"

I went immediately into Hirshhorn's office to report. He was busy, as he usually was, on his "piano." He acknowledged my presence with a glance as he continued shouting into the phone. Instead of my normal practice of standing beside his desk, paper in hand, waiting for a brief pause in his "piano playing," on this occasion I picked up one of the beautiful antique chairs that graced his office, placed it near his desk, and sat down. When he finally put down the phone he glanced at me and asked, "Somethin' special?"

"Yes Joe," I replied. "We seem to be into gold values at Quirke. Bob called me twice on the subject today."

"Ore grade?" asked Joe. For privacy I lowered my voice and leaned over the front of his desk.

"In the ounces," I replied, "from one-half to over eleven ounces and across the full conglomerate section, eight to ten feet, and in three drill holes spaced about one hundred feet apart."

"But gold?" asked Hirshhorn unbelievingly. I nodded in the affirmative.

"Are you sure?" he insisted.

I said, "We've checked out the Preston assay lab. They say there's no salting there."

Joe grabbed for one of the phones with his left hand. His right hand shot towards the score of direct-line buttons.

"Don't!" I said. "If this is for real, Joe, that gold will still be there tomorrow and the day after and the day after. If it's not for real, we could all go to jail. The core's on its way to Toronto. It will be double-checked here tonight, and we'll know for sure in a day or two. In the meantime we keep drilling. The gold could actually be in place but as a small pocket and we'd be stung. Let's play it cool."

"Cool!" Joe said loudly, as a command to himself. Then he broke into a song, playing loudly on the phrase, "Let's play it cool," until his alarmed secretary peered into the room.

Next morning the news was bad. Dr. Langford reported that the microscopic study of several core specimens revealed no gold present. The only evidence of gold at all, and there had not been much, occurred only as a smear mixed with brass on the outside of the cylindrical rock core, obviously derived from the brass diamond-studded drilling bits used. The circumstantial evidence suggested that particles of high-grade gold ore from some outside source had been deliberately dropped, by persons unknown, into the two-inch-diameter drill hole. There the revolving drill bit had broken it down and distributed it into the sludge and upon the external surface of the recovered core, sections of which were slit longitudinally for assaying.

There were suspects among recent visitors to the drilling sites, and certain of these were placed under observation. In a small log cabin on the shore of Quirke Lake, where visitors stayed overnight, we found, in the corner of a windowsill, small fragments of gold quartz ore probably identical to the material employed in this criminal scheme. However, we decided to let the matter drop and be forgotten. Hirshhorn accepted the disappointment philosphically – without a song. He knew that whoever may have dropped the high-grade into the drill hole, would likely have been either someone trying to make a "fast buck" or a troublemaker. In any event we didn't take the bait.

Financing the Peach/Pronto Development

Joe Hirshhorn played the key role in securing the funds for the development of the Pronto mine. With the help of Preston East Dome Mines, he also arranged the funding for the parent corporation, to which we gave the name Algom Uranium Mines, which financed all our Elliot Lake mines. Algom Uranium became Rio Algom upon its transfer to the Rio Tinto Company of England. This British group began later to provide the major capital funding required to bring all of Algom Uranium's other mines – Nordic, Quirke, Spanish, Panel, and Milliken – into production.

Hirshhorn's method of securing funds was typical of that period. He proceeded along one of two routes. If he held a large share position in a dormant corporation which had failed to be successful in earlier ventures, he might elect to rejuvenate that company as his vehicle. This would not only benefit him, since a second "vendor-promoter" block of stock was available to him, it would delight and benefit all earlier shareholders. In this manner Hirshhorn rejuvenated several dormant corporations – his "cats and dogs," he called them. In utilizing such companies to finance the staking, Joe had available for his immediate use a number of corporation vehicles, thus avoiding time-consuming incorporation of new companies.

The other route open to Hirshhorn was to form a new limited syndicate, securing for his efforts the allowable vendor-promoter's block of units in that syndicate (up to 25 per cent of total authorized), and sell for cash, to a few associates, a sufficient number of additional units in the syndicate to realize the modest amounts of high-risk, and, he hoped, high-return monies required for the first speculative steps of exploratory drilling. This was the procedure Joe used for the Peach Syndicate. The relatively few early purchasers who acquired Peach shares at $1 a share, realized within six months, an increase in value to $135 per share.

The high-risk "seed money" provided by the Peach Syndicate had to be supplemented soon, of course, by the much larger capital investment of $6 million for the development of the mine and mill. With an indicated ore body and a government purchase contract of $55 million for the entire production during the first five years that would completely amortize all capital and operating costs and provide an adequate profit, Hirshhorn had relatively little difficulty in persuading prominent Canadian brokers to provide the equity financing necessary to bring Pronto into production. The underwriting for the development of the Pronto mine was quickly over-subscribed.

At the time of Pronto's major financing, Hirshhorn again turned to Thayer Lindsley, one of the "giants" not only of mining in Canada and the United States but throughout the world. However, Lindsley's advisers, as noted earlier, advised against investing into the Pronto project. Nonetheless, Hirshhorn and I developed a close and warm relationship with this extraordinarily successful man.

Lindsley was born and spent the first fifteen years of his life in Japan, assimilating much of that country's rich culture. Resettled with his parents in the United States, he studied at Harvard and graduated with a B.A. in 1903. He was academically gifted, standing well ahead of his classmate, Franklin D. Roosevelt. In 1904 Lindsley received a second academic degree from Harvard in civil engineering. Work on various construction projects across the United States followed. He also completed graduate studies in geological engineering at Columbia University. After serving as an artillery officer during the First World War, Lindsley took over an iron mine in Oregon, rehabilitating it to profitable status, earning a modest capital profit, and demonstrating his entrepreneurial ability.

Following his success in Oregon, Lindsley came to Canada. In association with other creative entrepreneurs, commencing with Joseph Errington, he began to put together the remarkable Ventures-Falconbridge mining-metallurgical empire. In the process, he and Joe Hirshhorn worked together intermittently, beginning in the 1930s with the Beattie gold mine development in Quebec. After I came to eastern Canada I worked briefly as a consultant on several smaller projects for Lindsley. One of these involved a placer-gold deposit in the Omineca district of British Columbia. Another was his Opemisca copper mine at Chibougamau, Quebec. I also advised Lindsley on two Ontario uranium deposits. One was a precursor to the Bicroft mine in Bancroft. The other was the Ranwick prospect in the Camray field. Although Hirshhorn and I rarely visited Lindsley at his Toronto or New York offices, and he rarely visited our Toronto office, we did spend several memorable evenings over dinner at Lindsley's Forest Hill residence.

Lindsley lived alone in his large house, with his books, reports, countless geological maps, and a remarkably able housekeeper-cook. He was aware of Hirshhorn's particular taste in foods, which included a lack of variety but an insistence on quality. Accordingly, Lindsley provided Joe's favourite meal: shrimp cocktail, prime rib of beef with horseradish, roast potatoes, and coffee. Lindsley would carve the roast for Joe and myself but would never share in the fine meal. Instead, his housekeeper placed before him a bowl of fresh fruit with a tiny jug of cream. He might take a few crackers and share a cheese tray with us, but that was his entire meal.

Following dinner Lindsley usually said, "Let's go upstairs." What we had come for was about to begin!

Upon entering Lindsley's study, Hirshhorn might ask, as he waved a cigar produced from his front pocket, "Can I have a cigar?"

"Of course, Joseph!" Lindsley would reply. Hirshhorn would then put the cigar in his mouth and start chewing it, but, to his credit, he never lit it. He knew that Lindsley was a non-smoker.

The floor of Lindsley's study was half-covered with huge, un-folded, coloured geological maps. "I have these ready," said Lindsley. "I thought they would interest you." Hirshhorn and I would kneel on the floor to study them, sometimes with the tall, thin, "El Greco" figure of Lindsley kneeling between us. He would talk, point, and raise questions, as he led us, as if on a magic Turkish carpet, flying around the world. "Franc, when were you last in Brazil? Now here. . . . Now Joseph, this is an area in Morocco – phosphate mines – I've just returned. I saw the strangest thing there – let me tell you about it. . . . Look over here, this is the Massif Centrale area of France. Note how the uranium deposits are distributed. I believe there are more to be found along here – and here, but acquisition of the land is a problem. Ever been to Greece, Joseph? This map shows a number of high-purity borax deposits. They are totally undeveloped. What a tragedy! The problem is . . ."

And we would lose all sense of time until suddenly, and all too quickly, the electric light started flickering. "Too bad," Lindsley would remark. "It's my housekeeper signalling me that she is leaving, it is eleven o'clock." And it always seemed the right time for us to go, too. So we'd shake hands with Lindsley and take our leave.

On the way home after one particular evening with Lindsley, Hirshhorn enthused, "That was strong liquor, Frankie-boy." (We had consumed no alcohol.) "No way I can sleep for hours now. T.L. puts me on fire. Watta man, watta man!"

And although we never did develop a partnership with Thayer Lindsley for which Joe hoped, we regarded him most highly. He was a uniquely remarkable man.

Algom Uranium – A Glue!

On July 15, 1953, we incorporated Algom Uranium Limited. Hirshhorn had wanted the name "Patrician" or "President" and so instructed Bill Bouck who was, of course, familiar with the P ritual. These two names, however, were disallowed by the Registrar of Companies. Bouck could not reach Hirshhorn to settle this question, but he rationalized that the existing Algoma Steel, Algoma Central Railroad, and Algoma Steamship corporations were an illustrious group that Hirshhorn could accept, so entered it as "Algoma Uranium." When the charter appeared, however, the name inscribed was "Algom." I was not present when the tragic news was given to Hirshhorn, but his secretary told me later that he loudly lamented in disgust, "Algom! Algom! A glue!"

Glue or not, I became president and managing director of Algom Uranium and Bill Bouck, vice president – the same positions we held in Pronto. Bill Hutchinson was appointed engineering consultant and Bob Hart the operating manager. The board of directors for Algom was practically the same as for Preston East Dome. As officers of this new company, we set in motion the work necessary to explore its mining claims following the staking of the Big Z. Seven months later, we had established that on Algom Uranium's property there were two major ore areas to which we gave the names, "Nordic" (on the middle section of the Big Z) and "Quirke" (on the northern section).

Despite our very encouraging start at developing ore, Hirshhorn found it difficult to arrange Algom's financing. Perhaps much of the problem was due to our ambitions for Algom. I had persuaded Hirshhorn, with the support of my engineering staff, that Nordic and Quirke could each support a daily production of 3,000 tons, that we had the technical capability and should plan for such production, and that both mines should be put into production simultaneously.

Several major Canadian mining corporations were either not interested in our project – "Sorry, our business is nickel" – "Our business is copper" – "Our business is steel-making" – or were wary – "Let's wait until Pronto can show a track record. We might consider some participation but never two at a time." None of those whom we approached encouraged us to think that we would succeed in interesting Canadian corporations in our venture. Even Rio Tinto's Canadian scouting group, which was based in Toronto had been kept fully informed by us of the first Pronto results, reportedly advised their British office that the grade of our ore was marginal and the economics of our development uncertain. When finally Rio Tinto reacted with interest, which later became total support, the initiative came from their scouting organization in Johannesburg, South Africa.

The polite interest and lukewarm discussions in Canada soon frustrated Hirshhorn, and so he began to make approaches in the United States. A small parade of high-level consultants and corporate officers from major corporations based in California, Arizona, Utah, Missouri, and elsewhere came to visit our Elliot Lake field. Two or three were cautiously willing to consider one producing mine – but not two!

On August 29, 1953, the Soviet Union exploded a hydrogen bomb. Soon afterwards the Eldorado Mining and Refining Company, the Canadian government crown corporation concerned with uranium and refining, announced it would enter into long-term purchase contracts with new Canadian mines producing uranium on behalf of the United States government. Pronto was the first in the Blind River region to secure such a contract. It should be noted here that Eldorado did not provide any "start-up" financing for private-sector uranium-mining companies, but the contracts negotiated with Eldorado were of central importance in enabling such private companies to arrange their own financing.

The first Eldorado contract with Pronto was for the delivery of $55 million worth of uranium oxide over six years. Later Algom received a contract for about $207 million worth of the same product from the Nordic and Quirke mines. Soon we had separate and additional contracts for the Panel, Spanish American, and Milliken mines. All of these were Hirshhorn enterprises.

Occasionally we were asked why we did not have one or two huge operating units rather than seven physically separate ones. Our rationale was that Eldorado preferred to evaluate each mine individually for production contracts. Then too, Hirshhorn found that such an approach made fund-raising easier. There were other practical, technical advantages. With a number of separate plants, the risk of loss of production or interruption from natural disaster, fire, or strikes, was minimized. Our several production units varied as to productivity and operating costs. Competitive morale remained high among our half-dozen mine managers and their staffs. A further advantage was that we had greater flexibility when production contracts were terminated. We also found a "second life" for two of the smaller ore treatment plants. One was used to process the copper-cobalt ore from our Pater mine and another for the copper-gold ore of our Anglo-Rouyn mine in Saskatchewan.

Other Mines Along the Big Z

In addition to the eight uranium mines developed by Technical Mine Consultants in the Blind River area (Pronto, Nordic, Quirke #1, Quirke #2, Buckles, Spanish American, Panel, Milliken, and our copper-cobalt mine, Pater), there were four other unassociated mines developed in the same district. These were Consolidated Denison, Canmet, Stanleigh, and Stanrock mines.

Denison Mines, like Rio Tinto, was not involved in the initial geological concept development of the region, nor in the initial high-risk exploratory drilling that provided strategic information about the ore bodies nor in the required metallurgical research necessary for product-processing. These important pathfinder steps were taken by the TMC-managed Hirshhorn group of companies and by the Hirshhorn-controlled Preston East Dome Mines company.

The claims that were to comprise the eventual Denison and Canmet mine holdings, however, were those staked by Art Stollery and his colleagues Jim Kenmay and Fred Jowsey, who had successfully claimed a large block of land along the northern section of the Big Z. This trio set about optioning their land to others. It is reported that Stollery's initial asking price was a million dollars, a price viewed as excessive by several of the parties he approached. Since Art Stollery was well-known both to me and to Hirshhorn, it was not surprising that he sought to sell his claims to our group. Joe Hirshhorn, however, was not well-disposed toward Stollery. It was later reported to me that Joe rejected Stollery's proposal "out of hand." If this was so, it was done without reference to either Bill Bouck or me. Stollery then turned to others, including Stephen Roman who reportedly agreed to pay him and his associates $30,000 in cash and 500,000 shares in the company subsequently known as Consolidated Denison Mines Limited. Roman was president and Stollery vice president of this company.

In 1954 when Stollery sold his group's claims to Roman, our group had already incorporated the Pronto and Algom Uranium companies. To that point, our exploration drilling indicated a probability – as opposed to a possibility – that our prospects would prove successful. In addition, of course, there were the major problems of developing additional ore reserves underground, resolving the uranium recovery problem, and, most importantly, securing production contracts from the Canadian government which would ensure the financial success of our uranium-mining operations.

Stephen Roman and Denison Mines

I first met Stephen Roman some years before he acquired the claims of Art Stollery and his colleagues in the Elliot Lake camp. From the outset I developed a considerable respect for Roman's intelligence, financial courage, and for the remarkably sound "intuitive timing" of his various activities in resource development. During his early years in the mining industry Roman had a single senior associate, John C. Puhky, who said little but was alert, intelligent, and presumably contributed to Roman's policy decisions.

I had met Roman when I was asked to look at a mineral prospect in northern Ontario, in October 1946. A prospector whose judgement I respected had called me from Chapleau, which is about one hundred miles north and slightly east of Sault Ste. Marie. "Franc," he said, "there's a new gold strike up here. You've got to come up and have a look at it."

We met in Chapleau where we arranged with the railway section men to put us on their "jigger" – the hand-pumped rail-repair car. They transported us along the track twelve or fifteen miles to a point called Groundhog. We tumbled off with our sleeping bags, tent, and grub. My prospector guide said, "Now we've got to find the fellow who made the discovery – Joe Burke. He's a trapper, a squaw-man, with at least one son. He has a cabin on the river."

From the elevated railroad trestle we soon spotted the lone log cabin on a little sandy cove on the Groundhog River. Leaving my companion to watch our gear, I made my way down the steep river bank to the cabin. There I met a surprised, but pleasant Indian woman who spoke English. She told me that Joe and their son were "in the bush" and wouldn't be back until close to sundown.

Joe Burke was a typical bushman and trapper. Brown and hard as nails, he had become almost an Indian, with all the bush wisdom and self-reliance required to survive in the wilderness. He was forthright in admitting he had made a discovery. "It's good," he said, "because you can see the gold."

When I asked Burke if he had made the discovery on his own, he replied, "No, I'm being grubstaked by the Concord Syndicate." That name was new to me so I asked who was behind the Syndicate. "The boss seems to be a fellow named Steve Roman. He buys our grub and I get an interest in the discovery, but it belongs to the Syndicate." I asked for and was given the Syndicate's address in Toronto.

The following day my partner and I travelled upstream to "get a feel for the geology and to prospect." The morning after, I was again on Joe Burke's doorstep and he and his son led me to his find.

Although the exposed area was limited to a patch of rusty rock exposed by the roots of a fallen tree, I was favourably impressed by what Burke showed me and congratulated him on his accomplishment and, I hoped, his eventual good fortune. I promised him I would get in touch with Roman when I got back to Toronto. However, I was doubtful that I could secure an option on the discovery since, on the day I had been shown his find, three other scouts, – including Jim McCrea Jr., whose father was president of Dome Mines – had all appeared on the scene.

Nonetheless, as soon as I returned to Chapleau I called my secretary at my Toronto office. "Please go to the Concord Syndicate office and ask for Stephen Roman," I said. "Tell him you have heard of the Concord Syndicate and ask if he has any remaining units to sell. If he says yes, buy some for yourself. Also tell him that your boss would like to meet him when he returns from the bush." I told her I would return promptly to Toronto to see Roman and also to organize some claim-staking in the area of the discovery for the account of Pioneer Gold Mines of B.C., whose business affairs in eastern Canada I was then handling.

When I left Groundhog I asked my prospector to remain behind to determine what staking had been done by Burke and possibly others. For this work, I helped him secure a canoe and an Indian helper.

On my return to Toronto, I met Stephen Roman, told him of my visit to the Joe Burke discovery, and asked if the prospect was available for option by Pioneer. He told me that Dome Mines had already made an acceptable offer and would develop the discovery, which it subsequently did. Some modest gold production followed.

Stephen Roman's company, Concord, had begun to acquire title to heavy oil lands and shallow well production in the Lloydminster field in Saskatchewan. Some time earlier, Imperial Oil, in large part through the drive of geologist Ted Link, had drilled the dramatically successful Leduc, Redwater, and Golden Spike wells in Alberta that had captured the attention of the oil world and the Canadian speculating public. Roman, shrewdly, was into the right thing – not quite in the right province but clearly at the right time. This is close to the perfect formula for success in financing speculative ventures. Roman's Concord enterprise appears to have made the most of the opportunity and this served as his springboard to later successes.

While Roman was not involved in the discovery of the mines in the Elliot Lake area, he did take a calculated and shrewd risk in the right thing, at the right place, and at the right time, when he acquired the claims staked by Stollery, Kenmay, and Jowsey.

Roman's corporate vehicle then, Denison Mines, attracted some excellent technical staff, including an outstanding and able general manager John Kostuik, as well as geologists who had earlier served Pronto. One of the latter, Ralph Benner, was placed in charge of Denison's early exploratory diamond-drilling. Earlier, when he was a young, energetic, and imaginative geologist, Benner had been among the staff I had persuaded to leave the dormant mine camp of Cobalt to join the Pronto mine staff.

After Benner had been with Pronto for about a year, Denison offered him a more lucrative salary. He came to me for my approval and blessing, which I readily gave. We shook hands on parting and remained friends. A test of this friendship came a couple of months later when he asked me to meet him to discuss "geology."

Given my bush schedule, I told Benner he'd have to catch me "on the fly." We finally met in a roadside restaurant near the Pronto mine. Drawing sketches on a paper napkin, he explained that in regard to his first drilling at Denison, he had finished drilling one hole and almost a second, but had found no ore. He was, quite properly, concerned. I asked if he would care to reveal to me the values found in the two holes, which he did.

I considered his rough sketch and the low assays and said "it looks rough, but there is a very slight improvement in values in that direction," I indicated with a stroke of a pen, "and also a slight thickening of the conglomerate in the same direction. I'd call that the direction of improvement trend, so spot your next hole to the east."

"But that's out in Quirke Lake," remarked Benner.

"Then get out there on the ice," I suggested.

Some days later I suggested to our Quirke project manager that when any of our prospectors had occasion to deliver radio-telephone messages (TMC had a more powerful and reliable two-way radio-telephone system and provided a casual courtesy service to bush neighbours) to Benner's shack or to his drilling foreman's camp, they have their Geigers turned on at all times. I was careful to emphasize, of course, that they were not to touch any core or boxes. Days passed. I thought no more about Benner's problem. Then, late one afternoon, a coded radio-telephone report reached me regarding our Quirke drillings. Included in it was a message to the effect that there was "high 'radac' in covered core-boxes at our neighbours." I realized that Benner and Denison had probably found ore.

The next day, October 19, 1954, I called the brokerage office in our building. "Keep buying Denison for my account," I said, "and keep in touch." On that day the value of Denison stock tripled in value, with the net result that I purchased almost one hundred thousand shares of Denison at an average cost of 70¢ a share, and sold them the same afternoon to generate a substantial profit. I felt quite pleased with myself, since I had never "scalped" on the market before.

I divided the entire profit equally between six or seven of my field crew, myself, and Hirshhorn.

Hirshhorn had been absent from Toronto and knew nothing of the "scalping" episode. I simply placed the five-digit cheque payable to him in the large stack of mail on his desk. On his return, he scanned his mail and then confronted me with the cheque. "What's this mean?" he asked. I told him. Instead of smiling, he frowned: "Don't ever try a trick like that again. I play the piano around here!" he exclaimed as he folded up the cheque and put it in his pocket, with feigned annoyance and probably a touch of envy.

About a year later, I learned from others that Ralph Benner's problem had been more than geological. He had set about examining the Denison claims staked earlier by Stollery and associates, and had discovered several major staking irregularities serious enough that large sections of the Denison property could have been re-staked and legitimately claimed by others. Only extreme secrecy and round-the-clock negotiations between a prominent Toronto lawyer and the mining court judge secured for Denison a qualified period of grace in which to correct existing irregularities and allow the claims to remain in Denison's hands.

In late 1956 my colleagues and I became involved in a contest of wits with Denison, relating to this north-east corner of Quirke Lake. Not only had Denison's staking irregularities taken place at this area of the lake, but much earlier, this had been the spot where Stollery and his party had confronted the TMC staking crew and bluffed them into thinking that he had everything in the area staked – actually he had only just begun staking! It seemed clear that a more definite agreement was necessary between Denison and TMC regarding the precise border between our Connecho claims and the Roman-controlled Canmet claims.

Since this border area was entirely under water, the original staking had involved numerous witness posts, which had been piled on the edge of the lake. On each of these posts, its intended position in the lake was inscribed. But the "freeze-up" and "break-up" of the winter's ice along the shoreline had moved some posts, and others had simply floated away. In addition, some of the posts were poplar and had served to satisfy the spring appetites of nearby beavers. So we met Roman and his most senior advisors to resolve this issue.

By this time, Rio Tinto of England was assuming a larger policy and management role in Elliot Lake activities. Thus our delegation at the meeting included Dr. Duncan Derry, of Rio Canadian Exploration. Bill Bouck, who, as a lawyer with great experience in mining law, was our leader in these negotiations, and John Edison was included as back-up legal counsel for Bouck and me. Stephen Roman, John Puhky, and one or two others acted for Denison. As it turned out, we met during the Suez Canal crisis: newspapers throughout the world were reporting on the movement of British naval vessels to the Canal Zone area. On being introduced to Dr. Derry, who had a marked British accent, Roman bristled and bluntly blurted, "What are you British trying to do? Start a third world war?" Despite this blustery beginning, however, the meeting proceeded.

Our group took the initiative by outlining two practical boundary positions, one of which we recommended that Denison choose. Roman said he would decide in a day or so and this he did, stating to us that Denison would have the option we had not recommended. We were delighted!

I had suggested to our group that we try a dangerous bluff by offering Roman the area I felt was of greater value, based on a few random but successful holes we had drilled through the ice during the winter. They had finally agreed to that ploy, rather nervously and only after considerable debate. The land we acquired in that settlement later became part of our successful all-under-water Panel mine.

When it became apparent that Denison would have an attractive ore-body at Elliot Lake, Roman sought a treasury share underwriting for it. He proposed to sell one million shares for one dollar net per share to the treasury, and had enlisted the assistance of a principal in the brokerage firm of Draper Dobie to place the stock.

At the same time I strongly recommended to Hirshhorn that we "try for control" of Denison and that the acquisition of that share-block would be an important step to that end. Hirshhorn was immediately interested and asked, "Where can we find a quick million bucks?"

I told him of my old corporate alma mater, Pioneer Gold Mines of B.C., controlled by Colonel Victor Spencer and associates and now managed by my good friend Dr. Howard James. Howard James had indicated to me that Pioneer wanted into uranium mining and had about $3 million in their treasury. Hirshhorn deflated that suggestion by saying he'd heard that Spencer was strongly anti-Semitic and he wouldn't deal with him. But after a few minutes of reflection, he was bursting with enthusiasm. "We'll swing it," he announced. "I'll talk to Charlie Burns of Burns Brothers about it. He knows Vic Spencer personally, and also Frank Ross, Spencer's vice president on the Pioneer board."

Two or three days later Charlie Burns called, inviting me to a meeting that afternoon in Colonel Spencer's suite at the Royal York Hotel in Toronto. At the meeting, besides Spencer, Burns, and myself, there were Frank Ross and a fifth person. Hirshhorn was not present. After some social banter – I knew Colonel Spencer quite well from earlier Pioneer days – the group quizzed me regarding Denison's merits. I stated, with considerable conviction, that it would be the next most important mine in the camp after we had our Quirke "in business." Burns confirmed that the million shares of Denison stock were indeed available at a mark-up between 25¢ and 50¢ per share, and foresaw no problem acquiring the million-share block. He also made reference to Hirshhorn's involvement, while assuring Spencer and Ross that I would manage the project. Colonel Spencer said that Pioneer would make $1.5 million available. I left the meeting convinced that we "had a deal."

Later that day Burns came to Hirshhorn's office and asked if I could "sit in." He recounted to Hirshhorn what had transpired at the earlier meeting. Hirshhorn quibbled a bit about the mark-ups for the Draper Dobie principal and Burns Brothers, but concluded with a general statement of approval. Other TMC business required that I fly to Beaverlodge the next day, and I was away from Toronto for a week. I was puzzled by the total lack of communication on Denison from TMC during that period. Immediately on my return to Toronto, Hirshhorn being absent I called Burns to learn what was happening on the "Denison deal." Coolly, and with a note of regret in his voice he said, "Ask Joe." I did, later, but all he would ever say was, "It blew up. Don't ask me any more." To this day, what happened remains a mystery to me, but whatever it was, it probably ruined our opportunity to gain control of Denison and thus of all uranium production in Elliot Lake.

The Buckles Mine – Our Golden Lever

The Buckles mine was another of our mines which had resulted from the Big Z staking operation. It was named for Harry Buckles, TMC's field manager. He was widely known in the exploration industry and highly respected by all who knew him. Among other things, he played a key role in the Northern Aerial Minerals Exploration Company which pioneered exploration by aircraft throughout Canada's northern regions following the First World War. Buckles walked with an unusual roll, a bit like a drunken sailor. Both of his legs had been broken in a remote mining area, where there had been no one with medical knowledge to attend him. His colleagues had placed him on a bunk and improvised splints for his legs. His bones knit well, but his legs were crooked. Despite his slightly deformed legs, Buckles moved with the strength and endurance of a grizzly bear. He had a heart of gold and had accumulated a great fund of stories. Along with his other associates, I developed the highest regard for Harry Buckles as a person and for his sound technical judgment.

When Joe Hirshhorn and I put the Rix-Athabasca into production in the early 1950s, Buckles managed the development of the mine for us. And when we organized and implemented our plans for staking the Big Z, Buckles was again indispensable.

Hirshhorn incorporated the Buckles Mining Company to facilitate the purchase of the few Charles Metivier "copper" claims that predated our regional staking. Although the Buckles uranium ore body was of modest size, the grade was above average and all of the ore was near the surface. Thus mining costs were minimal. This ore body was of crucial importance to us in the development of, and in securing production contracts for, other mines we brought into production later. Eldorado Mining and Refining was prepared to issue contracts to companies having viable operations that could meet a five-year delivery schedule and start production within an early stated deadline.

Since we could build mills more quickly than we could sink shafts and develop underground ore, we used the Buckles mine to provide ore for initial processing by the mills of two other mines, until such times as the underground ore development of the latter could catch up to the stringent Canadian government delivery schedules. Had we not been able to use the Buckles mine in this way, we could not have achieved the necessary production in time to secure substantial contracts for the Spanish American and Milliken mines.

It was I who had suggested to Hirshhorn that we use the Buckles mine in this manner, if it was acceptable to Eldorado. When word came that it was acceptable, a rare beam of praise shone from Hirshhorn's highly expressive Semitic face as he exclaimed, "Frankie-boy, you must be one of Us!"

The Pater Mine – Found on a Stroll

Another property we staked in 1953 was the Pater copper-cobalt deposit. While it did not share the limelight with our uranium mines, since in large part it was privately owned, financed, and operated, its subsequent development indicated that mineralization in the area was not limited to uranium ores. More importantly, it proved again the dictum that: "Mines are not found, they are made!"

One day, while at our base camp on Highway 17, shortly before the Pronto came into production and while several exploratory drills were at work testing the Big Z, I said to Don Smith, the first project engineer at Pronto, "Let's go for a walk along the tracks for a change of scenery." The CNR tracks follow the north shore of Lake Huron closely at this point. For no particular reason, we walked east, toward Sudbury.

The water, rocky shoreline, and forest provided beautiful scenery and a tranquil change of pace from work. After we had walked about two miles, we came to a point where the rail line, built about 1910, cut through a ridge of rock. I can't pass a rock, boulder or outcrop of any kind, without at least glancing at it. Rocks, to me, have a charm which seems to go unnoticed by the overwhelming majority of people. Like Shakespeare I know there are "books in the running brooks" and "sermons in stones." I have heard them! Rocks "talk," and occasionally "sing" to me.

That day, I glanced at a particular rock; an unsightly, black, soot-encrusted rock. Still, I was prompted to scratch it with my prospector's pick and examine it more carefully. I remember saying to Don Smith, "You know, the remarkable Murray fault system passes near here. This fault zone splits the Sudbury nickel basin along its axis. It can be traced about 150 miles to the shore of Lake Superior near Batchawana Bay. This graphite shear zone could be a strand of it." As I scratched, some small green specks appeared.

"Look," I exclaimed, "those specks could be copper or nickel staining. I want you to return here later with a sample sack and, after scraping away the soot and grease, take some samples of that staining. We'll find out what it is."

In due course the samples were taken and assayed. Copper *was* indicated, but only as a few tenths of 1 per cent, not nearly adequate for economic production. Nevertheless, I was intrigued. I concluded that the structural setting and evidence of copper was sufficiently encouraging for one shallow drillhole. Later a hole was drilled. The shear zone was well-defined but the copper content was only slightly improved. Still I requested that as time and equipment permitted two additional deeper holes be drilled. All of these holes revealed some copper and some revealed cobalt. The grade was still low, but it improved at a frustratingly slow pace as they cut deeper and deeper.

Finally, at a vertical depth of about four hundred feet, we identified the top of a remarkable ore body. It was almost two thousand feet long and about twenty feet wide. It averaged over 2 per cent copper and .25 per cent cobalt. This ore body became the basis of the Pater copper mine, from which much copper and cobalt was mined to considerable depth by the Rio Tinto group. The ore was milled in the nearby converted Pronto plant when our larger, lower-cost mills replaced Pronto as a primary uranium producer.

Rio Tinto Enters the Picture

When we found and began to plan for the development of the Pater deposit, Joe Hirshhorn and I were eagerly searching for a major financial backer whose resources matched our vision of the dramatic scale on which our Big Z mines merited being developed. That search took an exciting turn in November 1954 as a result of a phone call from South Africa.

Joe Hirshhorn took a long-distance call that day and shouted through the open door between our offices, "Franc, there's some bird on the line calling from Johannesburg. He wants to talk to you. I'll listen in." I picked up the phone. A man with a cultured voice introduced himself.

"This is Oscar Weiss. You may not know me. I am a geophysicist based here in Johannesburg."

Later I learned that he was the geophysicist who, through the use of the newly developed magnetometer, had succeeded in tracing the length of the deeply buried and fabulously rich Witwatersrand gold reef for several additional miles, gaining international acclaim for the feat. Weiss had become a person of wealth and well-earned prestige. Fortunately this had not reduced his drive and ambition to make even more discoveries. He had been persuaded by Rio Tinto, London, to organize and manage various exploration syndicates, including one in Canada called "Ownamin," a contraction of *Oscar Weiss North America Minerals.*

After he had introduced himself on the telephone, Oscar Weiss said, "I have read, with much interest, the report in the *Northern Miner* of September 1954 of your work in the Blind River area on uranium-bearing conglomerates. Were you quoted properly?" I assured him that the *Northern Miner* report was correct. Then he asked, "Have you assayed that conglomerate for gold?"

I replied, "Yes, but to the present, no gold is indicated."

After two or three more questions, Weiss asked, "May I come and see you and Joseph?"

Before I could answer, Hirshhorn broke into the conversation, exclaiming, "Sure!"

"How soon?" Weiss asked.

Hirshhorn answered, "As soon as you like!"

Weiss then said, "I'll be there in a couple of days."

Some time later I learned that after Weiss had placed that initial call to us, he had phoned J. N. V. (Val) Duncan, Managing Director of Rio Tinto in London. Duncan is reported to have replied to Weiss, "Oscar, I have already had a report from Dr. Duncan Derry and Dr. Earl Gillanders concerning this activity, as well as a copy of the single-page memo which the geologist, Joubin, gave to our Ownamin office some time ago. Derry and Gillanders do not appear very optimistic on the subject."

Despite the lack of enthusiasm for our Big Z project on the part of Rio Tinto's Canadian advisers, Weiss told Val Duncan that he was going to Toronto. Two or three days later he arrived.

Oscar Weiss is an imposingly tall, well-groomed man of commanding appearance. The elegance of his appearance was more than matched by the quality of his mind. It is rare for a man to be both a creative scientist and an astute financier, but Weiss was both and more. He was clearly a decisive businessman and this quickly became apparent to Hirshhorn. Indeed he and Hirshhorn "hit it off" immediately, as did Weiss and I.

When Weiss had read the report in the September 1954 *Northern Miner*, which had appeared on the front page, he had appreciated fully the significance of a particular technical sentence I had employed in the article: "The ore bed appears to be a Proterozoic age basal quartz conglomerate overlying Archean crystalline rocks." He had said to me on the telephone, "You are describing the Witwatersrand gold-uranium deposits."

After Hirshhorn and I had talked to Weiss for about an hour during our first meeting, he turned to Hirshhorn and asked, "Do you mind if I place a long-distance call, Joseph?"

"Sure, go ahead," said Joe.

So, in our presence, Weiss called Duncan in London and said, "Val, you must listen to me. Can you get here quickly? This appears to be important." Weiss replaced the phone, saying, "Mr. Duncan will be here as soon as possible."

A day or so before Oscar Weiss first phoned us from South Africa, Joe Hirshhorn had received a phone call from Sam Harris, a friend and distinguished New York lawyer. Harris had reported that one of his senior law partners, Hans Frank, had told Rio Tinto in London of our Blind River uranium discoveries. Rio is reported to have evinced some interest to Frank concerning our activities. Hirshhorn told Harris that in our ongoing search for financial backers we had reached a tentative understanding with Canadian bankers to underwrite an Algom Uranium $40-million issue. This arrangement, Joe thought, might preclude our having discussions with Rio Tinto. Sam Harris assured Hirshhorn that, in his view, the arrangements completed with the Canadian banks would not constitute a major impediment to Rio Tinto's participation, if they so elected.

At the end of the Second World War, a brilliant British investment banker, Sir Mark Turner, had become the managing director of the Rio Tinto Zinc Corporation. He persuaded Val Duncan, a gifted organizer, to join the company. Val had trained as a barrister and had played a key role in the work of the British Coal Authority at the end of the Second World War. In the early 1950s, he succeeded Sir Mark Turner as managing director of Rio Tinto. One of his first responsibilities was to negotiate the sale and return of a major interest in the Rio Tinto mines in Spain to Spanish control. However, the British group were to continue as technical managers for some years. It is understood that the sale to a group of Spanish bankers involved a payment of $20 million to Rio Tinto Zinc. When the consortium of Spanish bankers began to pay Rio Tinto the $20 million, the question arose as to how and where this money should be re-invested.

After assuming office as managing director of Rio Tinto, Val Duncan had launched an exploration program in South Africa. Rio also began to take an interest in Canada and, in 1953, in Australia. Through the leadership and energy Val Duncan invested in Rio Tinto it gradually began to emerge as a dynamic world-wide mining company. Duncan encouraged Rio's Canadian development through the appointment of Oscar Weiss as the company's principal adviser on its development in North America. It was in this capacity that Weiss had called Duncan about our Big Z project.

Before Hirshhorn, Bill Bouck, and I met with Val Duncan, Weiss told us that he was a man of outstanding integrity and ability. "Duncan," said Weiss "has demonstrated remarkable business acumen and fairness, particularly in his negotiations concerning the historic Rio Tinto mines in Spain. He is regarded in London as having one of the sharpest business minds in Britain."

As soon as our discussions with Duncan began to develop, we became increasingly aware of the correctness of Weiss's assessment. Hirshhorn, Duncan, and I quickly developed excellent rapport. Both Hirshhorn and I knew that we needed financial support in the order of $40 million to develop the major ore deposits we had discovered on the scale they merited. We were also aware that there would be major advantages to securing the necessary financing from a financial group with major involvement in mining rather than from a group of banks, given our need of expertise in large-scale technical developments. There was, as well, the ultimate need for probably two or three hundred million dollars for the several production facilities we felt were justified. Hirshhorn told Duncan of the understanding he had reached with Canadian bankers, and that it would be necessary for Rio to reconcile its role with that of the Canadian banks. Duncan agreed to this.

When Duncan commenced his initial negotiations with us, he was anxious to work out the general terms for a deal that he could submit to the Rio Tinto directors in London for approval. Hirshhorn, and even Bill Bouck, felt uneasy with Duncan's suggested procedure. They were afraid it might only lead to protracted negotiations. Hirshhorn told Duncan we had been seeking a financial partner with the imagination and courage necessary to understand and accept the extent of the development we had in mind.

With typical bluntness, Hirshhorn said to Duncan, "We think you are that man." Duncan was silent for a moment, then said, "I shall give you a final answer in the morning." The next morning, he told us that Rio Tinto would commit itself in principle to an agreement under which Rio Tinto would advance substantial early funding to

Algom Uranium Limited and that we would mutually agree on the basis for raising all the additional funds required.

On February 21, 1955, a letter setting out the details of the initial agreement between the two companies was signed on behalf of Rio Tinto by Val Duncan and Sir Mark Turner, and on behalf of Algom Uranium by myself as president, and by Mr. L. I. Hall, our secretary-treasurer. The negotiations which Hirshhorn, Bill Bouck, and I had had with Val Duncan and Oscar Weiss had prepared the way for the formal agreement embodied in that letter.

Of crucial assistance in our reaching agreement so quickly was the receipt by Algom Uranium of a Letter of Intent, dated two weeks earlier, from Eldorado Mining and Refining Limited. It provided for the sale, by 1962, of Algom Uranium's Quirke Mine's production to a total value of nearly $206 million. This production contract, and several other contracts that followed, had been negotiated earlier by John Aird and myself, with the expert technical support of our TMS staff.

After the formal agreements between our group and Rio Tinto were finally signed on March 15,1955, Rio Tinto officials gradually became more deeply involved in the direction and day-by-day operations of Algom Uranium. Five directors representing Rio's interests were elected to the Board of Algom Uranium: Val Duncan, Dr. Duncan Derry, Dr. Earl B. Gillanders, Bill Malone, and Bryce Mac-Kenzie. Bill Bouck, Senator Salter Hayden – one of Hirshhorn's legal advisers – Joe Hirshhorn, and I, as president, continued as members of the Algom board. Dr. Earl Gillanders was appointed managing director.

The impressive consortium organized by Rio Tinto to finance our Big Z mines included Commonwealth Development Finance Company Ltd., N. M. Rothschild & Sons, Robert Benson, Lonsdale & Company Ltd., Group Lambert, Sogemines Ltd., and Amsterdam Overseas Corporation. North American institutions involved in the consortium were Model, Roland & Stone of New York, Gairdner & Company Ltd., and Burns Bros. and Denton of Toronto.

The economic power of the group Rio Tinto had brought together to finance the long-term development of our properties on the Big Z gave us great assurance as we developed and gradually implemented plans for the community now known as Elliot Lake. We were determined to ensure that it would be the finest mining community in Canada.

XI

Creating Canada's Uranium Capital and a Museum for Art and Sculpture

In the United States the name *Hirshhorn* is identified with the museum of art and sculpture on The Mall in Washington, D.C. In Canada the name is identified with the town of Elliot Lake which came into being through the financing Joe Hirshhorn arranged for the development of the mining properties on the Big Z.

From boyhood onwards, Joe Hirshhorn was interested in making money and in collecting art. The two went hand-in-hand. Thus, when the mining properties we had begun to develop on the Big Z proved sufficiently attractive for Rio Tinto to invest in them, and gave Joe his "big pay day," he was able to realize his long-time dream of a world-class museum. That museum might have been located in Canada rather than the United States.

Building a New Town

As development of the obviously large ore bodies of Quirke, Denison, Panel, and Spanish American proceeded along the northern sections of the Big Z, and of Nordic and Milliken on the middle section, it became apparent that the creation of a new community of substantial size in the centre of this area, would be essential and desirable.

The Pronto and Pater mines on the southern section of the Big Z were practically on the Trans-Canada Highway and thus did not face the same problems. Those who worked at the Pronto and Pater settled happily with their families along the beautiful shore of Lake Lauzon and in a small new subdivision we built at the edge of the older Blind River community. Nearby were the hamlets of Algoma Mills, Spragge, and Cutler. The well-established cities of Sudbury and Sault Ste. Marie were about 75 miles to the east and west, respectively, of the Pronto mine site, by paved highway and railroad.

The development of the uranium mines on the Big Z began shortly after the copper and zinc deposits discovered in 1953 near Lake Manitouwadge in north-eastern Ontario were brought into production. To maintain and to improve the living and social standards of such relatively remote frontier mining and industrial communities, a special branch of the Ontario government responsible for municipal planning and development had been formed somewhat earlier. This department had been created to co-ordinate the interests of other ministries such as Mines, Natural Resources, Education, and Health, and to work with private-sector enterprises providing the economic justification of such new community development.

By an Order-In-Council of October 13, 1955, the Ontario government appointed an "Improvement Development Committee for the Elliot Lake Area." This committee of three persons – Dr. E. B. Gillanders as vice chairman, W. E. Willoughby, a Toronto real-estate executive and director of Denison Mines, and myself as chairman – was to work in close co-operation with the officials of the Ontario government. We were extremely fortunate in securing at an early stage the services of Percy Lorne Brown as secretary-treasurer of the committee. Brown had had invaluable experience as a municipal clerk of various frontier communities and was well-versed in the intricacies of inter-governmental bureaucracy. We functioned effectively as a harmonious, four-man, non-elective administrative municipal board.

We were responsible for the "Elliot Lake Improvement District," the largest "municipality" in all of Canada. It covered in excess of three hundred square miles over which we had complete administrative, legal, police, and planning authority. The large size of the area was to ensure the prevention of "squatting" anywhere near our settled centres, the town, or the plant sites.

The committee's first problems were the selection of a central townsite and an access route to it from "outside." We enlisted Harry Buckles, Bob Hart, Bill Hutchinson, and Professor George Langford of the University of Toronto to recommend three optional sites. Dr. Langford had had previous municipal and environmental planning experience. Then we considered their three choices and selected one situated at the south-easterly end of Elliot Lake between it and Nordic Lake. A delegation, representative of all government departments involved, visited this site and approved it.

Now we had to come up with a name for the new town. The first suggestion was made by Ontario's Assistant Deputy Minister of Mines, who proposed "Joubin" or "Joubinville." I declined the honour, but offered another suggestion – "Nordic," after a nearby lake and a northern people involved in mining, whom I greatly admire. Other suggestions followed. The name "Elliot Lake" was finally chosen.

An important factor in the choice of the site was access to it. Buckles and Hart scouted out various road routes from Highway 17 and located one old overgrown logging road that provided a relatively straight-line access for the seventeen-mile route from the highway to the site. The general straightness of this old route was quite extraordinary given the terrain of many lakes, deep muskeg swamps, winding rivers, and rocky ridges. Technical Mine Consultants and Preston quickly re-opened the old roadway for bulldozer, tractor-trailer, and jeep use during the summer months, and for more efficient trucks and trailers during the frozen and snow-packed winter months. The principal obstacle on the road was appropriately named "Unnecessary Hill." Most of the mines on the northern section of the Big Z were developed, as were the mills and much of the townsite, using this first "Buckles-Hart" Highway." Then a year or so later the provincial government graded, drained, and surfaced Highway 619 which closely follows the "Buckles-Hart" route.

After the choice and naming of the townsite and the choice of an access road to it, we appointed Marshall, Macklin and Monaghan as the town's engineering consultants. Our initial directions to them were that we wanted a totally modern and beautiful town that would be comfortable for its citizens while blending in with the natural beauty of the region.

The growth of Elliot Lake was rapid. Over fifteen hundred trailer homes quickly appeared and the committee's pleas to the Municipal Planning Board resulted in the passage of Ontario's first provincial legislation governing trailer parks, later known as mobile home communities.

The responsibilities of our committee grew. I was at some time or other titular head of the Police Department, School Board, and Fire Department, and was even Game Warden until I could delegate these major responsibilities to others. Fortunately, there was no lack of "others." Frontier towns, by their very nature, attract the adventurous, the energetic, the resourceful, and the independent. Luckily, from its beginning, we had a number of such popular and effective volunteer leaders in Elliot Lake. One of these was Jack Gauthier.

"Mr. Elliot Lake"

Soon after the location of the site for Elliot Lake was made known, but before any activity had commenced there save for the presence of a few surveyors, I arrived one day in a small pontoon aircraft. I had come for two reasons: I wished to look over the planned roadways going north to the probable mine sites and to check the progress of several drilling crews. As our aircraft taxied towards a sandy beach, a small pile of gasoline drums came into view along with the burly figure of a man standing beside them. "Who's that?" I asked my companion. "We have no drills working around here."

"I don't know, looks like a stranger," was the answer. The plane floated to the shoreline. I stepped off and approached the man, who was moving slowly toward me.

Somehow, I thought, this man could mean trouble. I had not yet entirely thrown off the veil of secrecy we had worked under in staking the area nor had I begun to realize fully that our hard-won mining claims would soon give birth to an entirely new town in an area which had been wilderness since the beginning of time.

I asked the stranger brusquely, "Are you one of our drill contractors?"

"No," he said, extending his hand. "I'm Jack Gauthier, the town's franchised oil and gas dealer."

"But," I protested, "there'll be no town for months – a year. Why, road construction is only starting. It takes time to develop a townsite, blast foundations, and build houses!"

"It also takes oil and gas for those bulldozers and compressors," said Gauthier. I looked carefully at this large, burly man with his engaging smile, flashing eyes, and warm friendly manner.

"You're right," I replied. "We'll need what you have to offer." As I came to know Gauthier better, my respect for him and for his commitment to the development of our new town grew apace.

And Gauthier became much more than Elliot Lake's supplier of oil and gas. With associates, he built the first hotel – with a restaurant and the first beer parlour. He helped a colleague, Ed Blahey, build the first shopping centre. In addition, Jack became involved in the erection of a fine Roman Catholic-managed hospital. Later he became a director of the Elliot Lake Centre for Continuing Education, which was concerned with cultural development in the community. He was a catalyst and participant in a variety of other local projects. The community needed "boosters and optimists" like him, particularly in its early days.

Jack was also a generous and genial host. The mighty and the famous came to his hotel as guests. I treasure in particular the memory of several occasions when Gauthier persuaded Prime Minister Lester Pearson ("Mike" as we knew him) to escape from Ottawa for a weekend visit to the growing Elliot Lake community (which was in the Algoma East political constituency that Pearson represented in Parliament). Gauthier also persuaded the dynamic Robert H. Saunders, chairman of Ontario Hydro, to share in these "Pearson meetings."

Such gatherings, held in a suite of rooms in Jack's hotel, often over a weekend, quickly became informal and totally relaxed when Jack would turn to Mike Pearson and announce, "Beer on the house! Bull session is open!" Then, to the other invited guests, he would add, "whale it to him, boys." And that was our cue to raise any questions, doubts, or problems that came to mind with our friendly and co-operative prime minister. It should be noted that few of the questions related to Elliot Lake. These were largely "good fellowship" affairs, spiced with humorous anecdotes and much joviality. Throughout it all Jack moved about in his genial manner as a perfect host.

Gauthier's greatest catch at one such meeting was Dean Acheson, former U.S. Secretary of State and counsellor to several American presidents. Joe Hirshhorn knew Acheson, having probably met him through his highly trusted American legal advisor, Sam Harris. Acheson commanded the respect of various important Wall Street brokers and major American multi-national mining corporations. Having concluded that except for the Pronto mines, major funding for our Big Z uranium mines could not be secured in Canada, Hirshhorn had decided to go after American funding. Although meetings to that end unfortunately came to nought, Acheson had found Hirshhorn to be a fascinating, colourful, and creative character, and the two had developed a continuing friendship.

On one occasion, Hirshhorn invited Dean Acheson and his wife to visit the burgeoning Elliot Lake community. Our wives – Hirshhorn's wife Lily, Mrs. Acheson, and my wife Mary – had gone off to do some painting, a hobby they all shared. Rain soon threatened, which meant ankle-deep mud everywhere, so we retreated to Gauthier's hotel. There we were quickly joined by others and regaled for a couple of hours by Acheson's witty anecdotes of life as an international diplomat. And what stories Acheson could tell! I remember especially a comment he made about General Charles DeGaulle, whom he seemed to respect highly as a person but not as a statesman, when he remarked, "He struck me as looking like a pear on top of two toothpicks!"

Hirshhorn and Acheson could have made a marvelous "Mutt and Jeff" comedy team – Hirshhorn was not much over five feet in height and Acheson was well over six feet. Joe's antics accompanying Acheson's tales, and his flamboyant gestures, were in perfect contrast to Acheson's patrician, aristocratic bearing and reserved manner.

Despite such camaraderie, optimism, much activity, and continuing growth at Elliot Lake (the population reached eighteen thousand by 1958), there were an increasing number of sceptics raising their voices about "the future of uranium." At the time, I referred to that mood as the "five-year phobia," stemming from the public knowledge that all our mines were operating under five-year production contracts with the Government of Canada on behalf of foreign purchasers (the United States and the United Kingdom).

During a number of public addresses I attempted to point out that the uranium mines were, in fact, not more vulnerable by such contracts, but to the contrary, actually privileged. Few producers of other metals, hydrocarbons or other commodities, had enjoyed such initial security. As well, I attempted to keep abreast of and share with the community developments in the peacetime utilization of nuclear materials. I was greatly impressed by what I learned. Jack Gauthier shared my enthusiasm and served as a veritable one-man Chamber of Commerce for Elliot Lake.

To a degree, the sceptics were correct in their pessimism. A sharp and painful hiatus did occur when those first contracts were terminated and Elliot Lake's initial boom faded. Happily, however, those who persevered and had faith in the future, including many of the original pioneers like Jack Gauthier, shared, in due course, in the rebirth and renewed prosperity of the mines and the community.

Collins' Community Hall and the Hirshhorn Museum

Not long after construction had first begun in Elliot Lake, I raised with Joe Hirshhorn the need for a community hall to serve as a multipurpose social centre, and also to honour the geologist, Dr. W. H. Collins, whose geological map of the Big Z had been so vital to our staking of the area. As I envisaged it, a versatile community hall would serve as a ballroom, a large banquet hall, a concert and entertainment centre, and, of equal importance, as a gymnasium. I proposed that Joe and I finance the cost of Collins Hall equally, and Joe readily agreed. Typically, however, he wanted to control things.

"Fine, fine," he said, seemingly oblivious to the details I had outlined. "We'll fill it with paintings and sculptures and call it the Hirshhorn Museum." Joe was as deeply committed to collecting art as he was to being successful in business. I fully respected this, but I was determined to make clear to him my conception of what type of community hall Elliot Lake needed.

"No, Joe," I replied, "that's not what the community needs. Temporary exhibitions may be okay, but you may be shooting for too high a cultural level in a mining-camp town. Besides, it should be known as the W. C. Collins Memorial Hall. That's half the reason for building it."

Hirshhorn frowned, then asked, "Our names?"

"Yes, Joe," I replied, "we'll have them on a brass plaque in the lobby, along with a short biography of Collins."

"Okay!" Joe replied, "Shoot!" So Collins Hall was built, and, to our mutual gratification, it served its purpose well. Some time later, however, Joe began to promote the idea of the "Hirshhorn Museum" a second time. This was entirely understandable considering his considerable life-long collection. Joe was beginning to look for a permanent location for it.

Soon after beginning to work with Joe, I had realized that his time was about equally divided between the business of finance and art. These two activities were inseparable in his life, and he worked intensely hard and successfully at both. Much of his working time in his office was devoted to interviews and correspondence with artists, dealers, and other collectors. More than half the surface area of desks, tables, windowsills, and chairs and all the wall space of his office complex was covered by an ever-changing movement of paintings and small sculptures. This was true for Joe's Toronto offices and even more so for his New York offices, between which he commuted weekly.

While Joe usually described his major interest as collecting of American moderns, his collection of paintings and sculpture included French and American pieces from the nineteenth and twentieth centuries.

Hirshhorn was highly subjective about his collecting and his collection. Although he confided in a few experts, he had strong independent convictions as to what he liked or did not like. He was primarily a collector, rarely selling any of the pieces he acquired. He bought to trade or to keep. He rarely discussed his paintings or sculpture in depth, except in moments when his exuberance concerning an older piece or a new acquisition would impulsively bubble over. When asked about a painting, Joe would invariably offer much biographic data concerning the artist. A painting or a piece of sculpture was much more than just an object to him.

He was characteristically a blunt, decisive, expressive, and colourful speaker, given to readily understood metaphors. His stock phrases for appraising art included: "It sings. It sends me. Fantabulous!" or "It shines," or negative one-word criticism like "Junk!"

On the whole, Joe was positive and encouraging to the younger artists who approached him, many of whom were totally unknown in the art world. From them he would sometimes buy everything they offered. When they called for an appointment they were never refused and would be told, "bring everything." Invariably, when they arrived at Hirshhorn's office, he would be busy with the buttons of his "piano," the complex telephone exchange on his desk, which he operated himself, with a score of almost constantly buzzing direct telephone lines to stockbrokers in several cities.

Joe would glance up and simply say "Spread them all out." If the visitor hesitated, wondering where to put them since everything was already covered with art, Joe's next directive would be "on the floor." Only when this exercise was complete would Hirshhorn lay his phones aside, get up from his desk, and quickly scrutinize the paintings. Rarely would he say "I'll take that one." Usually, if he was suitably impressed, he would ask, "How much for the works?"

If the artist, usually timid and non-competitive, failed to state a price in the ensuing few seconds, Hirshhorn would quote a figure, perhaps in the low hundreds of dollars, them promptly return to his "piano" and the world of risk capital financing.

Without a word, and usually tearless, the visitor would often quietly roll up his or her works and depart. If the offer was accepted, Hirshhorn would occasionally call me through the open doorway separating our offices to help in picking up the paintings spread out like a collage over much of his floor. In the process he might confide to me his complete evaluation of the lot by scrutinizing a single piece for a few seconds and saying "Not bad. A nice kid. Maybe – some day!"

Hirshhorn would often say, regarding his risk capital funding of prospectors, "I'm a crap-shooter. I gamble on character. Lots of times, that's all there is." His attitude towards aspiring artists appeared to be much the same.

Hirshhorn's performance in sophisticated galleries of New York, "The Major League," he called them, was somewhat different. On the few occasions I was present, he would quickly sweep through the show, companions following at a distance. He might pause a dozen times in scanning a hundred paintings. Three or four might arrest his attention for more than a minute and the purchase, if any, would be made from these. On one occasion, in a Greenwich Village gallery, his exuberance could not be contained, and he broke into an ecstatic jig before a Stuart Davis oil. Arms, legs, hips, and a cigar all gyrating together, he called out loudly, "This sends me! It sings! It sings!" Although I listened attentively, I heard no singing save Hirshhorn's.

The great majority of Hirshhorn's collection to which I was exposed were works from 1945 to 1955 in the abstract expressionist mode. At first, I was not at ease in this near-total saturation with abstract moderns. Most of my earlier exposure to art had come from the older schools of great classic European art shown in the galleries of several of the world's great national museums which I had visited with my family. I felt that modern artists of the abstract school were short-term faddists, or as Hirshhorn would say, when he suspected deceit of any kind, "A con job!" Gradually, however, I gazed at the abstract paintings that lined our office walls, often with some technical problem on my mind, I found certain of them relaxing, in the sense that they provided a welcome mental diversion. And with some of them, I could enjoy an experience common to me during my years of outdoor life, when, for entertainment, my imagination would play with the flames or the curling smoke of a campfire in the evenings, the configuration of clouds in the sky by day, or the celestial constellations by night.

Then it dawned on me that even these unnatural two-dimensional images could, in certain cases, provide a mental stimulus. Perhaps after all, these works were not all calculated "con jobs." In fact, most of the artists whom I had met appeared to be intensely sincere, if unconventional. Undoubtedly they were applying their best in creativity and skill toward the conjuring up of these images. To reconcile my judgement of "art" with that of Hirshhorn's I attempted to arrive at a universal definition, which is "Art is an expression in any medium that stimulates the imagination of the viewer." Tried out on Hirshhorn, his reaction had been, "Not bad!"

After Collins Hall was built in Elliot Lake, I wasn't surprised to learn that Joe had developed plans for a museum and cultural community to be called "Hirshhornville." It was to be built near the Pronto mine on Highway 17, the main traffic corridor between Sudbury and Sault Ste. Marie, a "gateway" to the States, he called it.

Throughout his career as a speculator and developer of mineral properties, Hirshhorn was always more interested, as I was, in the exploration rather than the production phase of the mining industry. The creative elements of search and discovery were what attracted us. The identification of potential mining treasure and the raising of the high-risk/high-return funds necessary to retrieve such treasure were the challenges that really stimulated Hirshhorn. Since Joe was basically so optimistic and enthusiastic, his plans for Elliot Lake were entirely different from those which usually shaped mining towns. After the development of our uranium mines became secure, Joe told all who would listen, "Now I want to build the most beautiful small town in the world nearby."

During our initial development of the Big Z, before Rio Tinto of London became involved, we had many prominent Canadian and international visitors to our properties. These included bankers, investors, leading technical specialists, well-known political figures, and members of the international press. Some came out of interest or by invitation, others simply upon their own volition. To ensure that his guests were well accommodated, Joe built a splendid retreat on the north shore of Lake Huron at a place known as Bootlegger's Bay, not far from the historically important "Location X."

Joe had asked the distinguished American architect, Philip Johnson, to design a quality retreat at modest cost. Johnson appears to have been more impressed by Hirshhorn's enthusiasm than by his reference to "modest cost." It was hardly modest. Upon completion, the villa was lavishly furnished by Hirshhorn and his wife at the time, Lily, who was an artist. This luxurious building served as an art gallery, an office, and a part-time residence for the Hirshhorns, and provided ample accommodation for guests. Many lively social events were held there. When I could break away from my day-to-day responsibilities, I attended some of them.

Hirshhorn's success with his Bootlegger's Bay retreat encouraged him to start thinking of enlarging this tiny oasis of art and art appreciation. Joe was especially determined that youngsters growing up in the area should have opportunities to become acquainted with art and to learn to love it as he had.

With Philip Johnson's advice and the assistance of architects Parkin and Associates of Toronto, Joe began to discuss plans for a new town on Highway 17 near our "first baby," the Pronto mine. The new town was to be called Hirshhorn or Hirshhornville. Although it was to provide housing nearby for about one hundred Pronto miners' families, it was to be entirely different from a traditional "industry town." The preliminary plans provided for a library, a concert hall, a printing plant capable of turning out a sixteen-page daily newspaper, a complete shopping centre, a multi-story office building, and, central to all this, an art gallery. The streets were to be spacious, appointed with outdoor sculpture and, wherever possible, lined with trees already growing on the site. The natural beauty of nearby Lake Lauzon would enhance the appearance of the entire community. Just how large the new community might become was not clear. One estimate was that the resident population would be about three thousand with generous accommodation for visitors.

The unique focus of Hirshhornville was to be its art centre. It was to be designed as a major attraction not only for residents, but also for tourists and others travelling by car or train along the busy traffic corridor to and from Sault Ste. Marie, a border city between Canada and the U.S.A.

When Hirshhorn made public his plans for "the world's most beautiful small town," his intention seems to have been to display many of his hundreds of paintings and fine sculptures throughout the new town. I remember him dreaming aloud about how he would display several monumental pieces he owned, and how he would commission Jacob Epstein and Henry Moore to create others. When his architect and planners were ready they requested Hirshhorn's approval to submit the project plans to the Ontario government's municipal planning authorities for official approval. Problems began to emerge immediately.

Government officials were doubtless amazed by the extent to which planning had already been completed. Perhaps they felt slighted that so grandiose a proposal should be presented to them following a good deal of publicity and without prior consultation. In any event, it seems they were stung. They responded to the mass of architectural design work by bluntly announcing that they must appraise and approve all engineering plans for water supply and sewage collection and disposal before anything further could be considered.

Needless to say, Hirshhorn was shocked. For weeks he was extremely unhappy. Occasionally, he would burst out to me, "I take to these guys the dream of my life. It's gonna cost me a bundle for what I feel the people need. It's my best effort and they shoot it all down by talkin' about sewers! To hell with them!"

As Joe's planning for Hirshhornville proceeded I had serious misgivings, and I told Joe about them. My uncertainty concerning Joe's plans for his new town deepened when certain of the celebrated architects he retained asked me in private conversation, "Is this one of Joe's gags? Is it for real? Will he really put up the money?" Finally my conscience compelled me to tell Hirshhorn that I wished to remain neutral in the unfolding public debate.

Hirshhorn announced his plans for his new town to the media late in July 1955. Canada's leading weekly business newspaper, *The Financial Post*, in its issue of July 30, 1955, carried the banner headline, "Picasso Finds New Home in Ontario's Wilderness." An entire page was devoted to a report on Joe Hirshhorn and his dream town. The same day, the *Montreal Star* carried a feature story under the headline "Canada to Have 'Loveliest Town.' " These were just two of many accounts carried in Canadian newspapers.

A month later, on Labour Day, a delegation of fourteen businessmen from Blind River, the nearest community to the proposed site of Joe's most beautiful town, met with him to ask him to abandon his entire plan. Joe was emotionally wounded. Everyone, it seemed, was pitted against him save for Father Skillen, the Catholic priest in Blind River who had been publicly enthusiastic about the new project.

Paradoxically, some eleven years later, when Hirshhorn presented his private art collection – valued by him at that time at more than $35 million – to the United States government, he became the target of poisonous attacks by an association of American cottagers in the Blind River area. They were resentful that Joe had given some 5,600 pieces of art to the "Hirshhorn Gallery and Sculpture Garden" in Washington, D.C. Incredibly, these cottagers declared publicly that

Hirshhorn had made no contribution to the cultural development of the region! I shook my head sadly as I read the copy of their letter to Hirshhorn which they sent to me. They charged that instead of keeping the promises he had made earlier, Joe had created a community which would attract, "in place of art, panhandlers, pimps, and prostitutes."

This letter troubled me profoundly. Its authors made no reference to the thousands of jobs Joe and his associates had created in Elliot Lake. There was no reference to Collins Hall or to Joe's efforts to create the world's most beautiful small town – which they had frustrated.

Elliot Lake

While Hirshhorn struggled in his efforts to be generous only to be finally rejected, I continued working with my colleagues, Gill Gillanders, Bert Willoughby, and Percy Brown, as a member of the Improvement District Management Board for the developing community of Elliot Lake.

Looking back on our efforts to develop the community I recall that one key problem we faced that troubled me greatly during the first two years was the passion workers and their families had for mobility, reflected in their gypsy-style living in trailers. Even after we had built, in record time, the first thousand modern, fully serviced, permanent family dwellings, with the co-operation and co-ordination of federal and provincial authorities and efficient contractors, many remained empty. Instead, probably a thousand campers or trailers were being used as homes. This high percentage of non-permanent dwellings created a variety of social and service problems that were resolved eventually only by the passage of government regulations.

That our skilled tradesmen, whom we viewed as permanent employees, lived in trailers, disturbed our mine and mill managers. I asked one manager to enquire discreetly why these workmen preferred trailers to our new homes equipped with every modern convenience. The explanation was not long in coming. As one workman said, "If I have a mobile home and go on shift any particular day and find the boss hassling me, I can tell him to go to hell and fast! I'm not tied to the job by a mortgage on a house. I can quit! And in an hour and a half I'm rolling down the highway with wife and kids – free!"

And free and fast it was indeed! There were cases in which bank balances were left uncollected and even formal requests for unemployment insurance were overlooked. Fortunately, with time, regulatory pressures, and a more mature emotional climate in Elliot Lake, this preoccupation with mobility abated and Elliot Lake became a well-established community.

The long-term prospects of single-industry towns, such as Elliot Lake, depend, of course, not merely on the extent of the mineral or other resources which bring such towns into being in the first place. Their future is inextricably tied to the attitudes of their residents and to the long-term policies of governments for single-industry towns. If such towns are to become dynamic, forward-looking, and of some permanence, those who live in them must contribute to the development of a sense of shared responsibility, essential toward evolving a vision of and pride in a community. Then too, government policies must be developed and implemented to foster the realization of such continuity.

Only through thoughtful co-operative planning and action on local, regional, and national levels will it be possible, in the future, for the boom-and-bust tendencies of many single-industry towns to be remedied, at least in some measure. The problem, of course, is that as the boom gradually develops, and then begins to expand, two attitudes seem to dominate.

Many who participate in the boom "ride it" for all it is worth. "Live it up while you can" seems to be their motto. Others say, "I know the bubble is going to burst sooner or later. But I also know how to get out before the party's over!" Both of these views are indicative of the self-centred, short-term attitudes which unfortunately often govern not only the actions of individuals but also the formation and implementation of public policy concerning single-industry towns. Self-interest prevails rather than a thoughtful, co-operative development and implementation of policy designed to advance both individual and community interest.

Fortunately, in the case of Elliot Lake, there were – and are – a considerable number of citizens committed to the public interest as well as their own needs. Their optimism and community spirit, combined with the developing reliance on nuclear power appear to have ensured the economic continuance of the community of Elliot Lake for the foreseeable future.

Elliot Lake has at least three unique advantages that ameliorate the problems of normally short-lived mining communities: its considerable natural beauty, relative freedom from industrial pollution, and its longevity. It is already three generations old and so has deeper social roots.

XII

My Rio Tinto Odyssey in Africa, Europe, Australasia, and Spain

In the early spring of 1955, after Joe Hirshhorn and I had completed our agreement with Rio Tinto for their purchase of the Pronto and the other Big Z mines, together with the Pater and Anglo-Rouyn base-metal mines, I handed over my responsibilities as managing director of all our mining operations to Dr. Earl Gillanders. He was a highly educated geologist with wide experience in the mining industry, including uranium mining and milling. This transfer of responsibilities was the end of a dynamic chapter in my life and the beginning of a new one.

Three months later, Paul Young, general manager of the Pronto mine, advised me that "everything is on track here. We should be ready for full plant operation within three months."

I reviewed in my mind the several larger projects on which we were engaged on the Big Z. Given the knowledge and energy of such competent and dynamic resident managers as Young, Godfrey, Olson, Airth, Jewett, and Upham, I was certain these projects would also soon be "on track." By the time Young wrote to me, Earl Gillanders was already demonstrating his remarkable technical and administrative abilities as Rio's new chief of Canadian mining operations.

After thorough reflection on these facts, I went into Joe Hirshhorn's office one day, as casually as I had on hundreds of occasions when I would say, "Enough for today, Joe. I'm heading home." But on that particular day, I sat down before him and said, "Joe, suddenly I'm terribly tired. I must get out of this goldfish bowl. I have to quit."

"But you can't quit," he replied instantly. "We're the champions!"

"Sure," I said, "but my philosophy is to quit as an *undefeated* champion. Those who don't, wind up punchy." There was a moment or two of silence. Then Joe said, "Frankie-boy, you know what this does to me. If you quit, I quit!"

I quickly responded by saying, "Joe, if you and I stay in this rat race for another year or two, we'll both wind up in a nut house! I'm going over to Bill's [Bouck's] office now to tell him I'm done."

As it happened, my withdrawal from all managerial activities after Rio Tinto took control coincided with Technical Mine Consultants' transfer of authority to Rio Tinto Management Services Limited. Algom Uranium Limited became Rio Algom Limited, and practically all Hirshhorn-controlled mining interests passed to the Rio Tinto Mining Company of Canada Limited, 40 per cent owned by Rio Tinto of London. I was replaced as president of Algom by Bill Bouck, who held the position briefly. During this period of major organizational change I was persuaded, however, to remain a director of Rio Algom.

Bill Bouck was succeeded as president by the Hon. Robert H. Winters. Later the Rt. Hon. C. D. Howe, who played a key role in Canada's development from 1935 to 1957 as a federal cabinet minister, became a director. Hirshhorn was persuaded to serve as the first chairman of the Rio Tinto Mining Company of Canada board, but was ill at ease in that largely ceremonial role, and his tenure was brief.

Joe Hirshhorn was now able to devote himself unreservedly to the development of his art collection and the creation and implementation of plans for the Hirshhorn Museum in Washington. Securing agreement to the arrangements which enabled him to give his art collection to the government of the United States and to have it housed in its own unique building in the centre of Washington was a major feat in itself which required much thought and energy on Joe's part during a considerable number of years. He was helped in this by well-placed American colleagues and friends. The Hirshhorn Museum in Washington stands as a permanent tribute to the man whose business acumen and drive, whose passion for art, and whose desire to share the pleasure of viewing his collection with people from all walks of life made it such a magnificent reality.

Our Peach prospect, which Joe had taken delight in calling "Peachie," was brought into production and began operations as Pronto Uranium Mines Limited in the late summer of 1955. I officiated at the opening ceremony and the party that followed with mixed emotions.

The Pronto mine was the first uranium producer brought into operation in what was to become the fabulous Blind River uranium field. And it had been put into production within its estimated capital budget in a remarkably short space of time. Less than two and a half years had passed since our exploratory drilling had begun there. Certainly this was an outstanding record of technical achievement and was made possible by the dedication of many people.

A difficult and strenuous challenge had been faced and won, and

I was elated by the technical and financial success we had achieved. But I was also saddened. The excitement and challenge of each succeeding day, as we had explored, developed, and prepared our properties on the Big Z for production, had now come to an end.

Joubin and Associates

My responsibilities for Joe Hirshhorn and the technical management of our several mining companies now completed, I decided to become an independent consulting geologist again and to move at my own pace rather than be the vortex of external circumstances.

Quite unexpectedly, Val Duncan suggested to me that Rio Tinto, London, would like me to serve him as an unofficial roving consultant, advising him on some of their major operations as well as proposed new ones in Africa, New Zealand, New Caledonia, Australia, and possibly Ireland. Major mining and metallurgical operations in Finland, Sweden, and what was then Belgian Congo, were also to be visited to develop a closer technical rapport with them.

About the same time, I was approached by the Algoma Central Railroad Company of Canada, through the interest of John B. Aird, then a board officer of the company. They wanted me to co-ordinate the systematic geological mapping for mineral potential of their extensive railroad lands bordering their line from Sault Ste. Marie to Franz, north-east of Wawa, together with some reconnaissance exploration from Franz to James Bay as part of the original "Algoma Central and Hudson Bay" concept. I could not forgo these two exciting challenges and I agreed to undertake both assignments.

Franc R. Joubin and Associates, Consulting Geologists, Ltd., was incorporated as my formal agency on July 31, 1956. I chose J. D. (Duke) Hague, an accountant and long-standing friend, to serve as office administrator and accountant. Miss C.A. Henning – later Mrs. Wolf – became my personal secretary, in which capacity she continued to help me efficiently and faithfully for over twenty-eight years. Donald H. James, son of my early patron Dr. Howard James, joined my group as a geologist, and Donald E. Smith and Norman Ursel joined as mining engineers. These were the permanent staff. They were assisted by varying numbers of university students who worked for us in the field during the summer months.

Together, under my general consulting direction, Smith and Ursel managed and supervised our work for Algoma Central throughout nearly five years of exploration for that organization. Donald James usually worked as my geological assistant on consulting missions, both in Canada and abroad. Like the earlier TMC group, Joubin and Associates was also a totally compatible, happy team and, in the judgement of our clients, technically efficient.

Assignments for Rio Tinto

During 1956 and the first half of 1957, I completed several tours overseas as advisor to Val Duncan of Rio Tinto. When I visited Val Duncan in London, England, in early 1956, he suggested that Rio Tinto would organize tours for me to South Africa and Rhodesia for the month of February, and to the Belgian Congo, with some reporting visits to the Brussels offices of the Société Minère du Haut Congo, in March. Later, in August, I would visit the Skellefte district mines of Sweden and the Outokompu Company in Finland.

I arrived in Johannesburg, South Africa, on February 12, 1956, and was greeted by Oscar Weiss. He introduced me to a geologist, Dr. Noel Sharpe, and a mining engineer, Bryan Penn, who were both members of Weiss's relatively new Mineral Search of Africa group. Weiss and Sharpe had prepared an extensive itinerary for me, with visits to operating gold, uranium, and diamond mines in South Africa and various undeveloped prospects of gold, copper, and nickel in Rhodesia (now Zimbabwe). Sharpe was my companion and field guide on all these tours.

When I went underground in the larger South African mines of the Witwatersrand, I was surprised at the racist protocol involved. I was taken to a mine visitors' and staff room provided for changing from one's ordinary street clothes to underground clothing, as is customary. Here, my regular clothes and shoes were carefully removed with the help of one or two black Africans serving as valets. Then I was provided with a pair of safety mining boots and immaculately clean white overalls. With a white shift-boss as guide, we descended by the shaft's "cage" into the humid, very high-temperature mines – among the deepest in the world.

As we walked about, we quickly became soaked in perspiration. The areas in which the ore is extracted – the *stopes* – were occasionally so confined that we doubled-up or even crawled on our knees to enable us to watch the crouching black miners at work. As rivulets of perspiration coursed over their naked torsos, they were engulfed by the deafening roar of the hand-held percussion drills boring holes in the flinty rock for the placement of dynamite to be exploded later by a white shift-boss. The black miners were not allowed to handle explosives.

Because of the depths of the mines, the temperature is almost unbearable. Water sprays could be used to settle the dust, but only sparingly. Copious use of water would raise the humidity and make working conditions utterly intolerable. Thus the miners worked practically in the nude, clad only in their helmets, boots, equipment belts, and the briefest of shorts. As they worked, their bodies glistening from the sweat, they were exposed to obvious danger from loose rock collapse, but, in addition, the average miner would have inhaled so much silica dust that at the end of his eighteen-month contract his career as a miner could possibly be terminated due to silicotic lungs. What I saw in the depths of the South African mines thirty years ago gave me a glimpse of wage slavery at its worst. It shocked me profoundly.

On returning to the surface, we undressed, showered, and dressed again in our regular clothing, with the help of a black valet. My shoes had been freshly shined. After that underground visit, I seemed to be substantially better "turned out" than I had been upon arrival!

Wherever I travelled in south or central Africa I encountered what I regarded as a totally excessive use of black Africans as servants. For example, white persons seldom drove their own vehicles. Rarely would they even open or close a gate. A coloured servant would always spring to the aid of a white man. At that time the majority of the white population expected or demanded this servile attention. I was unaccustomed to such human abasement and could not believe that intelligent people would tolerate such overt racism.

While I was in Johannesburg, I had discussions with Bryan Penn, the mining engineer then engaged in engineering studies on the economic feasibility of mining a huge, low-grade, multi-mineral deposit and appraising the wisdom of Rio Tinto's investing in this deposit of copper, tin, iron sulphide, phosphate rock, and vermiculite mica. Clearly, Penn was convinced that it would be a good investment. Events proved, slowly but dramatically, that Penn's judgment was sound. A decade later, in 1966, the mining world would regard the Palabora, as the property was known, as one of South Africa's great mines, producing, among other products, more than one hundred thousand tons of copper a year.

After several informative visits to various mines, and discussions in Johannesburg, I set off with Sharpe in his plane for the north, to visit Salisbury, Lusaka, Tchisamba, Ndola, and Gatooma in the Rhodesias, before leaving him to enter the Belgian Congo – now Zaire. The prime objective of the northern trip was to study an area south of the "copper belt" where Sharpe was directing an extensive geochemical soil reconnaissance survey searching for Zambian-type copper deposits. Sharpe's program was probably one of the first of its kind in that region. Thus it was of considerable research interest as well as being a practical prospecting exercise.

The project manager of the geo-chemical survey field camp there was a Canadian, Dr. James Bichan, a geologist, who surprised me by greeting me by name! I had first met Bichan in the Val d'Or gold district of Quebec and later in the Beaverlodge uranium area of Saskatchewan. (He served for a time as Saskatchewan's Deputy Minister of Mines.) The world is, indeed, small for exploration geologists!

The second objective of our tour was to visit a nickel outcrop discovery near Gatooma, later known as the Empress Nickel, of which Sharpe had spoken to me earlier. In Johannesburg he had handed me, for examination, a well-weathered piece of porous rock, saying, "Please don't laugh at this story!"

Sharpe told me the rock had been brought to him not long before by a relatively wealthy white woman who, he thought, was the wife of a legislator in South Africa. She frequently visited the Rhodesias as a self-appointed Christian missionary. In the course of a recent preaching tour she had been handed a rock (of which I held a piece) by a native African. She had told Sharpe that upon examining the rock she knew instinctively that it was an act of the Creator. Like the gold of Havilah described in the Book of Genesis, "It was good!" There would certainly be a rich mine at its source, and the wealth derived from it would further her work in bringing Christianity to the natives. Furthermore, she would sell the "mine" to the Rio Tinto Company for the equivalent of £1 million sterling – "cash!" Sharpe paused at this point in his story to allow me a look at the rock in my hand.

With due reverence and solemnity, I removed my 10-X magnifying lens from my pocket and peered at the rock.

"Those tiny green specks – I'm not sure what they are," I said. "They could be specks of copper or nickel oxide. Perhaps even a mica or a chrome mineral. In any event it should be analysed."

Sharpe said this had already been done and that the sample indicated a high nickel content. He continued the story. Sharpe had returned with the woman to Gatooma. In a nearby hamlet they located the boy who had given the woman the rock and he led them on foot to the outcrop where he had found it. This outcrop was most unusual. The rock ridge was worn bare as if a lion had repeatedly lounged upon it, which the native boy said was the case. Natives avoided the area for that reason. Sharpe had forthwith instructed his geo-chemical crew, working not far away, to survey this adjoining plain area. They had done so and had quickly determined that the outcrop and surrounding area revealed an abnormal nickel content.

Oscar Weiss had negotiated an exploration option with the woman who insisted, with religious zeal, that she could consider no reduction in her original price, which had been agreed upon. Sharpe had instructed his field crew to pit the area of high nickel soil and attempt to expose a greater area of solid rock for examination. That was the state of affairs when he and I returned to the scene.

Sharpe and I stood before an area which was already pitted at probably a dozen points. The pits were not unlike small wells averaging about thirty-six inches in diameter and from twelve to fifteen feet deep. Sharpe was worried. No pit had reached solid rock and although the surface soil had indicated an abnormal nickel content, this diminished with the depth of the pit instead of increasing. I had no ready answers to this problem, but asked to be lowered by rope into several of the pits so that I might examine them in some detail.

The pits were humid, cool, and comfortable. All had the same general appearance – a rich reddish-brown coloured soil with no solid rock apparent. Finally, after examining several pits, I sensed that I was touching rock when my feet reached the bottom of one particular pit. I lowered myself to a squatting position at the bottom and began raking between my knees with the point of my geological pick. Instead of solid rock I found angular broken fragments. Because they were angular I realized they were close to their source. Using my hat as a basket, I collected four or five apple-size pieces and called to be hoisted back to the surface.

I had found what I wanted. In two of the lumps there were walnut-size kernels of relatively fresh, dark green-grey-coloured rock. I handed a fragment to Noel Sharpe who was kneeling beside me. He examined it with his hand lens. "May I laugh now?" I asked Sharpe.

"Of course," he replied. "What's the verdict?"

"This," I replied, "is a gabbroic type of rock identical in appearance to the several hundreds of pounds of the stuff I've cracked in the Sudbury nickel basin ore piles. It is the perfect host rock for nickel, with or without copper. You've got to drill!" That was on February 29, 1956. On a return visit later in August that year, I saw the well-mineralized drill cores from several successful holes.

Eventually, the prospect developed into the modestly important Empress Nickel Mine. And the lady preacher, I was informed, was paid in full. Probably Val Duncan would agree that she too had the gift of "Sacred Fire"!

By Jeep from Rhodesia to the Congo

After visiting various producing copper mines in the Zambian copper belt, I travelled from Lusaka to Élisabethville by jeep, driven by a most unusual Ugandan, Andrew Ssengooba. As we two rattled along over the long-dried clay track that served as a rarely used jeep road, there was much time to talk and observe.

One particularly vivid sight that struck me was large areas of dead and fallen trees similar to the charred burnt-over areas I had occasionally traversed in the wake of a forest fire when prospecting in British Columbia. In the border area between Rhodesia and the Belgian Congo, however, these had been caused by giant ants which had simply devoured the forested areas. Many of what seemed to be dead tree stumps and trunks were actually huge, abandoned ant-hills, two or three feet in diameter and twelve to fifteen feet high. Andrew told me that some of the native people used such ant hills, when still occupied by ants, as burial mounds. The human bones would be retrieved, sometimes after only a few days, for ritual and ornamental use. Within that short period the ants would render the bones as clean and attractive as pieces of ivory.

Save for such scenes, and our conversation, the day-long trip was generally a lonely and uneventful affair. The one small group of people we did encounter on the entire trip actually caused an incident. About five young women were walking toward Rhodesia from the Congo, their tall, lean figures and high-piled hair attractively covered with bright materials trimmed with colourful brass and ceramic jewellery of local origin. They carried their personal property in small, scarf-wrapped bundles. Despite Andrew's gentle protests, I made him stop so that I could photograph the group, which I did. I then expressed my thanks with a smile and a wave of the hand. But the women were not pleased. As I moved toward the jeep with its motor idling, where Andrew waited, they quickly encircled me. A couple of them held out their hands as the entire group excitedly chattered to me in a language I did not understand.

I assumed that the women wanted me to give them money, so I dug into my pants pocket, drew out all my coins, which were mainly copper and brass, and dumped them into the women's outstretched hands. To my surprise the coins were forcefully flung into the bush alongside the road. The chattering became even more agitated. I quickly retreated to my seat beside Andrew in the jeep and we roared away.

"What did I do to anger them?" I asked him when we were out of sight. "Didn't I offer enough money?"

"Not exactly," replied Andrew, as his round pleasant face broke into a huge smile. "They were a band of better-class prostitutes, trekking to the copper mines. And you scorned their dignity."

"But how?" I protested, but Andrew felt he had said it all. The grin stayed on his face for a long time.

I might have come a long way, but I was still abysmally naïve in the worldly ways of such ladies, starting with Zada in Bridge River, the "Hollywood" ladies on Vancouver Island, and now these African ladies of "easy" but not "cheap" virtue!

Andrew was a bright young man. Although he was employed in Rhodesia, his home was near Kampala in Uganda, where he had completed his secondary education and passed the British university entrance examinations with the tutorial assistance of a dedicated Anglican clergyman.

"Did you study in your village?" I asked him.

"Oh, no," he replied, "our village is only a tiny place. The Anglican mission school was about fifteen miles away."

"So you boarded at the mission school?"

"No, I went there daily from our village."

"How?" I persisted. "On bicycle, or by foot?"

"No," he replied, "I had no bicycle and it took too long to walk. So I ran."

"You ran there and back daily?" I asked incredulously.

"Yes," was the modest reply.

"And you want to continue to university?"

"Yes," he replied, "and my Anglican tutor feels I should. I have passed the British university entrance examinations. It would like to study law and perhaps some day serve in my country's government."

When Andrew and I parted company in Élisabethville, I wrote down his address and that of his clergyman adviser, along with details of his education. I felt a compulsion to pursue the matter further.

In answer to my enquiry, the Anglican tutor in Uganda replied, "Andrew is a most extraordinary young man. It would be a tragedy if he were unable to go to university, for which he is fully qualified." Seven years later, on June 21, 1963, Andrew wrote to thank me for the realization of his dream. He reported that he had completed his legal studies in the Middle Temple in London, England, and would be called to the bar on July 6, thereafter authorized to practise law in Britain and in his native country, Uganda.

During six of those intervening years, Andrew and I had maintained an on-going correspondence, meeting for evenings together each time I passed through London. I remember in particular Andrew's reply to one of the earliest questions I put to him. "What," I asked, soon after his arrival in London," impresses you most about this huge modern city?" He thought for a moment and I sensed mental confusion. "I'll make it easier for you," I added, "name just one thing!"

Almost instantly, he replied, "the eggs."

Rather taken aback, I asked, "But what is so different about the eggs in London?" His reply was most interesting.

"When I finish my classes each day," said Andrew, "I return directly to my room and organize my notes while they are fresh in my mind. Afterwards I have a meal and tidy up my room. When I'm not tired, I go for a walk in the cool of the evening. I look in shop windows, particularly those displaying meat and dairy products. Those eggs! They always give me a special thrill. So many of them, all in neat rows in trays! They look so clean and beautiful. I often return to the same store windows just to look at the eggs."

Baffled as I was at his response, the significance of the eggs became clearer to me in later years. During my extensive travels in some of the poorest nations of the world, particularly in the more impoverished rural areas, I was to learn that the egg is a precious commodity. Often, it is a symbol. Most of the people who live in these countries are too poor to possess meat-producing animals. The chicken, however, is almost universally present. And yet a small group of five or six terribly "rooster-pecked" hens might only product three or four eggs a week. It is no wonder such eggs are often treasured.

Placed on a shelf or in some other safe place in the family's dwelling, eggs are usually reserved for older grandparents or ailing members of the family. On special occasions the egg is served to honour a family guest. Early in my work overseas I learned that declining such an honour is viewed as disdainful and will lead to mutual embarrassment. Thus, my custom was to accept and to consume with obvious relish any egg, cooked or raw, of any vintage, which was offered me – often in a single gulp!

Fortunately, the story of Andrew is a success story. In Kampala, Uganda, Andrew practised law, and later with business associates developed a moderately prosperous sugar plantation and sugar refinery. By 1981 Andrew had a happy family of ten children. In the interim, they had miraculously survived Idi Amin's murderous years in power and the terrorism that has followed.

Following Amin's expulsion, Andrew was elected to the Ugandan Parliament. He had finally achieved the objective he had chosen for himself years earlier. I was indeed privileged to have been able to help him.

Visiting the Société Minère Operations in the Congo (Zaire)

Following my drive with Andrew to the Congo, I was treated royally by the senior technical officers of the Société Minère du Haut Congo, at their bases in Élisabethville, Jadotville, Kipushi, and Shinkolobwe, and at their mines and metallurgical complexes. I also felt much more at ease socially. The pervasive oppressiveness of the leaden blanket of South African apartheid, and the less extreme but ever-present colour distinction in Rhodesia, had been lifted here. The Congo (like most Latin-dominated colonies or ex-colonies – as opposed to the British, German, or Dutch) was much more liberal in its racial relationships, as I was to learn later in my United Nations work.

Regal old-world social protocol was nonetheless displayed at times. For example, one "dressed" for a staff dinner, with jacket and tie, or even in a borrowed tuxedo. At dinner, the table was covered with fine linen, porcelain, and silver. Curiously, it was in the Congo that I was first introduced by my Belgian hosts to fresh caviar and steak tartar and some of Europe's finest wines. They may have been a long way from Belgium, but in true colonial form, mentally and socially they were still there.

I was enormously impressed with the mineral wealth of the Congo. There were deposits of gold, copper, germanium, zinc, and uranium, many of which were under lucrative production. Most of this production was controlled by the Société Minère du Haut Congo, my hosts. They had hoped, in vain, that I might help with one particular technical problem: this was the quickly approaching exhaustion of the once-famous Shinkolobwe uranium-gold deposit. They had reached, quite clearly, the bottom of that particular treasure chest. Not one of the several uranium discoveries they had made, and which they showed to me, offered much hope of success. Our visit to one of their prospects, however, turned into a rather frightening experience.

Joseph Derricks, the company's exploration geologist in the Congo (who later became the global exploration vice-president and senior official of the parent corporation) and I were visiting various prospects. We were travelling by jeep near the Shinkolobwe mine, across a high plateau, notorious for the presence of the tse-tse fly, an insect whose sting can cause a fatal creeping paralysis. We stopped at midday beside the baked-clay track, to dine and rest. Our two black attendants erected an awning to protect us from the searing sun. Under it they set up a folding card table with linen, cutlery, and two folding chairs. Then they opened a picnic hamper containing fresh, crusty bread, cheeses, cold meats, and a bottle of red wine. After our meal, the table was cleared, but Derricks and I remained in our seats, heads resting on folded forearms, to enjoy a nap until the midday heat had subsided. Our two attendants padded quietly and unobstrusively around us. Suddenly, I was awakened by a shout, and a sharp blow on my bare right arm. Derricks and one of the attendants grabbed and held me by the elbow. Both peered anxiously at the crushed body of an insect on my bloodied forearm. Derricks said the Africans thought it was a deadly tse-tse fly. "It may not be so," he said. "But we mustn't take a chance. Let's get out of here fast and head for the closest village to find a doctor."

A wild jeep ride followed, during which Derricks yelled at me, at intervals, asking if I could feel any pain or swelling. Fortunately, I couldn't. Finally, we reached a small village, the jeep stopped, and a small circle of curious Africans gathered around. An individual in a plain blue uniform stepped forward. I assumed he was probably the local head man or constable. He listened to our attendant's story, peered at my arm with the tiny pink spot – and shook his head in the negative. A huge sense of relief flowed over me.

What Future in Southern Africa?

The overall impressions I gained during my 1956 African tours were mixed, and in certain particulars, highly unfavourable. I was shocked by the extent to which the tremendously dynamic, efficient, and profitable gold- and diamond-mining industries of South Africa depended on the crudest form of wage slavery and even more appalled that those whose labour was so essential were treated with such contempt away from the workplace. I sensed, on purely pragmatic grounds, that such abuse of vital manpower could not continue. In human terms, South Africa's was a totally unstable system. Sooner or later it must fall apart, probably not by rebellion nor "strike action" – which would be tragically suicidal – but by the relatively simple passive withdrawal of labour by a unified black people.

The mine labourers were recruited for eighteen-month contracts by agents of the companies. I was told that those who accepted work in the mines did so to earn and save a small amount of capital to purchase a bit of livestock, or even a bride of good family in their agricultural village of origin. Intelligent native leaders, I reasoned, would prevail upon increasing numbers of potential mine workers to ignore work in the mines since any financial advantage gained through such work would be more than outweighed by the damage caused to their lungs and general health.

In other sections of Africa I found that better social and economic conditions prevailed throughout the Zambian copper belt and even more so, I thought, in the Congo mining industry.

Perhaps I placed too high a significance on the social factor in the overall economic balance. Nonetheless, I concluded that mining industry investments would deteriorate first in South Africa and perhaps last in the Congo. Consequently, I was convinced in 1956 that it would be prudent for foreign investors in the mining industries in those countries to liquidate their assets for re-investment in other Commonwealth countries, such as Canada and Australia. During the following three decades many companies did this. Indeed, social and political turmoil did wreak havoc upon the foreign-owned mining enterprises in the Rhodesian copper belt and in the Congo.

Despite the rising tide of criticism from outside South Africa concerning apartheid, and increased levels of violence and military activity in the country itself, it has remained politically, socially, and economically relatively unchanged. Those who control South African politics are determined to ensure that white dominance will prevail. Nonetheless, substantial European capital has been discreetly withdrawn from that sector of Africa. Paradoxically, American capital appears to be taking its place.

In Sweden and Finland

The contrasts I saw in the mining industries in Africa and those in Scandinavia were enormous. The very rich ores of some of the African mines, largely the product of unglaciated, tropical-zone surface enrichment, are totally absent in the northern glaciated regions of Scandinavia.

Because their ores are of poorer quality, and their costs are higher, the Swedes and the Finns have developed, of necessity, extraordinary resourcefulness in the efficient mechanization of mining and metallurgical operations. They have developed such high levels of expertise in these areas that they probably realize as much, or more, from the manufacture and sale abroad of mining and metallurgical equipment as they do from their mineral production.

In Sweden, most of my time was devoted to tours of the Boliden Company operations in the northern Skellefte mining belt. It was a revelation to note the sophistication of their exploration techniques and to admire the ingenuity and efficiency of their operations. And the social conduct of the senior technical people I met was immeasurably more informal and convivial than in Africa.

In Finland, my primary technical tour took me to the remarkable Outokompu nickel-copper-chrome mine in the east, and the unique smelting furnaces in the south which had been developed to treat very complex ores. At the smelter site in Porvoo I felt completely at home, since senior technical personnel there had travelled widely in Canada. Socially, I also felt at home, since my wife's family had emigrated to Canada from Finland. I felt at home for yet another reason; the climate, geology, topography, and vegetation were identical to that of the glaciated Pre-Cambrian Shield areas of Canada.

While a wide variety of minerals occur in Finland's Precambrian rock, mineral production is modest and the country has neither coal nor oil. In addition to the nickel-copper-chrome mine at Outokompu, which I visited, limited quantities of iron, vanadium, and titanium are mined near Kajaani in central Finland and iron at Akaslompola in the north-west near the Swedish border.

In Finland, inviting someone to take a sauna with you is a sign of friendship and a clear indication that you have nothing to hide from one another. I was staying at a most luxurious lodge during my travels, and was persuaded by my hosts, some Finnish executives, to spend an hour with them in the sauna. While I demonstrated unusual ability to endure the high temperature I declined their invitation to take a dip in a partially ice-covered lake nearby. My hosts told me, with much delight, that my ability to take the heat in the lodge's sauna equalled the record set there a year earlier by Gene Tunney, the former world heavyweight boxing champion!

I greatly enjoyed my visit to Scandinavia, particularly the time I spent in Finland where I would return on several later technical missions. My tour of mining sites in Ireland was also memorable, but for different reasons.

To the Emerald Isle

There is not much mining in Ireland, but in September 1956, Rio Tinto sent me to the Irish Republic for two weeks to observe and report on new mining discoveries and developments. One of these, the Northgate, where there were hopes of mining copper, lead, and zinc, had been initiated largely by Canadian entrepreneurs, including several promoters and geologists whom I knew. Among these were Pat Hughes, who had served his apprenticeship as a prospector with Technical Mine Consultants in Athabaska, Wild Bill Richardson of Goldfields Uranium, Ranald Macdonald, who had worked for me, and broker mine-makers Harry and Bud Knight, J. L. Goad, and Gilbert LaBine.

I toured some of the active mining areas in Ireland with G. L. Murphy, a senior geologist of the Irish Geological Survey who had been a key adviser concerning some of the earlier discoveries. Murphy, a well-informed and delightful host and companion, was the first person to suggest that I visit Blarney Castle and that "for business reasons" I kiss the Blarney Stone.

During one trip in Murphy's car, a Volkswagen Beetle, we became lost. We crawled slowly along amidst driving rain in what resembled a gutter. It was a narrow single-lane road sunk between high banks on both sides, lined with prickly gorse shrubbery and crowned with fieldstone fences. Suddenly we saw a head covered with a large sou'wester poke above the wall. Murphy stopped the car and scrambled through the gorse up to the fence to ask for directions.

I caught a glimpse of an old, craggy, stubble-covered face and a gnarled bare hand pointing out a direction. A feeling of relief that we now knew where we were, coupled with sympathy for the old man, came over me. I removed from my packsack a bottle of Canadian rye whiskey which, I had been told by Canadian friends was regarded as a magic elixir by the Irish, good for any emergency. I got out of the car and waved the bottle at Murphy. He took it, unscrewed the top, and passed it to our benefactor. I watched as the old man studied the label on the bottle carefully, hesitated, brusquely said something to Murphy, then placed the bottle to his mouth and drank for what seemed an interminably long time before handing the bottle back.

When Murphy returned to the car, I asked, "What did the old man say?"

"You'd never guess," replied Murphy. "He looked at the bottle, then barked, 'Shur, lad, an' 'tis Protestant whisky y're offerin' me.' With that said, he lifted the bottle to his mouth. I thought he would drink forever!"

My assessment of the mineral prospects I saw in southern Ireland was that a fair potential for economic lead-silver deposits was apparent and that some exploration and development were justified. I would have liked to have been able to prepare a much more encouraging report on mineral prospects in Ireland. Throughout my life I have enjoyed my occasional association with men of Irish blood. Unfortunately, however, our sharing of Celtic roots can in no way enhance the mineral potential of the Emerald Isle.

Travels in Australasia

My tour of mining properties on behalf of Rio Tinto took me not only to southern Africa, Scandinavia, and Ireland, but also to more distant sections of the world. In January 1957 I flew to New Zealand and New Caledonia, going on to Australia in February of that year.

In Auckland, New Zealand, my host and guide was Dr. Gordon Williams, Dean and Professor of Geology, at the University of Otago, Dunedin, who also served as a consultant to Rio Tinto in New Zealand. (Later he became one of my respected colleagues in the United Nations service when, about fifteen years later, our paths crossed in the Middle East.)

On my first trip to New Zealand, Dr. Williams and I travelled up the west coast of North Island, from Auckland, and returned by road along the east coast. The purpose of this journey was to examine several minor mineral occurrences of mercury-bearing hot springs, iron sulphide deposits, and some large iron-titanium beach-sand deposits. We also visited an apparently exhausted gold deposit – the Waipu.

As I drove through New Zealand I was highly impressed by its scenic beauty. The many small but lovely rock and sand beaches along the coastline were a delight to behold, as were the charm and cleanliness of the smaller towns. These were reminiscent of the English countryside in architecture and layout, but seemed more lively, given the sunny climate and profusion of lovely tropical flowers, shrubs, and trees everywhere.

I doubted then if I would ever see a more beautiful resort area than the hot-spring spa region of Rotorua with its charming old, British-colonial-styled mansions set in a rainbow sea of British roses and tropical bougainvillea. As well, the Wairakei hot-spring area, then under development for geo-thermal electricity production, was another absolutely spectacular scene with several high-pressure steam jets in action.

I was greatly surprised by the remarkable topography of North Island. From the lush low elevation of Rotorua I could see the snow-capped peak of a 9,000-foot-high mountain near Lake Taupo. Some years later I was reminded of this unusual sight as I stood beside an equator monument at Nanyuki in Kenya, gazing in awe at the snow-clad peak of Mount Kilimanjaro not far distant.

After we arrived in Wellington, Dr. Williams left to return to his university duties in Dunedin. I was then joined by Ben Dickenson, Rio Tinto's technical consultant in Australia. He became my guide for the remainder of my stay in New Zealand, and later, throughout eastern Australia.

After meeting the officials and technical specialists of New Zealand's Geological Survey, Mines Department and Mineral Research

Laboratories, Dickenson and I flew to Nelson on South Island. There we spent a week visiting the recently discovered Buller Gorge uranium deposits. These discoveries were in a heavily forested and mountainous area, access to which required much rugged effort on foot after a helicopter flight.

Buller Gorge is an important tourist attraction. It bears the name of a remarkable Englishman who had connections with both Canada and New Zealand. Charles Buller, who became a member of the British House of Commons in 1830 was one of a small group of English political radicals who effected valuable reforms in Britain's colonial policy. He came to Canada in 1838 with Lord Durham following the rebellions in Upper and Lower Canada the preceding year. Later Buller contributed to the development of policies of the British government which benefited New Zealanders and for which they still remember him.

Although I was exhausted each day after the strenuous field activities in which I engaged as I toured New Zealand, I was quickly revived by some food, a little drink, and, principally, by Ben Dickenson's enthusiasm and optimism. Educated as a mining engineer, Dickenson, who served as deputy minister of mines on one of the Australian state governments, was a natural and talented mine-finder and mine-maker. He contributed immeasurably to Rio Tinto's subsequent growth in Australia. By the early 1980s, 19 per cent of Rio Tinto Zinc's profits came from their operations in Australia.

A non-technical highlight of my journey to New Zealand was a visit to the birthplace of the internationally renowned physicist Ernest Rutherford. Rutherford, the head of the Cavendish Laboratory in the University of Cambridge from 1919 until his death in 1937, had been engaged in research concerning ionizing radiation at McGill University in Canada from 1898 to 1907. It was during this period of eight years that Rutherford and his colleagues at the McGill laboratory established the science of radioactivity on a sound and substantial basis.

Rutherford's primary school near Nelson was an old but well cared for building, resembling perfectly the "little red schoolhouse" so common to rural parts of Canada until the 1960s. In one such "little red schoolhouse" in northern Alberta, my wife Mary had taught a multi-grade class for eight years as a young teacher. As I marvelled at the simplicity of the building and its furnishings, I realized once more that fine minds can be kindled and motivated to supreme greatness without all the comfortable and costly facilities deemed so essential in many of our modern schools.

Somewhat to my surprise I found no plaque or monument honouring Rutherford, at or near the schoolhouse, although later, at the coastal community of Westport, some distance away, I did see a monument to Rutherford beside the local church. That monument stands in a tiny plot of land where I found some green onions growing through the coarse grass, I enjoy onions so, with due reverence I plucked and ate one. It occurred to me that the great Cambridge scientist might have been greatly amused at the sight of a Canadian uranium prospector paying homage to him while munching on an onion.

While I was at the schoolhouse I had been shown some original letters the retired janitor of the school had received from his ex-student friend Rutherford. Among various questions the janitor had asked the Nobel Laureate in Physics was: "Do you think it will ever be possible to employ the power of the atom to generate commercial electricity?" Rutherford's reply was negative. The idea of obtaining power from the nucleus of the atom, wrote Rutherford, was just so much "moonshine – so much fanciful thinking." This had been Rutherford's considered view in 1932 when two of his most outstanding students, John Cockcroft and Ernest Walton, split the lithium atom. What enormous change had occurred, I thought to myself, within twenty-five years!

My visit to New Zealand was highly informative and most enjoyable. What I saw and learned confirmed what I had read earlier. Although a wide variety of minerals occur in New Zealand, including uranium at Buller Gorge for which there was considerable hope when I was there, only gold had proven to be present in sufficient quantity to merit commercial operations for a sustained period. Indeed, gold had become a major export in the early decades of New Zealand's development after increasing numbers of Europeans began to arrive as settlers from 1840 onwards. In national terms, however, the pastoral industry, particularly sheep-ranching, has been much more significant.

In marked contrast to New Zealand's rather limited mineral resources are the rich deposits of New Caledonia, the largest island in the French overseas territory. It is in the southwest Pacific Ocean east of Australia and north of New Zealand. It would be the next stop in my Rio Tinto odyssey.

New Caledonia was discovered in 1774 by the British explorer,

James Cook, the most celebrated navigator to explore the Pacific. Cook gave the island the name Caledonia, which the Romans had used for Scotland. Britain, however, like France and the United States, was reluctant to become involved in the costly responsibility of administering and defending a distant island of unknown potential.

After the establishment of a French Roman Catholic mission on the island in 1843, the French government began to take an interest in New Caledonia. It was annexed by France in 1853 and the richness of its mineral deposits, particularly nickel and chromium, subsequently became recognized. Before the Second World War the island was producing about 10 per cent of the world's nickel and slightly less than that when I spent two weeks there in 1957 visiting the operations of the Société Le Nickel deposits and works and the Tiebaghi chrome deposits. The Le Nickel Company was viewed as an "in-law" of Rio Tinto, London, since the European Rothschilds were deeply involved financially in both.

New Caledonia is a beautiful tropical island, 248 miles long and 31 miles wide, with steep slopes covered with lush vegetation. Its southern shoreline, an expanse of beautiful sandy beaches bordering the Coral Sea, is immortalized in the song, "Bali ha'i," composed for the musical *South Pacific*. I walked along one of those beaches and, yes, I am certain I heard the melody of that haunting song drifting up from the surf as it gently lapped the sandy shore.

In terms of its human history, New Caledonia is a paradox. As a relatively distant, isolated island from the former colonial region of French Indo-China (Thailand, Cambodia, Vietnam), it served from 1864 to 1894 as a penal colony for Indo-Chinese political dissenters, as French Guiana and Devil's Island had served in northern South America. After some prodding, my reluctant French guide showed me some of the long-abandoned prison cell blocks and torture chambers. Nature, in its wisdom and patience, had almost totally enveloped these hideous buildings in a jungle growth of tangled vines, many of which were thorny, some, paradoxically, in exquisite bloom. Where there had been profound agony, now there was indescribable beauty.

New Caledonia is a treasure house – an economic geologist's dream realized. The entire island is a great mass of ultra-basic rock thrust up from great depth in the Earth's core along a deep crustal fracture, a *plate edge*. The original rock material contains abnormal quantities of nickel, chromium, cobalt, iron, manganese, and vanadium. But there is more! The tropical climate, with its cyclical rains and dry periods, combined with the saline vapours of the surrounding ocean and intense solar radiation, has resulted in considerable disintegration, decomposition, and reconstruction of the original rock into enriched mineral concentrates through natural processes not unlike, although much slower than, those involved in man-made metallurgical works. The end result of these natural phenomena is that large areas of the island's soil, to considerable depth in places, have become secondarily enriched ores, technically called *laterites* and *placers*.

This geological state was recognized early by the island's colonial masters. The penal population was put to work manually exploiting this natural wealth of the soil until mechanization gradually replaced human labour. The relative world scarcity of nickel and chromium continued to increase the economic importance of the New Caledonia deposits, once estimated to contain one-third of the world's nickel. By 1957, when I visited these operations, they were fully modern in every respect. It never occurred to me, at that time, that the huge mining complex at Kuaoua on New Caledonia's east coast would become the focal point in the struggle for independence in 1985.

New Caledonia's capital, Noumea, a port on the south-western corner of the island, now has a population of about fifty thousand. Its city-planning and architecture displayed, in the late 1950s, much evidence of its early wealth and Latin elegance, although the ravages of the tropical climate have taken their toll.

The French officials and technical specialists I met in New Caledonia were co-operative, able, and charming. I was also most favourably impressed by the Indo-Chinese population. Small, even dainty in appearance, they were quick, bright, and amazingly tough when muscular effort was required.

On the day of my departure, I was stricken by a frightening fever of unknown origin. Since I did not wish to alarm my hosts, I sought an independent physician in Noumea for assistance. Although the physician to whom the hotel manager took me appeared untidy, his office was reasonably presentable. The doctor seemed totally confident in his diagnosis of my complaint, and an inoculation by hypodermic needle into my left upper arm was quickly administered. A short time later, I boarded the aircraft for the long flight from Noumea to Darwin, Australia. While I have no recollection of the boarding, nor of the flight, I do remember, in a confused manner, arriving in Darwin and being greeted by Ben Dickenson. My left arm seemed totally paralysed and I had double, sometimes triple, vision. After two days of hospital rest, I fully recovered. To my alarm I was then told that the doctor in Noumea had given me a massive injection of opium. At least it had eliminated the fever!

Australia and Tasmania

Soon after the first European settlers arrived in Australia in 1788, following the exploratory voyages of James Cook and others, they found coal near Sydney and alluvial gold to the west of the settlement there. Later, gold was discovered in Victoria and then in western Australia. These discoveries stimulated widespread prospecting and the development of rich mineral deposits in various sections of the country.

The principal gold rush occurred in the colony of Victoria. While gold production there passed its peak by 1857, the population of that colony in 1860 had increased from 77,000 in 1850 to 540,000. During the same period Australia's population grew from 500,000 to about 1,150,000. This rapid growth in population fostered industrialization, the construction of railways, and the continuing search for minerals as the population spread out across the continent.

The opening up of Australia's resources of all the major minerals – coal, copper, iron, lead, nickel, tin, zinc, silver, and gold – contributed to the economic boom of the 1880s. Especially significant was the discovery during that decade of additional deposits of gold and copper, and in particular of silver and lead at Broken Hill near the border between South Australia and New South Wales. After Britain's Australian colonies entered into federation and emerged as the Commonwealth of Australia on January 1, 1901, the search for mineral deposits and money to develop them continued as important aspects of the economic life of the new nation.

Uranium was first discovered in Australia in 1906, near Olary in South Australia about two hundred miles north-east of Port Pirie, and the site was appropriately named Radium Hill. Although the ore body was quite complex, the extraction of radium and uranium was carried on until 1916. The second uranium discovery was made in 1949 by a bushman, Jack White, in a north-western township of Australia's Northern Territory with the unusual name of Rum Jungle.

Jack White, who apparently eked out a living by prospecting and hunting for animals and selling their skins, was searching for kangaroos in Rum Jungle when he came across a pit which, it seems, had been dug by prospectors searching for copper. White's curiosity stimulated him to examine the pit, and he recognized the presence of uranium ores, over which the Australian government had exclusive jurisdiction at that time. When White's discovery became known, the government arranged for a comprehensive exploration program to be carried out. The following year another uranium deposit was discovered nearby.

After my short stay in the Darwin hospital to recover from the fever and effects of the inoculation, Ben Dickenson and I visited the Rum Jungle operation, about sixty miles south of Darwin. I was particularly interested to visit the mine-site, a community called Batchelor, which had been established to accommodate the miners and their families, since it was, in a sense, the Australian counterpart to the town of Elliot Lake. Milling operations had begun there in January 1953. The combined production of the Radium Hill and the Rum Jungle mines had reached a total of about one million pounds of uranium oxide by the mid 1950s.

From Rum Jungle, Ben Dickenson and I flew to Mount Isa, a mining community in Queensland near the border of the Northern Territory and slightly more than two hundred miles south of the Gulf of Carpentaria. Mining had been carried on in that area since John Campbell Miles's discovery of silver-lead ore in 1923; he had named one of his properties after his sister, Isabelle. Following the Second World War and the new interest in uranium, prospectors became active in that section of Queensland. Among the prospectors were Clem Walton and Norman McConachy.

In 1954, Walton and McConachy were prospecting east of Mount Isa, near the community of Cloncurry. As the two men travelled along the dry bed of a creek their truck broke down. Walton worked to get the truck going and McConachy decided to use their Geiger counter to check for radioactivity. A rich deposit of uraninite, later established as having reserves of 3 million tons of rich ore, was discovered. The deposit was called the Mary Kathleen, in honour of McConachy's wife, who had died not long before. After thorough examination of the prospect, it was clear that a major open-pit mining operation should be undertaken.

By the time the decision was taken to develop the Mary Kathleen deposit, Joe Hirshhorn and I had agreed with Rio Tinto, London, that they would play the central role in financing the development of our uranium properties on the north shore of Lake Huron, in Ontario. Rio's knowledge of uranium developments in Canada no doubt added to their world-wide appreciation of financial opportunities in that sector of the mining industry. They became involved in the financing of the Mary Kathleen deposit.

A contract was completed with the United Kingdom Atomic Energy Authority for the purchase of £40 million of uranium oxide. That was a substantial contract, given that the initial arrangements Joe Hirshhorn and I made with Rio Tinto had involved only $40 million. Given this background I visited the Mary Kathleen site with much interest.

The Mary Kathleen is located in the Northwest Uplands of Queensland. That particular area is characterized by Pre-Cambrian rocks of the Australian Shield, which trend north-northwest to the border of the Northern Territory. Since the nearest town in this semi-arid area, Cloncurry, is about fifty miles from the mine-site, it was necessary to plan for the creation of a community near the Mary Kathleen, just as it had been necessary to create the community of Elliot Lake near the mines on the Big Z. At the Mary Kathleen the lack of water was a major problem which could only be resolved through the creation of an artificial lake. A dam was constructed across the Cornella River. Like many other rivers in Australia, however, the Cornella is almost dry for a considerable period each year. Thus it was relatively easy to construct the dam in such a way that the new Lake Cornella covered an area of about three square miles. When the rains came the dam was capable of trapping a large volume of water. It was carried nine miles in a pipeline to the mine-site.

During my visit to Australia I went to Melbourne to meet with directors and officers of Rio Tinto, Australia, and with principals of other mining and metallurgical corporations with which Rio was associated or engaged in discussions concerning long-term development of Rio's interests in that part of the world. Through my discussions I learned that two other Canadian geologists I knew well – Dr. William Gross, with whom I had worked briefly in the early Hirshhorn days, and Dr. Desmond Kidd, with whom I worked in north-central British Columbia in the early 1940s – had been in Australia on consulting assignments earlier.

After my enjoyable, though brief, visit to Sydney – which gave me the impression that it is the San Francisco of the southern hemisphere – Ben Dickenson, a dynamic promoter named Mouson, a coal consultant, and I, went to visit the impressive coalfields near Newcastle, New South Wales. I was interested to learn that this busy port city had originated about 1800 as the Coal River Penal Settlement.

With a small group of the directors of Rio Tinto, Australia, I also visited Tasmania. This island state of the Commonwealth of Australia, lying about 150 miles south of the State of Victoria, has a total area of slightly over twenty-five thousand square miles, most of them mountainous. We went to Tasmania to visit the tin-mining operations at Roseberry and the Mt. Lyell copper operations near Risdom. Gold had been discovered in Roseberry Creek and lead ore at nearby Mt. Read in 1893. Lead smelters went into operation there just before the First World War, but the high zinc content of the ore made the enterprise unprofitable. This difficulty was overcome with the development of new processing methods, and mining operations were begun again in 1936.

Mining activities at Mt. Lyell, as in other areas of Australia, began with gold, then silver, and later base metals. Over 90 per cent of Tasmania's copper is mined at Mt. Lyell. The directors of Rio Tinto were particularly interested in the operations of Electrolytic Zinc at Risdom since they were then considering its acquisition. Subsequently, the Australian operations of Rio Tinto and Consolidated Zinc were amalgamated and Conzinc Riotinto of Australia was created. A decade or so after my visit to Tasmania, major new underground copper deposits began to be developed near Mt. Lyell.

My visit to Australia made me aware of the dynamic state of mineral discoveries there and I gained some appreciation of its vast mineral potential. What I saw and learned gave me the impression that only the surface of that vast potential had been scratched. I left Australia with the firm conviction that its boom in mineral exploration and development would continue and that it would be marked by occasional discoveries of spectacular dimensions.

When my Rio Tinto colleagues and I parted in Tasmania they flew to Melbourne while I went to Sydney for a final conference with Dickenson and a flight to Canada. Several months after I returned to Canada I went to Spain to visit the mines which had given the Rio Tinto organization its name.

Rio Tinto Operations in Spain

From the time Joe Hirshhorn and I had first met with Oscar Weiss and then Val Duncan, they had spoken of the mines along the Rio

Tinto in Spain. My interest had been whetted and I was therefore delighted when Rio Tinto invited me to visit those mines, and related metallurgical operations, in the late summer of 1957.

The Rio Tinto – the pink river – wanders for sixty miles or so through south-western Spain, southward past the village of Palos and out into the Gulf of Cadiz. Palos is about fifty miles west of the historic city of Seville, at the entrance to the harbour of Huelva, an ancient Andalusian city. It was from Palos that Christopher Columbus embarked on his celebrated voyage to America, and to which he returned.

The barren arid hills which form the northern border of the plain through which the Rio Tinto wanders, contain minor gold deposits and some of the largest and earliest-known copper deposits in Europe. These deposits have been worked for more than three thousand years. The colour of the river changes from brilliant brick-red to green just below the place where the great ore bodies of the Rio Tinto are located, near the town of Nerva. Much of the colouring of the river is due to impure iron- and copper-bearing solutions which have permeated from their source rocks into the river. It was this unusual colouration which attracted ancient adventurer-prospectors, bringing them to the richest copper deposits of the ancient world.

The mineral deposits on the Rio Tinto in Spain have been known and intermittently exploited since the time of the ancient Phoenicians and Romans. In the Roman era, the deposits were producing copper from smelted ore (as huge piles of smelter slag from that period testified at the time of my visit). However, the initial attraction of these deposits was undoubtedly the freed gold present in the rusty soil that overlay the huge copper deposits below. This gold was in the form of tiny grains in the soil, which, because of its iron content, became rusted over time. As the gold was sought and recovered, the brilliantly coloured green and azure-blue carbonate and silicates, formed from the surface alteration of copper sulphides, were also prized.

In 1872, a London-based syndicate of financiers from Britain and Bremen, in Germany, purchased the Rio Tinto deposits from the government of Spain. This syndicate operated and continuously developed these deposits until 1954 when majority ownership was returned to the Spanish government and Spanish nationals.

I had read something of the history of the development of the Rio Tinto deposits but it was most interesting to see the site with my own eyes and to visit the attractive small archeological museum there. The Rio Tinto Company had carefully retrieved, restored, and placed on display in their mine-site museum, many primitive and ancient implements and artifacts recovered during the course of mine operations. These included ancient coins, candlesticks, glassware, mining implements, and other items which, together, provided a fascinating view of some of the treasures and tools of the ancient world.

Although the majority ownership of the mines had been returned to the Spanish government, the widespread regard for the ability and recognized dependability of the Rio Tinto Company and for its management by Val Duncan, resulted in the Spanish government appointing that company to continue as manager of the mines.

Historically, copper and pyrites, with lesser quantities of gold and zinc, had been the primary products of the Rio Tinto mines. The pyrites (an iron and sulphur mineral) had supplied much of Europe for decades as the source of sulphur for the production of sulphuric acid, a most important reagent in many metallurgical and chemical processes. Now major sour-gas discoveries containing appreciable sulphur had been made in south-central France. These discoveries made available abundant by-product supplies of elemental sulphur for the sulphuric acid market at a highly competitive cost compared to pyrite-source sulphur.

I viewed the site of the Rio Tinto mines with mixed reactions. The gently rolling hills, as far as I could see, were totally devoid of natural or cultivated growth and were composed of arid sands. The company had been struggling for some years, in vain it appeared, to restore vegetation to the hills rendered barren by centuries of despoilment through the cutting and burning of trees to provide heat for the smelting of ore and the generation of steam. Herds of grazing goats had devoured what brush and ground cover remained.

Still the arid sands and the large rectangular leaching lagoons of green, blue, yellow, and pink liquids were colourful. Areas of granular black slag piles from Roman times were still visible. I walked over and examined them with wonder and curiosity, marvelling at the apparent efficiency of metal extraction two thousand years ago.

The combined open-pit and underground mine-workings were an amazing mix of modern and ancient methods. In the open-pit bottom were trucks, loaders, and hoists at work. In the many small lateral and older workings around the edges of the pit, men were working manually. The manual workers were recovering the rich leftovers of ore from corners and crevices where machinery could not be employed. There was a strong stench of sulphur everywhere in the lateral workings and occasionally a wisp of smoke. Increasing ground pressure from the whittling away of ore pillars could cause the pyrite to ignite and burn.

After visiting two or three of these underground corners I really felt I was looking into an actual picture of the biblical Hell. The workers were clothed only in tattered cloth shorts or leather aprons and sandals and their bare torsos shone and reeked of sweat. The stench of sulphur in the air, the naked bodies blackened by the sooty ore, the noise, the feverish picking for meagre leftovers, all combined to give the impression that it was the abode of the damned.

Amazingly, the workers' communities on the surface were in sharp contrast. The workers had large families of cleanly dressed children who played happily. There were tiny vegetable gardens and flowers in pots blooming everywhere. The people of the mining community appeared well, vigorous, and sociable.

After touring the mining and leach treatment works in the company of Rio's highly capable technical managers (who were mostly British), and travelling on the ore transport railroad to the works and seaport of Huelva from which the products of the Rio Tinto mines were shipped, I went on to Madrid. There, I met various government officials and Rio Tinto's senior Spanish representatives. While these meetings were more social than technical, there was much interest by the new Spanish owners in my impressions of the operations, including their economic prospects. I told them that I was most favourably impressed by what I had seen and optimistic about their future. In due course, I felt, new ore bodies would be found; indeed, they were.

When I returned to London and reported to Val Duncan, he asked me to participate in two or three other small meetings with senior Rio Tinto directors, among them a key member of the Rothschild family, a family which had played a leading financial role in Rio Tinto for over a century.

Over lunch with one of Duncan's senior aides I was told that Val Duncan wished to appoint a senior full-time international technical consultant of my type who would travel widely and be based in London, England. I did not realize immediately that this was, in fact, a discreet invitation for me to consider such a full-time post. But even if I had done so, my reply would have been a regretful, "No, I cherish my freedom." Nonetheless, my respect for Rio Tinto as a company and Val Duncan and his colleagues as remarkable people, remained unchanged.

My overseas consulting for Rio Tinto completed, my colleagues and I, as Franc R. Joubin Associates, provided Rio with monthly reviews of developments in mining exploration across Canada, with our assessment of their importance. These reports went directly to Val Duncan in London, with copies to Robert Winters, head of Rio Tinto in Canada. After one year they were terminated, ostensibly because Winters felt that Rio Tinto, Canada, was competent to survey and assess the Canadian national scene. However, our monthly reviews were quickly requested by others and granted to a Canadian bank when Rio opted out.

While I was consulting overseas for Rio Tinto, my colleagues in Joubin Associates had been deeply involved in the large Algoma Central Railway lands geological assessment project. Despite the importance of this work, and despite having now overcome the accumulated weariness which the high-tempo Hirshhorn years had produced, I wanted a more comprehensive challenge. A variety of factors now combined to produce such a challenge in Canada.

XIII

New Challenges in Canada

British Columbia has always held a particular attraction for me. It is, after all, where I grew up and where my mother remained until her death. I keep going back there. So when Howard James suggested early in 1958 that I could help Pioneer Mines again, I was immediately interested.

Pioneer, in Howard's view, was on its last legs. "We have very limited ore reserves left above our cut-off grade of .25 ounces of gold per ton. Our costs continue to rise and no increase in the price of gold above $35 an ounce is yet in sight. Why don't you help me with it?" Here was the exciting challenge I had been seeking.

I knew something about Pioneer's problems and had some clear ideas on how they might be resolved, at least in part. In the early 1940s, while I was working for Pioneer and completing my Master's degree in geology at UBC, I had undertaken a comprehensive study of the geology of the region encompassing the Pioneer and Bralorne mines and the adjoining properties.

My reason for undertaking this study, of what is known as the "Cadwallader Gold Belt," was to arrive at an understanding of the gold ore body environment for that district, the better to find new ore bodies (and also as a probable research project for a doctoral thesis, were I to pursue that objective.) In carrying out this study, I had had the enthusiastic support of the several mine geologists in the area and I had been able to gain comprehensive data on the region's gold deposits.

While I decided not to use the data for academic purposes it readily qualified me to become registered as a professional consulting geologist in British Columbia. (Later my study was published by the Canadian Institute of Mining and Metallurgy with assistance from the Geological Survey of Canada. It remains a standard scientific reference on the gold deposits of the Cadwallader Belt).

Both the Pioneer and Bralorne mines were on the Cadwallader Gold Belt, less than two miles apart. Nonetheless, they had always operated separately. I became convinced that bringing them together in a single company would be advantageous in a number of ways. I decided to accept the challenges involved in amalgamating these important British Columbia mines.

Since my early experience in British Columbia and the Bridge River Valley had played such formative roles in my life, I must digress briefly to outline some of the challenges involved in the early development of the province and its mineral potential.

While Spaniards were probably the first Europeans to explore and to claim the north-western section of North America's Pacific coastline, it was the later-arriving British who gained control of that area. Captain James Cook began geological exploration of the coast in 1779, and was followed by other British under Captain George Vancouver, a naval officer and explorer who had served with Cook.

During the first half of the nineteenth century, British Columbia was largely under the control of fur traders. Finally, in 1849, the British government declared Vancouver Island a British colony and entrusted its colonization to the Hudson Bay Company. Nine years later the mainland was made a separate colony under the name British Columbia. The two colonies were united under the latter name in 1866. The emergence of both colonies and their ultimate union were hastened by two separate discoveries of gold.

In the spring of 1850 the wife of a chief of the Haida Indians on the west coast of Moresby Island in the Queen Charlotte Islands found a nugget of gold weighing nearly five ounces. When fur traders at Fort Simpson learned of the discovery they determined to find its source. Eight miners arrived in July 1851, but were able to secure gold only through barter with the Indians. Later, free gold was discovered at Mitchell Harbour, but the Indians, not yet bitten by the "gold bug," sent the white men away. In 1854, James Houston of Langley claimed he had found coarse gold in the Tranquille River just west of Kamloops. Not long afterwards it was reported that an Indian filling his cupped hands with water from a stream saw a shining pebble. Quickly he plucked it from the water. It was a gold nugget.

When word of these discoveries reached the California gold fields, and beyond, thousands of fortune seekers rushed northwards. Twenty thousand Americans arrived during the next three or four years. They were joined by Canadians, British, and Australians, each of whom had completed the long and difficult journey to the Fraser Valley.

During the years 1858 to 1865 dramatic discoveries were made as thousands of prospectors arrived in Victoria, crossed to the mainland and made their way up the Fraser River. Beginning at Maria Bay on the Fraser, near the site of the community now known as Chilliwack, prospectors panned for gold along the Fraser Canyon and the rivers and creeks which flowed into it. Half a million dollars in gold was reported to have been taken out between June and October of 1858. The discovery of such wealth lured the prospectors on as they moved up the Fraser and nearby rivers sampling as they went. Soon men were panning for gold along almost the entire four hundred miles of the Fraser River from Hope to Prince George.

As prospectors worked their way up the Fraser and its tributaries, many found gold in the alluvial beds. But their findings were modest in comparison with what was to come. The first Cariboo diggings were commenced beside the Quesnel River, which flows into the Fraser about sixty miles south of Prince George. There, prospectors found it was much more profitable to dig for gold rather than merely to pan. In 1861, diggings along nearby Williams Creek seemed so abundant in gold that it was called the richest creek in the world.

The gold rush town, south and slightly east of Prince George, which became known as Barkerville, soon had a population of nearly three thousand people and was described as the largest Canadian "city" west of Toronto. In its peak year of 1863, nearly $4 million in gold was recovered. At Barkerville gold lay below the surface requiring digging and capital beyond the means of ordinary prospectors.

Members of the Royal Engineers were sent from England to survey the route northward from Yale along the Fraser River in preparation for the construction of the Cariboo Road to Barkerville on the western edge of the Cariboo Mountains. The amazing feat of constructing the road along the wall of the Fraser Canyon was begun in 1864 and completed within two years. When the road was open, a great tide of prospectors swept up the valleys of the Fraser, the Thompson, and their tributaries.

While British Columbia's great Cariboo gold rush reached its peak in the mid 1860s and gold production began to decline for a time, the prospectors and those who came to meet their needs began to open up the interior of the new British colony. Some of those who remained had followed the Fraser north past its junction with the Thompson River, where the settlement named Lytton was established, and onward to the site of the present village of Lillooet at the foot of the Cascade Mountains, above the west bank of the Fraser.

This village, which took its name from the wild onions which were found in abundance there, had sprung into being in 1858 as prospectors moved northwards.

A few of the prospectors who arrived in Lillooet began to search for gold in the Bridge River Valley, then up the Hurley and Cadwallader Creek. It was in this isolated but most pleasant region of British Columbia that its richest and longest-lasting mines, the Pioneer and the Bralorne, were developed.

The Pioneer Mine

Gold was first discovered in the gravel beds of the Bridge River Valley in 1858. While other discoveries of alluvial gold followed, nearly three decades passed before the strike was made on the Cadwallader Creek which ultimately produced the Pioneer Mine.

Serious, though vain, attempts were made to extract the gold from the quartz vein source by milling by Harry Atwood and William Allen in 1897, by F. Kinder and Arthur Noel until 1911, and then by Adolphus Williams and Frank Holten. Pioneer Gold Mines was incorporated by Holten in 1915. It was not until 1920–24, however, that David Sloan, the first professionally trained engineer to assume the challenge, eventually succeeded with financial associates, in not only efficiently milling the ore, but also in developing richer sources of ore.

Sloan had an old tunnel on the property cleaned out and soon found some promising ore. This encouraged him to continue. Arnold Hoffman, in his 1947 book *Free Gold: The Story of Canadian Mining*, reported what happened next.

> He [Sloan] started a crosscut toward a projected shear zone where he had decided a sizable gold vein might be located. His calculations were only too accurate, for he had not spent more than $4,000 of the original $8,000 before he hit the Pioneer vein squarely. It was almost too good to be true. From that moment the history of the mine reads like a chapter of the *Arabian Nights*. One pocket containing little more than two tons of ore yielded $200,000 in a handpicking operation. Another, said to be the richest block of ground ever mined in Canada, provided 5,000 ounces of gold, $1,900,000 from 900 tons. Sloan's syndicate did exceedingly well. From 1928

to the present (1946), the Pioneer has produced more than $25,000,000 of which $9,301,793 has gone into dividends.

Sloan had confidence in his own estimate of the Pioneer's potential and was determined that it would be realized. Working closely with Colonel Victor Spencer, who had bought out other partners and become president when Pioneer Gold Mines Limited was incorporated the following year, Sloan, as managing director, played the central role in Pioneer's development as a great gold mine and as a fine community for its employees.

As a mining engineer Sloan knew how to get the ore out of the mine and recover the gold from it, but his knowledge of geology – the art of finding new ore sources – was inadequate. Thus, in 1932, he persuaded Dr. Howard James, who had earned his doctorate in geology and had considerable mining experience, to become mine geologist at Pioneer. When David Sloan died in early August 1935, from injuries incurred in an airplane accident, James was appointed to carry on his work as general manager of the mine.

I had secured my first summer job with Pioneer several months before David Sloan's untimely death and before Howard James had assumed responsibility for the operation of the mine. Two years later, in the spring of 1937, I became a permanent member of Pioneer's staff and continued, as earlier described, in the company's service in western and later eastern Canada for over ten years. Following that I handled specific assignments for Pioneer and retained my close friendship with Howard. Accordingly, I was knowledgeable as to the aged mine's problems and keen to help Howard James resolve them, if possible, when in late 1955 we discussed the matter. The opportunity of merging with Pioneer the equally languishing Bralorne Mine on one side and a block of relatively untested claims on the other added an exiting dimension to the problem.

The Bralorne Mine

In 1897, three prospectors, William Young, Nat Coughlan, and John Williams, came into the Bridge River Valley from Lillooet, arriving at Cadwallader Creek, where they staked three claims, calling them the Lorne, Golden Key, and Marquis. These three claims, with others added later, eventually formed the primary holdings of Bralorne Mines.

There followed about three years of indifferent gold production from the crude milling of vein quartz operated by that syndicate.

During the period 1900–16, William Sloan (no relation to the Pioneer's David Sloan) joined with Arthur Noel and his wife Delina to equip and operate a mill on the Lorne claim. The mill was not successful, but the Noels, particularly Delina, persisted in their faith in the mine. This remarkable woman shared in the day-by-day efforts to develop the mine. She also attracted national attention through her skill as a hunter, particularly of grizzly bears of world-record size. She continued as an active prospector in the Bridge River area until well after her eightieth birthday, and remained a close friend of my wife Mary and me.

The Lorne claim was purchased from the Noels by the Stobie Furlong financial brokerage company in 1928 and organized as the Lorne Gold Mine Limited. A million-dollar ore body was soon developed but financial difficulties were encountered with the onset of the Great Depression. Work ground to a halt. The following year, the Bralco Development and Investment Company, headed by Austin Taylor, acquired control of the Lorne and renamed it Bralorne.

The first gold ingot was poured at the Bralorne two years later and the company then paid its first dividends. By 1937 the Bralorne operations extended about a mile deep from the surface and had a hundred or so miles of lateral workings. At its greatest depths the temperature reached as high as 130° F (it was one of the hottest mines in Canada) and the rock pressure was considerable. Despite these problems it maintained a good safety record and a good financial record.

Amalgamating the Bralorne and Pioneer Operations

When I became re-involved in the Pioneer in 1958 I was, in a professional sense, returning home. I had gained my first professional experience in prospecting and mining in the Bridge River Valley and my appreciation of the life and work of those who had developed these mines had grown rather than diminished over the years. I was pleased to be given the opportunity to help restore them to their former glory.

Howard James had spent most of his professional career as Pioneer's chief operating officer, working tirelessly for the company with outstanding results. Now he was faced with the serious problem of declining ore reserves, rising costs, and a seemingly permanent $35-per-ounce value for his product. I was eager to help him for both personal and professional reasons. Howard had provided me with employment during the difficult Great Depression years which made it possible to complete my university education. He had encouraged me to pursue studies in geology when I was at a cross-roads between that science and chemistry.

In mid-1958 John Aird and I, with two smaller participants, purchased from Victor Spencer and Frank Ross, the principal shareholders of Pioneer, and from Austin Taylor, Senior, the principal shareholder of Bralorne, their stock holdings in their respective companies for approximately the prevailing market price. These men made as a condition of their sale that they would wish some continued representation on the new board of the new company, Bralorne Pioneer Mines Limited.

Practically all of the directors of the new company had substantial experience in successful enterprises. Karl Springer and Mel O'Brien were Austin Taylor's representatives, while the Hon. Frank Ross and Ernest Bull represented Victor Spencer. Dr. W. A. McElmoyle of Victoria, a major individual shareholder, was also a director. I served as president and John Aird as vice-president. Ira B. Joralemon, a long-time consultant to Bralorne and a friend of mine, and Howard James were appointed geological consultants to the new organization. Clearly, this was an excellent board of directors.

When the new board had been appointed, we addressed ourselves to the twin problems of mine and plant modernization and the development of additional ore reserves. In the late 1930s the Pioneer Mine was regarded, for a year or two, as one of the richest gold mines in the world, processing five hundred tons of ore daily at one ounce of gold per ton.

Throughout the 1940s and 1950s the average ore grade of both mines had been consistently about one-half ounce of gold per ton. Hobbled with a gold value of $30 to $35 per ounce during this long period, the mines could not profitably treat material containing less than one-quarter ounce of gold per ton. Although we continually expected an increase in the value of gold, it did not materialize until ten years later; too late to reward our merger group's efforts.

To revitalize the operations of the Bralorne and Pioneer, I concluded that unification of management, administrative staff, and labour was essential. This involved a re-alignment of the senior management and the infusion of younger and more modern direction in the operation of the new enterprise. The ventilation of the mine workings in the excessively hot depths of the Bralorne was improved and the earlier two separate ore treatment plants were replaced by a totally modern new mill. The general productivity of mining operations was considerably improved. The average production of the new company was increased and maintained at the rate of 100,000 ounces of gold annually during my period of management, which ended in the early 1960s.

The unification of the operations of the two separate mine-sites resulted in a considerable reduction of personnel at all levels. The labour force was cut in half through centralizing operations at the Bralorne, the use of more modern equipment, and more or less closing the Pioneer. The Bralorne and Pioneer mines had been labour-intensive companies; now they were becoming capital-intensive and fewer miners were involved in the higher physical risk and drudgery categories of the operation.

We were successful in the Bralorne in increasing the higher-grade ore reserves, but only at increasing depth where we remained frustrated by the excessive heat, rock pressure, and, at that time, inadequate mine access to solve those problems.

The same problems, excessive heat and ventilation, aborted a determined effort to explore between and below the Pioneer mine ore area from existing deep Bralorne deep workings. However, the greatest frustration of all to me – as an explorer and developer as opposed to an operator – was the inability to explore from existing Pioneer mine workings the virgin area of favourable geology adjoining the mine to the east. These claims were then controlled by a major eastern Canadian mining company with whom John Aird and I could not complete a joint venture agreement.

These earlier frustrations of our 1958 merger group remain still to be tested by a new generation of mine developers, immeasurably assisted by the fact that they could be rewarded with golden treasure worth twenty times more today than would have been the case had we reached it.

Ma Murray, who had helped make the Bridge River Valley a home for me when I had worked there in the 1930s, was one of those who made me feel particularly welcome during the 1950s. She was delighted at the prospect of the Bralorne and Pioneer being operated jointly, and her reception was so generous that I was embarrassed. In her newspaper she described my return to join and modernize the Bralorne and Pioneer mines as "The Second Coming." This all-too-generous overstatement caused me to hide for a month!

When we amalgamated the two mines and modernized their equipment we ensured that the most modern safety arrangements and devices were in place and that safety crews received the training necessary to deal with all emergencies. The value of such training was illustrated dramatically the year after our new company came into being.

On June 3, 1960, the headlines of both the *Vancouver Sun* and the *Vancouver Province* reported a cave-in at the unrelated Golden Contact mine a few miles from the Bralorne and Pioneer. Two miners had been either entombed or crushed to death underground. The others had fortunately escaped. As soon as the accident was reported to me, I immediately sent two of our highly trained mine-rescue teams to the Golden Contact to do everything possible. The twelve well-trained men of our mine-rescue crew worked three men at a time in intensive three-hour shifts to drive a new tunnel through hundreds of tons of solid and broken rock to reach the area where the rock collapse had occurred. They worked with all possible speed non-stop for thirty hours. At last they broke through and reached the two trapped miners, who were badly bruised but not otherwise injured. The anxiety and suspense were over, and the relief and joy felt by both rescuers and the group of relatives and friends who had been keeping a long vigil was wonderful.

Life soon returned to normal in the Bridge River Valley, but normal is never precisely the same after a mining accident. The accident becomes part of the collective memory and that influences, to a degree, how people think about the mine and mining. But life goes on. Miners and their families are hardy, hopeful people.

We Try to Acquire Britannia Mining

As the president of Bralorne Pioneer I had overall executive responsibility for its operations and development. When our new company was functioning effectively, in consultation with my vice-president John Aird I began to search for growth opportunities for it. One opportunity arose through the closing down of the celebrated Britannia Mining and Smelting operation at Britannia Beach about twenty miles north of Vancouver on Howe Sound.

Although the presence of copper in the Howe Sound area had been known since 1865, it was not until the 1880s that Oliver Furry, a trapper – and what an appropriate name! – discovered the property which became the site of the Britannia mine. Furry sold the property to Leo Boscowitz, a Victoria fur dealer, who subsequently sold it to a financial group in the United States. Control of the company was still held in the United States when I began to take a special interest in it. Its operations had been closed down, in part, apparently, because of deaths in the Shley family of New York, which controlled the mine through the Howe Sound Company.

For many years the Britannia mine, just south of Squamish, had served as the railroad terminus to the Bridge River gold fields. I was quite familiar with the mine and its senior staff. My judgement was that the Britannia property was still of considerable value for a variety of reasons.

The large area of land included in the Britannia property contained valuable untouched timber. As well, the hydro-electric generation rights of an attractive watershed and a fully developed generation plant were involved. Readily available and untouched gravel deposits, of value to the aggregate stone market in nearby Vancouver, an ocean port site, and ocean frontage were also included and finally, I was not convinced that the full potential for additional copper-gold ore had been investigated.

As I was to soon to find out, one thing unexpectedly led to another when I telephoned the head of the Howe Sound Company in New York. I learned that the company had divested itself of all its assets to various purchasers. Further pursuit led me to the principals who had acquired the mine. I explained my interest on behalf of Bralorne Pioneer Mine and was asked how serious I was. I told the principal that I could be in his New York office within one week with a certified cheque for $1 million as evidence of good faith if they were interested in its sale.

"I like your style," was the answer. "Come and see me this week anyway, although I can give you no answer for a month. Don't bother with the cheque on your first visit!"

When I arrived in his New York office I was greeted, to my surprise, by F. A. McGonigle, a Canadian mining engineer and a graduate of UBC who was highly regarded in eastern American mining circles and who knew of my accomplishments. McGonigle, the newly appointed vice-president of the Howe Sound Company, had briefed his chief on my background.

The three of us were going over my proposal for the purchase of Britannia when its new president suddenly said: "Look, we have one other nibble from a representative of Japanese interests. They could be interested in the purchase of the mine; they want more information. An American mining equipment company, Emco, have purchased all the mine's mobile equipment. We have asked a consultant, Dr. Tolman, to study the geological plans and tell us if any significant copper-ore potential remains on the property. Any decision to sell depends on his recommendations."

"But look," he added, "let's talk about another Howe Sound property which is much on my mind. Ever heard of the El Potosi silver mines of Chihuahua, Mexico?"

"Only textbook knowledge that it's one of the world's great old silver mines going back to the time of the Conquistadors," I replied.

"Yes," came the rejoinder, "but right now it's a loser. We've got to make up our minds fast on how to handle it. Fritz says you can handle it. Why don't you help us on that evaluation while we're waiting for Tolman's report on the Britannia?"

It was shrewd of them to link the two issues – what I wanted and what they wanted. I can resist any temptation save a professional challenge and I knew that exercise would stimulate me greatly. I would earn a good fee and at the same time I might be able to move closer to my goal of purchasing the Britannia mine.

"Okay," I replied. "I'll 'vet' the Potosi."

I spent most of March 1959 in northern Mexico studying the Potosi mine which is located about eight miles over a rocky road from Chihuahua, a city of modest size. My work there was extremely interesting for technical, historical, and socio-economic reasons. That section of northern Mexico, directly south of El Paso, Texas, had produced silver and lead intermittently for about four centuries. Indeed, to that time, the state of Chihuahua had produced about one half of Mexico's lead and zinc output, about a third of its gold, and much of its uranium.

In Mexico, silver and gold are produced, to a considerable degree, as by-products of lead, zinc, and copper. But the El Potosi was exclusively a silver producer, probably one of Mexico's top six silver mines. Its production had contributed to the enormous quantities of silver taken to Europe from the new world after the discovery of America.

When I arrived at the Potosi mine-site, in the arid, semi-desert of the state of Chihuahua, I found the readily accessible hillsides were riddled with exposed workings, many of which had been exploited for perhaps several centuries. Some of these workings were now in mechanized production. Others were still being worked manually by individuals who had negotiated small-scale leases. I learned that some of the hillside sites were centres of illicit mining – "high-grading" – of silver.

Some of the smaller, more remote sections of underground workings were still being mined as in centuries past – by candlelight, hand-held hammer, and chisel. The small quantities of silver-lead-zinc ore recovered were carried in leather bags on the heads or back of wiry men who, because of the heat, were half-naked as they climbed "chicken ladders" – notched poles – from the depths of the mine to the surface.

These "high-graders" were literally thieves. They were driven to their illegal activities by need of money to feed their large families, to buy beer for themselves, and to pay the village priest his tithe so that he too might have some funds for the upkeep of the church and for food and wine. They – and the priest – probably considered the silver which the high-graders sold to agents in the nearby village as bounty from Heaven.

There was no concerted effort by the company to stop the practice, but when a high-grader was caught by some mine administrator stumbling upon the culprit, the penalty applied was no more than seizure of the stolen silver, of which probably one-half would reach the company's vaults, the balance often being retained by the apprehender as a reward to himself for his alertness. This way of dealing with offences is called "Mexican justice," not always in a derogatory sense.

My evaluation of this once-great, but now aged, mine was, for me, an emotional experience not unlike composing an obituary for a long-time friend. I knew that many thousands of men had given the best years of their lives working there. It was a place consecrated by toil. Now it was coming to an end.

In mining circles there is an old saying that "a good mine dies hard." It seems to keep on struggling to yield good ore. This was true in the case of the Potosi. Its mining staff were doing everything they could to prolong its life through the search for new ore.

Although my recommendation was that my clients should dispose of the Potosi silver mine, it was coupled with the introduction to them of another *gringo* (foreign-owned) company nearby. The operators of this company, which operated a zinc smelter, had conveyed to me their interest in new sources of zinc. Zinc was present in the Potosi mine in small amounts but these had been scorned in the past. Silver was far more glamorous. Whether the reincarnation of the Potosi silver mine as a modest zinc mine proved possible, I do not know. If it didn't, then the high-graders would have the Potosi mine all to themselves, enabling them to enrich their own communities instead of the coffers of some foreign operation. I was reminded on my last day in the nearby community of Chihuahua that in the midst of major adversity even terminal old age need not be sorrowful. Perhaps the high-graders would prove that this would also be true for the venerable Potosi.

I was exploring the ancient city of Chihuahua and casually strolled towards its central square, with all of its classical Spanish charm, to admire the statues which dominated it. Nearby were a number of ancient wooden benches supported by elegant cast-iron bracketry painted black.

On one of these benches sat a very old couple, simply dressed, wearing sandals, with tattered straw hats covering their wispy white hair. They clung to one another, The man had his arm around the woman's shoulders. In his hand he held her two hands, loosely clasped together on her lap. Both gazed, motionless, their faces turned slightly upward, directly into the warm sun. When I saw them, from perhaps one hundred feet away, I actually thought they were part of the sculpture. Only when I was perhaps fifty feet from them did I realize they were alive!

Slowly, I reached for my camera. As I removed it from its case, I edged closer to photograph the entire scene with the elderly couple as its centre. Suddenly, I realized from their fixedly staring, wide-open eyes that they were probably both blind . . . and yet, despite this tragedy, complete tranquillity and contentment were clearly evident on each of their wrinkled faces. Even in the middle of that public square I felt I was invading their personal privacy. I could not take the photograph. In fact, there was no need for me to do so. That scene is one of the most touching and beautiful pictures stored in my treasury of memories.

Soon after completing my study of the Potosi mine for the Howe Sound successors, I was advised that Dr. Tolman had recommended that they retain the Britannia mine. So it did not become the property of Bralorne Pioneer as I had hoped it might. This major disappointment contributed, with other factors, to my decision to sell my interest in Bralorne Pioneer.

Throughout my career as a prospector, geologist, and developer of mining properties I have gained satisfaction primarily in the discovery of new mineral prospects and their development. Because I prefer outdoor, personal exploration involvement to the constant management responsibilities of mine production, the latter has never attracted me.

When a highly attractive financial offer for share equity in our new company was made to our small group by an American syndicate, I readily sold my holdings. Others of our original group elected to remain involved.

While I no longer have a financial interest in mining properties there my attachment to my friends in the Bridge River Valley has remained undiminished to this day. I still occasionally visit the district, enjoying the role of "guru" to a younger generation struggling to bring about still another rejuvenation of that historic old camp.

The successful amalgamation of the Pioneer and the Bralorne, and the sale of my financial interest in the new company, enabled me to devote more time to meeting a new challenge. I began to search not for gold in its solid form but for "liquid gold" – for oil.

Prospecting for Oil and Gas in Sun and Snow

Early in the 1960s I began to take a special interest in hydrocarbon exploration. As an economic geologist I was interested in any and all treasure recoverable from the rocks. I was also a crusader looking for challenges. I had succeeded in the realm of hard-rock geology with important uranium, copper, and gold discoveries so I thought I might explore the potential of soft-rock geology. For one thing, some important electronic tools, including air-borne magnetometers, had been found useful in the exploration of the sea-floor and its riches. They had been used about this time to gain the first clues that much oil and gas might possibly exist beneath the North Sea. I was intrigued. Why couldn't I do the same elsewhere? I had been interested in such possibilities for some years anyway, so I figured now was a good time to give it a try!

Over a decade earlier I had sat with an Inuit companion on a rock knoll beside our campsite at Little Whale River on the east coast of Hudson Bay. Gazing westward over the vast expanse of the bay, I felt certain that there must be treasure within that huge sedimentary basin, but, I had mused, that temptation must wait. Some years later,

I had been similarly tempted while on the Caribbean island of Jamaica. Then I had persuaded the Hon. Norman Manley, the widely respected lawyer who was prime minister of Jamaica from 1955 to 1962, to allow a syndicate I had formed to study onshore and offshore oil and gas potential in and around his island country. To ensure that we had the necessary technical expertise for such a study, our syndicate, comprised of Sir Denys Lawson, former Lord Mayor of London, England; John Aird; myself; and several others had engaged Dr. T. A. Link, the petroleum geologist of Leduc, Redwater, and Golden Spike fame, and a younger petroleum geologist of his choice, Ronald D. Johnson of Calgary. They went to Jamaica to work with me on the study. Unfortunately, evidence from our field research was discouraging and the Cariboil Study Syndicate was disbanded.

However, a year or so after this, I received a small booklet in the mail from the Geological Survey of Canada, described as GSC Paper 59.13 by Margaret E. Bower. This booklet outlined the geophysical significance of an air-borne magnetic flight-line (a magnetometer towed from an airplane) just offshore of Hudson Bay's western and southern coastlines. This report came as a pleasant surprise to me. A year or two earlier, while serving as a member of the GSC Advisory Council, I had suggested to the senior officer of the GSC, Dr. J. M. Harrison, that such a survey be made to provide some fundamental data on the geology, and particularly on the thickness of the Hudson Bay sedimentary basin.

There was a second reason for my pleasure in this report. Although there was no data on the central section of the Hudson Bay basin (which normally would be the section of maximum thickness and for that reason the best area for an oil and gas search), the line which had been flown indicated clearly a marked thickening of the sedimentary formation seaward. There was even a marginally attractive exploration thickness close to the Manitoba coastline. As I reflected on these facts, a plan of action gradually became clear to me.

A comprehensive study should be made, I decided, to determine the oil and gas offshore potential of the Hudson Bay basin. This vast offshore region, including Hudson and James bays cover some eight hundred thousand square miles, about one-fifth the area of Canada. As the vehicle to carry forward my plan to search for oil and gas in this huge area, a group was formed called Société Générale des Pétroles, registered later under the English acronym, *Sogepet*. (I had chosen a French name because I had French clients in mind for the initial financing.)

Sogepet was formed during July and August 1962 as a syndicate. Its members were Air Marshal Wilfred Curtis, retired from the Royal Canadian Air Force and now an insurance executive; Joseph Sedgwick, a leading Canadian barrister; James Manley, a friend and solicitor; and myself. Initially, Steven Low, a stockbroker known to Air Marshal Curtis undertook the early financing of our activities. Later Low withdrew from the syndicate and was succeeded by Roy Jodrey, Senior, and two colleagues from Nova Scotia. I functioned as president and chief executive officer of the group. Our senior technical adviser was Ronald D. Johnson, with whom Ted Link and I had worked in Jamaica. One of the major problems facing our group at the outset was to determine whether the federal or the provincial government(s) controlled the offshore areas in Hudson Bay.

Duff Roblin, then premier of Manitoba, had been one of our "winter neighbours" in Jamaica. Occasionally he and I had met in the evenings. On one occasion he had said, "You prospect for everyone else, Franc, why don't you do something for us in Manitoba?" And so I decided to see him in Winnipeg. I explained that Sogepet wished to look for oil and gas in Hudson Bay, that it might be found in the Manitoba offshore and that I had come seeking his answer to the question: "Who owns what out there in Hudson Bay?"

Fortunately, the political situation in Canada at that time was favourable as far as our proposed project was concerned. John Diefenbaker, leader of the Conservative Party, was then prime minister of Canada. Roblin, also a Conservative, was in power in Manitoba, and the Conservative Party, under John Robarts, also governed in Ontario. Given this political context, Roblin was able to say with confidence, "I think we can work it out. Let me try!"

Within a couple of weeks or so, Joe Sedgwick called me to say, "We have informal but written assurance in the form of a personal letter from the prime minister that there is an understanding between Ottawa and the provinces that we can proceed with exploration. The thrust of this understanding is that the federal government will lay down the rules and be 'in charge.'" Whatever the results of our exploration, we would be dealt with "no more onerously than under existing regulations which apply to the land mass in the provinces." The Canadian Department of Energy, Mines and Resources issued the necessary authorization to our group.

The first oil and gas exploration permits ever filed in the Hudson

Bay offshore area were filed in the names of Sedgwick, Curtis, Manley, and myself. These permits covered the Manitoba coastline and extended for about forty miles offshore. Thus began a technical challenge and a labour of love that has captivated me ever since, and that continues to this day.

After we had secured the exploration permits, we needed the funding for field operations. Our best prospect for this I had thought could be the Rio Tinto–Rothschild group in Europe. Val Duncan of Rio Tinto had teasingly invited me, and in the presence of Guy de Rothschild and another Rio Tinto board member, to "bring to our attention – and first – any other schemes like Blind River." I felt that Hudson Bay offshore oil exploration would qualify.

I phoned Val Duncan and gave him the story. He was interested, but cautious. Rio Tinto had sold their substantial oil and gas equities to British Petroleum (BP) for shares in the latter he informed me. Nonetheless, Duncan said he would phone the chairman of BP, tell him what I had said, and ask him to phone me. When the chairman phoned, he listened attentively to what I had to say. Then he remarked: "A most exciting concept, Joubin, but for us you are six months too late. We have become part of a syndicate that proposes to do the same as you propose – but in the North Sea!"

With a certain loss of ardour, I turned to the Calgary "oil patch." Ron Johnson suggested that we approach the principals of the Aquitaine Company of Canada, at that time newly arrived in Canada from France. They already had become the Cinderella of the Canadian industry because of their imaginative and courageous financing and resultant discoveries of the Rainbow and Zama oilfields in Alberta. The Aquitaine officials were favourably impressed by our presentation and agreed to "farm into" our project and pay all the initial drilling costs of a test well in exchange for 50 per cent equity in our lands.

Our Kaskattama (Kaska) "slim-hole" well, on the south-west coast of Hudson Bay near the mouth of the Nelson River, was an exploration success. It revealed several sections of good oil-environment-type rock and, most importantly, it penetrated at shallow depth several hundred feet of porous reefal rock containing residual bitumen. This was convincing evidence that oil reserves were probably present elsewhere in the huge Hudson Bay basin at greater depth.

When news of the results of our shallow, coastline Kaska well became known, an immense exploration rush into the region began. Almost the entire water surface of Hudson Bay, totalling in excess of

100 million acres, was applied for and granted to over a score of major oil companies from all over America and several from Europe.

Fortunately, by that time Sogepet had gained the support not only of the Aquitaine Company but also of the Consumers Gas Company, which had become the prime shareholder of our newly formed public company. Accordingly, Sogepet's equity base became spread over much of the Hudson Bay area through various "farm-out" and "farm-in" deals, under which land equity is exchanged for exploration funding. As a result, of course, our real equity in each of many on-going project areas became reduced, but our area coverage greatly enlarged.

Sogepet's acceptance by Aquitaine and the dramatic encouragement of the Kaska well produced prominence and promise, but also problems for us. Now we were in the international major league of oil exploration companies and the dues would be high.

Probably for the first (and undoubtedly for the last) time in modern Canadian oil-exploration history, Sogepet set about raising $1 million by elevating its small syndicate into a public share company and selling its stock for $1 a share, as speculative gold-mining ventures had commonly been financed in earlier Bay Street days.

The issue was quickly sold and, in the process, a principal in this junior financing introduced us to the remarkable entrepreneur and successful corporate president of the Consumers Gas Company, Okah Jones. Jones was intrigued by the Hudson Bay dream and the spark kindled by the Kaska well. His company agreed to finance the first $2 million of Sogepet's exploration expenditures with the option of converting such advances into Sogepet shares should they so elect. This was all discussed at a lunch shared by my friend William F. Mitchell, Okah Jones, and myself. The deal terms were roughed out the next day on the back of a used envelope by George Carpenter, Okah's aide, and myself and refined by Mitchell. Bill Mitchell, who had much high-level global experience in the oil and gas industry, became my highly effective vice-president at Sogepet for many years.

Little did we realize then that the relationship would lead to private sector and government expenditures totalling about $100 million over the next twenty years – and the prize is not yet won!

It is noteworthy that direct cash demands upon Sogepet's portion of this gross sum, exclusive of Consumer's $2 million, had been about $1 million, thanks to many astute farm-out arrangements and constant federal and Ontario and Quebec provincial government endorsement, and some subsidy toward our objectives. Of particular professional pride to my colleagues and me is that our exploration dream for the Hudson Bay basin has been shared and contributed to by a dozen private-sector oil and gas corporations of international stature, including the largest such independent corporation in the world, Armand Hammer's Occidental Oil through its Canadian subsidiary.

And the hunt continues. Since the first shallow slim-hole Kaska well uncorked the bottle, five major exploratory (wildcat) offshore wells have been drilled by our group. These wells, in addition to considerable technical field and research effort by scientific agencies of the federal government, have added significantly to the technical data base of new knowledge concerning Hudson Bay.

We have yet to find oil and gas in economic form or quantity, however, I remain convinced that both are present in the Hudson Bay basin. I still hope and work toward witnessing the proof of a prophecy made on June 30, 1715, by Captain James Knight, first Governor-in-Chief of the lands and waters of Hudson Bay, who wrote of his domain:

> This next summer, if please God spare me life and health, I design to go to the northward where there is an absolute necessity of settling a trade – to which I believe and am well satisfied that all the rest of this Country will be nothing in matter of profit to what will be in a few years found there.

Like Captain Knight I am convinced that Canadians have much to gain through the careful development of the economic potential of Hudson Bay. Enjoyment of the benefits which could flow from the effecting of that development, however, will take time, patience, and thoughtful and substantial investments of human ability and money. I am not lacking in personal self-confidence as to my technical expectations for the Hudson Bay region. A similar model concept, the huge Dimenex-Occidental gas region in north offshore Trinidad, developed by me in my United Nations service, was proven after a decade of effort to be a dramatic success.

The Simcoe Canal Concept: An Up-date for the St. Lawrence Seaway

Another challenging project to which I devoted considerable thought and some field study in the early 1960s would have seen the construction of a major new canal linking Lake Ontario, Georgian Bay, and Lake Huron.

This concept envisaged an addition to the St. Lawrence Seaway system which would make possible the shipping of goods and travel by water from Lake Ontario to the upper Great Lakes through a waterway 450 miles shorter than the present route. Such an addition would reduce pressure on the troublesome Welland Canal sector of the present route. It would also contribute to the development of a valuable new dimension for the enhancement of economic life and tourism in the province of Ontario.

I commissioned helicopter surveys and a careful engineering study – by an able staff engineer, Norman Ursel – on the feasibility of a major commercial ship-canal following, for the most part, existing waterways from near Port Hope on Lake Ontario to Washago on Lake Simcoe, to Georgian Bay, and thence to Lake Huron. At the time this preliminary work was done we did not look into other infrastructure facilities which might be linked to the canal project.

Officials of the governments of Canada and Ontario to whom I presented the concept were "intrigued" or "interested" but no more. I sent a copy of the study to Joe Hirshhorn at his retirement home on the French Riviera. As expected, Hirshhorn replied, "Visit here. My neighbour, Rothschild, is a natural for it."

Joe discussed the idea with Rothschild, who reportedly said, "Please Joseph, no talk of new canals for a while – until we can put the Suez Canal disaster out of our minds." Hirshhorn and I concluded that the concept would require time before its merits would be appreciated. More than a quarter of a century has now passed and, in my view, the value of the concept has improved with age.

Hirshhorn not only had an amazingly good sense of timing, of knowing when a business deal could be put together and sold, he knew how to organize a team and to make sure it won. One of the members of his Canadian team was Ed Parker.

Ed Parker, Ryerson, Hirshhorn, and Purple Trousers

Two or three years after I entered into partnership with Joe Hirshhorn, he had asked me to find someone to help him with his mail and publicity matters. After considering a number of persons I selected Ed Parker. Ed joined Technical Mine Consultants as its Public Relations Officer and served with distinction in that capacity during the years that followed. When Rio Tinto took over, Parker continued to handle public relations for the new company, Rio Algom, until some years later when he set up his own successful public relations company. After we went our separate professional ways, Parker and I kept in touch. He was a warm, friendly, and talented person, always optimistic – a most engaging and genial colleague.

Ed Parker had grown up in the dynamic Jewish community in Winnipeg and had first learned about journalism from his father. Later, after he graduated from the University of Manitoba, he worked as a journalist, played a key role in the development of a recreational association for federal civil servants in Ottawa, and subsequently went to Regina, Saskatchewan, to handle press relations for Premier Tommy Douglas. After the Ryerson Institute of Technology was established in Toronto in 1948, Parker organized its journalism and graphic arts program. He came to TMC from Ryerson.

While Joe Hirshhorn had approved of Parker's appointment initially, he had doubts about him. The reason for this was that on his first day at work Parker had worn a pair of brilliant blue-purple trousers that would have put a peacock to shame. "What pants!" Joe had exploded. "You often wear pants like that? I can't stand them. Keep out of my sight today. Don't come back with them on tomorrow!" And that was the end of that problem. It was also the beginning of a long and mutually beneficial relationship between the two men.

Parker attended to Joe's public relations needs in a most efficient, lively, and faithful manner. Even after Joe's death, Parker remained a trusted friend and adviser of Joe's son Gordon, who frequently came to him for advice and counsel. As a man of wide experience, Hirshhorn was no doubt anxious to ensure that his son would share in his good fortune of friendship with Parker. Joe's wish was fulfilled as Ed and the young Hirshhorn were in close touch right up until Ed's death in late March 1988.

When Ed Parker introduced me to Ryerson it had only two substantial buildings. But it wasn't Ryerson's buildings or lack of them that interested me. My primary focus of attention was its teaching program.

I was, and remain, strongly attracted to vocational education as North America's equivalent of the historically effective British and European apprenticeship training systems which were critical in the development of industrialism in the western world. I still believe that most crafts, trades, and some professions are best taught by "hands-on" training. Only recently has Canada opted for the teaching of "technicians" and "technologists," as opposed to the almost exclusive pre-occupation with academic training at the university level.

Traditionally, prior to the early 1960s, Canadian universities were primarily places for a select few. The teachers of the teachers, the theorists, masters of research, those with serious interests in esoteric knowledge, and the members of the scholarly, scientific, and cultural professions, are those whom, in my view, society should support in its universities. I feel it is wasteful and socially inefficient to debase the university, as is the norm today, by turning it into a mass-attendance "brain factory" for social or technical employment, or, worse still, to use the university as an agency for the securing of social esteem. Canada needs a variety of distinctive types of post-secondary educational institutions in addition to the university model.

Thus it was with great interest and pleasure that I met principal Howard Kerr and his colleagues and worked with them in the development of Ryerson in the mid 1950s and early 1960s. At that time, Ryerson came under the supervision of the provincial Department of Education. Principal Kerr, as the head of Ryerson, received advice and guidance in policy matters from various advisory committees then under the able, overall chairmanship of Col. D. F. MacRae. I served on two of the organizing committees – Industrial Chemistry and Fund Raising.

After Ryerson's initial 1948 group of about 250 students had completed their studies and demonstrated their skills in the work-place, enrolment in Ryerson began to rise. Graduates became widely accepted in business and industry and contributed to the growing regard for their school. As Ryerson became established, the government of Ontario considered the desirability of granting it self-governing status. In 1962, Premier John Robarts invited several individuals, including myself, to examine this matter, and we recommended that Ryerson become a self-governing polytechnical institute. In March 1963, Minister of Education William G. Davis introduced an Act which was passed in the Ontario Legislature to give Ryerson such status. I was invited to become one of the founding governors.

Our immediate problems, as governors, were the continuing growth of Ryerson's enrolment and the need to expand its facilities. Ryerson's enrolment grew from 1948's 250 to about 2,300 nine years later, and was projected to rise to 10,000 by 1970. The demand for graduates exceeded the supply. The need for more and more space soon led to questions about Ryerson's location. After much consideration it was decided that the Institute should remain on its original site and that it should be enlarged. Nearby lands were purchased and buildings built. The curriculum was expanded according to demand. The name was changed to Ryerson Polytechnical Institute. It had now become a key institution in Ontario's post-secondary technical education system.

My deepening involvement during the 1960s in the United Nations' Technical Service overseas necessitated my retirement, in 1966, from the Ryerson board. While I derived great satisfaction from my association with the institute, I was troubled by its gradual drift away from its original commitment to high quality "hands-on" technical education and toward becoming yet another more abstract degree-granting university.

Ryerson had a great opportunity to plough a deep and increasingly fertile furrow in this vitally important field of technical education. My earnest hope was that by uniting practical learning in the factory and field with classroom learning in the institute, Ryerson would contribute to the revitalization of Canada's programs of technical education.

My Other Involvements in Canadian Social Life

During the years 1959 to 1962, when my principal professional activity was the direction of the Bralorne Pioneer Gold Mines, I regularly visited British Columbia on business. This worked in well with frequent visits to my ailing mother in Vancouver.

John Aird, my colleague in Bralorne Pioneer Mines, often accompanied me on my visits to Vancouver. Since we were both directors of the Canadian Mental Health Association (CMHA), we frequently made stopovers in provincial capitals between Toronto and Vancouver to help the heads of the CMHA's provincial branches resolve organizational or administrative problems. We were also involved in the evaluation of the research efforts of various individuals and agencies receiving grants from the association.

During these visits through western Canada, we met with professors of psychiatry and psychiatrists in private practice to discuss association-funded research on which they were engaged, and to encourage them to publish the results of their research. I took a particular interest in such publications, for I knew that while all research results are not, by any means, of equal merit, publication is one of the primary ways whereby knowledge is advanced. In addition, I knew, of course, that many younger scholars were encountering major problems in having their work published. I resolved to do something about this latter problem.

Since my studies at the University of British Columbia had prepared me for a profession and under difficult financial circumstances, I had a practical appreciation of this latter problem and how it could frustrate equally ambitious and financially handicapped persons. Accordingly, in March 1961, I established, anonymously, the "Intellectual Prospecting Fund" at UBC. Its sole administrator was the remarkable educator, Walter H. Gage, who had inspired me when I first became a student during the Great Depression, and who later became a trusted friend.

Toward the end of his distinguished career, Gage became UBC's president. His tenure in that office was immortalized by students as "The Age of Gage." In 1975, the year of his retirement from the presidency, an album of tributes from former colleagues and students was prepared. My contribution to that volume read as follows:

> It was the fall of 1931 and two years deep into the Great Depression. The Groper was a nice enough kid of 20, matriculated two years earlier from Victoria high school. Lots of ambition, but no family. No drag and no job other than casual work swamping on a coal-delivery truck. No money, save $190.00 frugally saved over two years. On impulse, the Groper visited Craigdarroch Castle, then makeshifting as Victoria College, and enrolled as a student to give it a try for the one term he could afford. Teaching there was a young "math prof" not much older than the Groper – a teaching genius with a deep human interest, and an inspired motivator. The Groper fell under his spell and despite many intervening obstacles

travelled the full educational route and was richly rewarded. The "math prof," of course, was Walter Gage, and I was the Groper.

While Gage was still a professor of mathematics at UBC, prior to his elevation to the presidency, I decided to approach him about my "fund." I told him I wanted to help junior faculty members with imaginative research concepts which were too unorthodox for institutional financing. Gage was agreeable and administered the Intellectual Prospecting Fund for several years with great success.

At the outset, this fund, which evolved from suggestions I received in the mid 1950s from Howard James and Professor Harry Gunning, was used mainly to provide financial help to junior faculty members, usually on their sabbatical leaves. Amongst the first of a number of publications, which resulted, in some measure, from the granting of this assistance, was a history of the immigration of Doukhobors to Canada. Another volume which appeared in part through the operation of this fund was *The Newman Brothers*, a comparative biography of John Henry Newman, widely celebrated for his classic *The Idea of a University*, and his much lesser known brother Francis. Several other volumes were published through assistance from this fund. One departure from the usual practice of assisting authors involved the allocation of funds to support a practical research project to develop "a talking machine to help the blind," a personal concern of Walter Gage.

Upon his retirement as president of UBC in 1975, Walter Gage recommended that the residual fund be contributed as "seed money" for the development of the University of British Columbia Press. To this I readily agreed.

During this same period, I participated in the launching of a totally private and unpublicized youth development program, inspired and carried out by three remarkable friends: Bert Fiddes, Alex Sutherland, and Howard James. Fiddes was a professional social worker. Howard James, my early patron and long-time friend and colleague, had served for two decades as the director of the Central City Mission on Vancouver's skid row and was widely known for his dedication to those who had reached rock bottom. And Alex Sutherland had previously served as a dedicated aide to both Fiddes and James. These three men readily carried out this project while I, as Hirshhorn would say, "found the moolah."

They identified likely prospects for rehabilitation, mainly teen-aged high-school dropouts, including several juvenile court referrals. My dedicated screener-counsellors were superlative. Of twenty candidates with whom we worked, only two failed us. All the rest became winners, some dramatically so.

Our method was based on individual counselling which was both informal and ongoing. In each case our initial aim was to identify and develop a high degree of motivation. In our efforts we drew on education at a variety of levels ranging from simple manual trade skills to advanced university education. Our only conditions were that our lads show satisfactory and continuous progress, and that when they had succeeded they were to each help another in the manner in which we had helped them.

Our vintage year was 1969; four of our boys graduated from UBC together, receiving degrees in Physical Education, Music, Law, and Medicine. This called for a party, and I still treasure a group photograph taken at that joyous celebration.

My Experiences with Igor Gouzenko

I was asked occasionally to assist specific individuals. One of the more unusual was Igor Gouzenko, whose defection from the Soviet Union in September 1945 became a significant international event.

A lieutenant in the Russian army, Gouzenko came to Canada in June 1943 to work as a cipher clerk in the Russian embassy in Ottawa. When he learned he was scheduled to return to the Soviet Union, he decided to defect.

Gouzenko's testimony – and the evidence contained in the briefcase filled with secret documents which he gave to the Canadian authorities – convinced a Royal Commission, set up by the government, that the Soviet Union was engaging in foreign espionage from its diplomatic base in Canada. The documents Gouzenko gave to Canadian officials revealed, among many other things, the activities of the spies Klaus Fuchs and Alan Nunn May, who were later convicted in Britain of passing secrets concerning atomic weapons to the Soviet Union.

My first meeting with Gouzenko occurred following a conversation I had with Fergus Cronin, then a Canadian reporter for a popular American weekly magazine. Sometime in the late 1950s, Cronin came to my office alone. He asked that the matter he wished to discuss with me remain confidential between us. When I agreed to keep the information confidential, Cronin then told me that he was reasonably close to Igor Gouzenko, who had read of me in the press and wished to meet me. "Why?" I asked.

Cronin could only offer a guess. "He prides himself on his writing ability. Perhaps he wants financial help with his writing."

I was aware of Gouzenko's much publicized defection, as well as of his first novel *Fall of a Titan*, which I had not read. I was intrigued by the opportunity to meet the man. Two or three days passed. A man appeared at my office and told the receptionist that he wished to see me. My office manager, Duke Hague, went out to meet him and the enigmatic visitor said, "Just tell Mr. Joubin that I am a friend of Fergus Cronin." The man was Igor Gouzenko.

He was a dark-complexioned individual, of medium height and strongly built. Despite his apparent physical strength he seemed always to be ill at ease, on guard. Given his defection and the danger of KGB retribution, this was perfectly understandable.

For some time, Gouzenko and I sat and chatted. His request was simple. There had been a change in personnel in a federal government office, some political or administrative realignment, which had resulted in the delay or discontinuance of a sum of money, which, to that time, had been paid to him regularly. Gouzenko made his point in a discreet manner, but it was quite clear: he needed money. Given his peculiar undercover status, he said, he could not go to a bank for a loan even though he had property that could serve as collateral. He therefore had to find some individual he could trust, in order to retain his anonymity. He feared assassination should his identity become known.

Gouzenko's story seemed to me believable and reasonable. I explained, however, that I was not involved in the mortgage business and would have to consider the proposal for a day or two. Explaining that he could not wait that long, he spoke of his urgent need for $1,000 immediately and told me that he had read of my activities in the press and seen photographs of me in newspapers. He said that his wife had told him that he could trust me. Given his extremely suspicious attitude toward everything and everyone, this was surprising.

During our first meeting, which lasted not more than half an hour, he asked if I had read his book. I told him I had not read it, but that as soon as I could find time I should like to do so. Gouzenko was curious about my activities as a prospector, but he fidgeted a great deal and was apparently not disposed to spend much time in conversation unrelated to his problem. When I asked how he would repay the loan, he glibly replied, "Oh, that's no problem. I have revenue from my book and the screen rights."

Making out a cheque for $1,000, I asked "to whom do I make it payable?"

"Just Mr. Brown." he replied. "I am Mr. Brown to everybody, including my children." He took the cheque, thanked me, and said it would soon be repaid. Before he left he assured me that he would be back soon regarding the mortgage, but that he would not make an appointment. He never made appointments. He just came or he didn't.

Gouzenko struck me as neither a pauper nor a con artist, but as belonging to a legion of struggling artists, poets, painters, writers, and inventors who have approached me over the years for modest help, not unlike another prospector asking for a grubstake.

After two or three weeks, Gouzenko suddenly appeared again. He apologized for not having the repayment for the first loan but reported that he was now ready to discuss the mortgage of his property. It would be difficult, he explained, to provide me with a traditional type of mortgage. Because of his undercover situation and alias, he could not be party to the usual mortgage documentation. I explained that I could not loan him the $3,000 to $5,000 he requested without collateral, and I would need to have some detailed knowledge of the assets he would put up as collateral. "That is understandable," he replied. I introduced him to Duke Hague, my accountant. Since Gouzenko appeared reasonably at ease with Hague, I suggested that Hague accompany him back to his home so that it might be appraised for some type of informal mortgage, Gouzenko agreed, but "not today," he said.

After Hague had visited Gouzenko's home he gave me a detailed report. My general impression was that everything seemed to be in order. Thus, under this curious "handshake mortgage agreement," I provided him with a further and larger sum of money. Later, Gouzenko suggested that I visit his home. By this time I had told my wife Mary about my new acquaintance. I asked Gouzenko if I might bring her with me. This seemed to upset him, and he said, "No, come alone."

The Gouzenkos did not live ostentatiously. Their moderately large, older, wood and stone house in a far western suburb of Toronto was set in a large lot surrounded by shrubbery and trees and approached by a long, treed lane. The dark, somewhat gloomy grounds seemed to me to be the right environment for a man who lived in the midst of conspiracy. Gouzenko and his wife Svetlana had two children, a boy and a girl, who were not at home on the occasion of my visit. Gouzenko explained that they were unaware of their father's true identity. This probably contributed, in part, to the conspiratorial manner about everything Gouzenko did, reflected so dramatically in the wearing of a paper bag over his head whenever he appeared on television. Each time I met him he gave the impression that there was an ongoing conspiracy to find and kill him.

Generous quantities of home-cooked food and wine were provided. Our conversation was general, animated, and frank, ranging over a variety of subjects largely unrelated to money. To my surprise, Gouzenko's wife, who was also an author and a most outgoing person, told me that she had been trained as an air force pilot in wartime Russia. My impression was that even a decade earlier she would have had considerable difficulty squeezing into the limited space of a fighter aircraft!

At this time, there was considerable discussion in the press concerning Gouzenko's book, *Fall of a Titan*. It had been reported that he had sold movie rights to this book to American interests for some $50,000, then a considerable sum of money. I raised this matter with Gouzenko and asked why he needed more money if he had done so well with his writing. His simple explanation was that money went through his hands like water. This certainly did not encourage me to give him any more!

Gouzenko complained to me repeatedly of the lack of appreciation shown by Canadian authorities for what he had done and the risks he had taken. In his long rambling discussion that evening he told me that his primary ambition, from early boyhood, had been to become a successful writer of historical novels. When he told me that, I couldn't help asking myself whether Gouzenko's highly unusual political situation could have been self-arranged to create real-life circumstances perfect for a historical novelist. That evening Gouzenko presented me with an autographed copy of *Fall of a Titan*, and Svetlana gave me an autographed copy of her book, *Before Igor*.

However, the amicable relationship between Gouzenko and myself soon became strained. After the first curious mortgage loan, he returned and proposed a second similar relationship. He asked me for a cash loan, "guaranteed" by an unregisterable mortgage on a multi-acre cottage property near Georgetown. He declined to give me a proper legal description for the property, pending, he said, a subdivision survey to be made. When I told him I would wait for such a survey, he repeatedly asked for, and in some cases was given, smaller sums of money. No survey documents ever appeared.

This awkward and unpleasant relationship continued until one day Hague drew my attention to a short news item stating that a Canadian bank was, in effect, black-listing Gouzenko for repeatedly issuing worthless cheques. Gouzenko's irresponsible financial habits had caught up with him. By this time I had had enough of his opportunism. He was abusing his western-world freedom. From that point on, my office turned him away.

Several years later, I received a letter from a firm of attorneys in Toronto advising me that they were acting for parties attempting to straighten out some of Gouzenko's earlier financial problems. They had partial information on some of his earlier transactions and my name was included in their records. Would I waive all my claims if I were given partial restitution? I agreed, and my account records for "Mr. Brown" were closed.

When I reflect on the Igor Gouzenko I knew, I think of him as a natural conspirator. He seemed to enjoy living the life of a master spy. His sudden appearances and disappearances, the circuitous routes he followed (he never took the elevator directly to or from the floor on which my office was located), his disguised voice on the telephone, all seemed to me to be staged. In my view, such precautions were not really needed. And many of the things he did increased rather than decreased public interest in him and his family, surely the exact opposite of what he should have intended.

As I sought to fathom Gouzenko's tortuous behaviour, I became convinced that he embodied much of the distrust, fear, and paranoia which the Cold War had stimulated in all of us. These characteristics were displayed by Gouzenko's use of disguises when he appeared in public. He was, of course, a defector who had sought asylum and had chosen to put himself and his family in their dangerous predicament. When Canadian authorities failed to treat him as generously as he assumed he merited, I think that his tendency to distrust others, particularly those in control of government agencies, deepened, as did his fear and paranoia. To a certain extent, his attitude toward governments, of course, was quite understandable.

Personal experience has taught me that ordinary people of different races and nationalities, working on one-to-one or small-group bases, can develop an enduring sense of trust, and through such trust harmonious relations, even though there are obstacles to overcome. Why is it that leading nations of the world can't seem to do the same? How might enduring co-operation be established rather than the absurd competition stimulated by the vested interests of the military-industrial agencies in both the Soviet Union and the United States? What, if anything, can ordinary citizens do to advance peace in world affairs? These were questions and issues for which I sought answers and which led to my deepening involvement in the movement for world peace.

My Commitment to World Peace

Since childhood I have been naturally tolerant of all peoples and races, together with their differences of language, customs, and beliefs. Early in life I became committed to the concept of "The Brotherhood of Man." This was something that had been taught to me by my mother, and it was something that I lived.

I spent my childhood on the edge of Victoria's Chinatown, attending school and playing with, among others, Chinese, East Indian, and Japanese chums. I was also conscious of being an outsider myself, French in British Columbia, which in those days was very British.

The Asians I knew were all servants or gardeners. During the Great Depression I had worked side-by-side with Chinese coal shovellers. Later, when my prospecting activities were based largely from Japanese fishing communities on the Pacific coast and in Indian villages, I had shared fully in the lives of these people, at work and at play and occasionally at worship.

As a college junior I had worked in the Students' International Relations Club, which attracted international philosophers and political leaders to its seminars. And at UBC my principal part-time activities, apart from study and working to survive, were reading about world affairs, attending lectures, and debating on every aspect of international history, political thought, and ideology.

My basic moral code was – and remains – the Ten Command-

ments, and high on that list is "thou shalt not kill," without qualification. The deaths of my father and my younger brother taught me
personally something of the ravages of war. I can honestly say that I
have never carried or used a firearm, except in target practice as part
of obligatory militia training at university. Had I been accepted (and
not rejected as I was) for military service, I would have served in the
medical corps. I am opposed resolutely to war, regarding it as an
entirely improper means for resolving international disputes. I do not
believe that peace can be defensive without being aggressive. Mankind
urgently needs a system of enforceable international law and an agency
that commands universal respect and trust to arbitrate differences,
or humanity is doomed.

When the indescribably horrifying results of the use of the atomic
bombs were first revealed at the end of the Second World War, I
was deeply shocked, seeing it as a barbarous crime committed by
the military forces of a "white Christian nation" upon a civilian
city of "the Asian race," remote from any war zone – not once,
but twice. In 1949, when I began to prospect for uranium, among
other metals, I did so in the hope that this tremendous new energy
source would, in fact, be used to serve humanity under strictly
controlled conditions (just as fire does). The realization that one
cubic inch of uranium can provide heat equivalent to burning thirteen hundred tons of environmentally despoiling coal was awe-
inspiring. Clearly, this metal, like other metals, could provide great
blessings to humanity, if not perverted by twisted minds.

I have worked hard over the years to promote the blessings of
uranium in every possible way and to overcome the curse that befell
its first use. One means of doing this, while contributing to the advancement of international peace, was through my association with
the Pugwash Conferences.

The late Cyrus Eaton, the Canadian-born American industrialist,
established and financed the Pugwash Conferences. Eaton, who may
have learned of my work through an article entitled "Joubin of Blind
River" in the August 1955 *Life* magazine, invited me to Cleveland to
tell him about the uranium mines in Elliot Lake. Through his financial
interests in railways and steel companies, Eaton had had for many
years a deep interest in mining. He had played leading roles in the
ventures of Steep Rock Iron mines in north-western Ontario and,
later, the Ungava Iron Ore Company in northern Quebec.

Eaton wondered if there was another mining investment opportunity for him at Elliot Lake. He was also interested in the developing technology of power reactors for peaceful purposes. He was a professed internationalist and "peace-nik."

I was much impressed by Eaton's sincerity and understanding of international developments. Some may regard Eaton and the Pugwash Conferences he initiated as long on generalities and short on specifics about peacemaking. Eaton's aim was simply to persuade world leaders to become committed to world peace and to use their intelligence and power to prevent war and to promote peace. In my view, Eaton's initiative was deceptively simple and yet highly effective. He was earnestly endeavouring, in his own words, "to make the world of the 'here and now' a more attractive place in which to live."

Stimulated by the declaration concerning the extreme perils of nuclear war that Albert Einstein and Bertrand Russell had signed in early April 1955, which urged governments to abolish nuclear weapons and to find peaceful means for the settlement of all matters of dispute among them, Eaton had turned his family home in Pugwash, about forty miles northwest of Truro, Nova Scotia, into a centre for the furtherance of international peace. It was his hope that authors, politicians, businessmen, public administrators, scholars, and scientists (over a score of Pugwash members are Nobel Laureates) from all over the world would come together in Pugwash to develop practical proposals for the implementation of plans whereby human beings could rid the world of military aggression and live in peace. The Pugwash Conferences, which began in 1955, made, and continue to make, important contributions to peace. The administrative headquarters is now in London, England.

Pugwash was, and is, an enabling facility for continuous research and debate among scientific advisers to policy makers of east and west. Its founding by Cyrus Eaton was a key step in a movement that has grown in strength and political importance. It is a "Thinkers Conference" organized around a series of seminars in which urgent issues of world concern are discussed. Pugwash Conferences are today held around the world, and on both sides of the Iron Curtain. I became a supporter nearly thirty years ago and have remained so to the present.

The East/West Roundtable was another agency which contributed to international understanding. I was introduced to it by Cyrus Eaton. It was a group of eastern and western European leaders who had the same general objectives as the Pugwash Conference, but were more politically oriented. It was, in essence, a representative but necessarily elitist forum – its members had almost all held high political office in their respective countries – for debate, study, and reconciliation of ideological differences toward amicable co-existence between the Eastern bloc countries and Western democracies.

At the time of my involvement with this group in the early 1960s the great majority of members were senior politicians or statesmen who held, or had held, important positions in national governments. Included in the group were a former president of France and a former president of Italy, along with several others of ministerial rank from five or six European countries. This difference in membership between the Roundtable and the Pugwash Conferences I found intriguing. Those at the East/West Roundtable were veterans of government policy-making and practice. They had wielded power but rarely had it seemed to their liking as internationalists. Their altruistic principles had been compromised. I was struck by the extent to which they spoke of their sense of frustration and helplessness while in positions of political power. I remember the lament of a former socialist prime minister of France, elected by the working-class vote of that country, whose political career was ended by a national strike.

I attended only two of the annual East/West Roundtable conferences, in Paris and Brussels, but did develop several long-lasting correspondence friendships with certain of the British participants, principally Philip Noel-Baker and Konni Zilliacus, both well-known British socialist political figures. Noel-Baker, the son of Canadian-born Quakers, was awarded the Nobel Peace Prize in 1959.

Participation in the Pugwash Conferences and the East/West Roundtable provided opportunities to meet and share in seminars with leaders and, more importantly, to contribute through discussion and publications toward establishing enduring bases for world peace through international co-operation. The knowledge and education I gained thereby inspired me to assist the Canadian physicist Dr. Norman Alcock when he told me about his plan for social research and peace education.

Alcock's pamphlet on peace, *The Bridge of Reason* first brought him to my attention early in 1961. I sought him out and complimented him on the content and argument of his essay and offered to purchase some copies for distribution. He personally delivered these to me, and we spent an hour or two in discussion.

During our conversation Alcock told me that, having sold his successful electronic research company, he was now going to direct his energies full-time to the advancement of peace.

I was immediately impressed by Alcock and the courageous sacrifice he proposed to make in the then largely uncharted sea of peace research. I learned that he had completed his training as a nuclear physicist in Montreal during and after the Second World War. There, he had been associated with some of the distinguished British scientists who had come to participate in the joint British-Canadian atomic research project administered by Canada's National Research Council. In 1946 he had engaged in research at Atomic Energy of Canada Ltd. at Chalk River, Ontario. In 1949, Alcock received his doctorate in physics from McGill University.

With two colleagues, Alcock established Isotope Products Ltd. in Oakville, Ontario, in 1950. The aim of these men was to use their knowledge of nuclear physics for peaceful purposes. Some years later, when Alcock and his colleagues sold their business and the decision was made to transfer it to the United States, he decided to remain in Canada.

In the autumn of 1959, Alcock resolved that he would devote himself to intensive, full-time peaceful studies as a way of contributing toward the creation of political and social systems necessary to counteract the ongoing development of a nuclear-armed world. Just as he had invested over twenty years in the study of science and in scientific activities, Alcock was convinced that he should now devote himself to the advancement of world peace in the same disciplined manner.

Upon completion of an initial study of the social sciences, Alcock wrote his thirty-eight-page booklet *The Bridge of Reason*, which he published at his own expense. In that highly thoughtful pamphlet, he set out his ideas concerning the promotion of peace.

Alcock argued that a network of peace research institutes should be brought into being as part of a comprehensive effort to reverse the drift toward nuclear war. Just as the scientific method and human rationality generally had played key roles in the phenomenal progress of technology (and in the advances in the biological sciences which had largely rid mankind of historic plagues and other infectious diseases), Alcock was convinced that the methods of science and reason could be used to rid the world of social diseases, one of the gravest of which is war. Thus he proposed that small groups of scientists and scholars of many countries should come together as the nuclei of the proposed network of peace research institutes, and they function as internationally oriented co-operatives for the advancement of peace.

In the development of his plans for an international network of peace research institutes, Alcock was aware that no single individual working alone was likely to come up with the analysis and methods necessary. He was conscious of the role that the "critical mass" played in a nuclear reaction. It was his hope that a dedicated group of peace researchers might be able to create the "critical mass" needed, at various strategic centres throughout the world, to outlaw nuclear war. The individuals involved in such an enterprise, Alcock recognized, would have to be persons of the highest professional standing within the communities from which they came. He was also aware that the peace research institutes which they created would have to work closely with governments while being independent from them. They would have to be able to gain the respect and support of the governments concerned while not being controlled or directed by them.

Following the publication in March 1961 of *The Bridge of Reason*, Alcock embarked upon a campaign to interest key individuals and institutions. The establishment of the Canadian Peace Research Institute was announced on November 2, 1961, by a director of the new Institute, the Rt. Rev. James S. Thomson, Moderator of the United Church of Canada, a former president of the University of Saskatchewan, and, earlier, a general manager of the Canadian Broadcasting Corporation. Dr. Thomson described the activities planned for the new Institute as "a crusade to make reason prevail . . . a rational down-to-earth program that can succeed if Canadians will establish the first Institute promptly and carry their example to several other countries."

Norman Alcock persuaded other influential Canadians to serve as directors of the new Canadian Peace Research Institute, including Dr. Brock Chisholm, first co-ordinator of the United Nations World Health Organization, and Dr. Pierre Dansereau, the world-renowned botanist and Dean of Science at the University of Montreal. Pierre Elliott Trudeau, who at that time was a member of the Faculty of Law at the University of Montreal, served as a member of the board until 1965. Other members included Walter C. Koerner, the British Columbia industrialist and philanthropist; Hugh L. Keenleyside, who had had a distinguished career in the Canadian diplomatic service; Gerard Pelletier, the journalist who later became a member of Prime

Minister Trudeau's cabinet; Mrs. W. P. Tucker, a key member of the women's movement in Canada; Dr. Francis G. Winspear, who had been a member of the faculty of the University of Alberta; and Dr. Kenneth E. Boulding, a distinguished economist, a Quaker, and author of many articles on peace research and related matters. Norman Alcock and I were also members of the board.

Norman Alcock regarded peace research as a profoundly serious and urgent undertaking, not unlike the development of international constitutional law. I shared that view with him entirely, as did an increasing number of Canadians, together with the news and broadcast media. Within a short period of time, following its founding in 1961, the Canadian Peace Research Institute had gained thousands of supporters across Canada. A publicly provided "start-up" fund of about a quarter of a million dollars, a considerable sum in those days, was raised to finance the initial work of the Institute, particularly the program of research which the board approved as part of its overall plan to launch this new agency.

As its name indicates, the primary function of the Institute was social research and data publication. Through the research activities of its members; through its monthly journal of original research on human attitudes, social behaviour, and a wide variety of issues related to peace and war; and through its peace research reviews, the Institute made highly significant contributions to the organization and integration of knowledge concerning war and peace. This work was, and is, of vital importance. Those responsible for the Institute's establishment and ongoing work recognized that if peace research is to be conducted on sound bases and to be effective in the prevention of war and the reduction of destructive violence, then such research must be co-ordinated, tested, made cumulative, command respect and trust, and be applicable. This is a difficult and complex undertaking. But just as mankind has been freed from slavery and various infectious world diseases and plagues through disciplined thought and co-ordinated action, the Institute sought to contribute to the improvement of knowledge concerning war and its causes and how they might be ameliorated.

Later, after Pierre Trudeau became prime minister of Canada, those of us who had worked with him in the early days of the Institute looked to him for new international initiatives. His quest for global peace and the establishment of Canada's new Institute for International Peace and Security confirmed our belief in his long-term commitment to those ideals which had led each of us to become associated with the Canadian Peace Research Institute.

Involvement in the work of the Institute was a key factor which led me to search for the best means (within my scope of training and experience as a geologist and developer of mineral resources) of serving as a technical missionary in the cause of world brotherhood. When I decided upon this goal, and before I became a full-time Technical Advisor to the United Nations posted to numerous fields abroad, I elected to visit and tour the People's Republic of China while in the east on a professional trip to Japan in 1961.

XIV

A Glimpse of the People's Republic of China

As a young boy on the outskirts of Victoria, I was fascinated by our Chinese next-door neighbours. I often participated in the many anniversaries and street festivals in nearby Chinatown with a swarm of Chinese youngsters about my own age. My favourite among the festival parades was one which took us, with accompanying gong music, to the Chinese cemetery near the Pacific Ocean. There, members of the Chinese community carefully disinterred the remains of their ancestors buried years before. Music was played to attract the good spirits and firecrackers were set off to drive away the evil spirits. The bones recovered from the graves were ceremoniously polished and packed carefully in small wooden boxes for return to China. As these solemn proceedings took place, the delightful aroma of roasting pork and other delicacies began to permeate the air. We would soon be sharing delicious food provided in generous quantities. My brother and I and our Chinese chums enjoyed this part of the ritual best.

Later, after I had graduated from high school and found myself engulfed in the Great Depression, the only full-time winter job I could secure was in a coalyard at a railroad siding on the edge of Victoria's Chinatown, where I worked alongside about a dozen Chinese labourers. Together we unloaded coal with hand shovels, then screened, sacked, and weighed it, finally delivering it door-to-door. It was hard and dirty work, but there were no shirkers. We were a brotherhood of shared labour, one of the noblest of all orders.

All who are familiar with the history of Victoria and Vancouver know that these cities were the initial destinations, and often the eventual homes for thousands of Chinese brought to Canada to help build our railroads or to work in our coal mines. While their contribution to the development of this country has not often been celebrated, they were important nineteenth-century Canadian pioneers. As a boy interested in prospecting, I had learned about the key role the Chinese had played as participants during all the major gold rushes in western North America – California, British Columbia, the Yukon, and Alaska.

I Decide to Visit China

I set in motion plans to persuade Chinese authorities to allow me to visit their country as a tourist and as a geologist. I hoped also that by visiting China I would contribute in some small way to a better Canadian understanding of that huge country's struggle for socio-political stability and perhaps also cultivate some scientific links between China and Canada.

It was about twelve years after the People's Republic of China had been proclaimed and Mao Tse-tung had become its chairman. Mao, through his political power and idealism, and Chou-en-lai, the prime minister, through his administrative and diplomatic skill, had consolidated their control of the vast country and its diverse population of about 700 million people. They had also secured the constructive economic and technical support of Communist allies such as the Soviet Union and Czechoslovakia, and others such as socialist Sweden, evidence of which I was to see in the large and obviously new or modernized transport and communication systems.

For clearly profound yet publicly unclear reasons, Mao and Chou had begun to remove the Russian presence from China, a move which was well advanced at the time of my visit. Pictures and statues of Lenin remained untouched, but portraits of Stalin had been replaced by those of Chairman Mao, save in the offices of a few absent-minded professors or scientists. Mao's "little red book" seemed to be the genuinely popular "bible" of the land. Every literate person – and there had been a literacy explosion in China from about 1955 onwards – carried a copy, and it was read publicly as avidly as we read newspapers, magazines, or paperback books. *Quotations from Chairman Mao Tse-tung* is essentially a summary of the seemingly countless essays Mao wrote on current Chinese history and desirable personal and group behaviour. I tried to secure a translation of the booklet before I went to China (and while I was there), not realizing that it would not appear in English until 1966.

I knew several of the small number of Canadians who had previously toured China, and I turned to them for information and guidance. Among these were Dr. J. G. Endicott, a clergyman who was born in China and was a friend of Chou-en-lai; Prof. J. Tuzo Wilson, internationally known geophysicist; and James S. Duncan and Walter L. Gordon, senior Canadian business executives.

The late 1950s and early 1960s was a most difficult period for a private individual wishing to visit China. During those years China was locked in a political struggle with the Soviet Union; relations with the United States were non-existent, in the formal diplomatic sense, given continuing American support for Chiang Kai-shek and his followers in Taiwan; and Chinese military and security personnel were seeking to strengthen their role in the leadership of their nation. It was not, by any means, a good time for a North American to come knocking at China's door to ask if he could come in. Nonetheless I was hopeful.

I flew to Hong King, then, as now, China's effective "back door" to the western world. There I presented myself to the trade commissioner of the People's Republic of China in his modest office. I showed him my Canadian passport and the letters of reference which several of my Canadian friends and acquaintances had written on my behalf to Chinese friends and Europeans resident in China. The Chinese contacts included senior persons in the government, the Academy of Science, the country's international trade bureaus, university professors in faculties of geology, geophysics, and languages, and members of the medical and social welfare professions. Probably the most important was Kuo Mo-jou, the chairman of the Chinese Peace Committee. Kuo was generally regarded as China's counterpart to George Bernard Shaw.

The trade commissioner gave me a feeling of optimism concerning my proposed visit. "Oh, yes," he said, "we have received other material regarding you from independent sources." He asked for my Hong Kong address and told me to return to his office the following morning for visa photographs. "You may have to wait two or three days, but keep in touch with my office," he added.

About the third day, the commissioner called me. "Everything is in order. If you come to my office with $17.50 in Hong Kong money, I shall give you your train tickets and the reservations for your compartment." The next morning I boarded the train and was on my way to China.

Travelling in China

Entering China alone in mid August 1961, I was to visit Canton for
two days; Peking (Beijing), the central capital, for five days; and
Chansha, Wuhan, and Chengchow briefly. Except for the short railroad trip from Shumchun, on the south-east border, to Canton, I
travelled entirely by air on a general south-to-north route, covering
about twenty-six hundred miles.

During my visit, I travelled, observed, and talked almost entirely
without the help of a guide or interpreter. I did this by choice, and
there was no effort by the Chinese to influence me otherwise. This
was not as difficult as one may think. In the course of much round-
the-world travelling, I had developed the knack of speedy adaptation
to circumstances ranging from the sublime to the ridiculous. Indeed,
after more than a week in Tokyo and Hong Kong fending off droves
of procurers, prostitutes, dope pushers, sex perverts, and runners, I
felt I could handle anything.

I had considerable freedom within China. My schedule of meetings
and visits to particular offices, factories, or laboratories, was arranged
in advance on the basis of what I had asked to see and what my hosts
suggested might be of special interest. I was never denied permission
to see things in which I indicated an interest.

Each morning I was met and escorted to my train or plane or
taken to an appointment mutually pre-determined. If there was no
apparent language problem I would thank and dismiss the guide after
confirming the arrangements for my next meeting. Attention was
always given courteously and efficiently to my transportation needs.

Usually each person I arranged to meet had a translator beside
him, when that was necessary, or an aide might guide me between
offices or through the plant. Generally after such appointments were
completed a car would be waiting to take me back to my hotel. During
my free time, when no appointments were scheduled, I was totally
on my own. When this was the case (which was not often), I went
out walking, just like a tourist on a cruise would do on arriving in
any port in the western world.

Although I carried a small amount of Chinese currency in my
pocket it was rarely needed, save for coins on buses. When I took a
taxi, or purchased larger items in a shop, I showed my hotel registration tag and initialled the invoice. At the end of my trip, before
being escorted to my return train to Hong Kong, I was presented

with a statement for total expenditures, which I thought was very reasonable. Payment was made with British sterling notes, which I was told was the only foreign currency then acceptable to them. I never found out how these scattered expenditures were controlled; when I enquired I was simply told, "Don't worry. We do."

My inability to speak Chinese was a handicap, but not a serious one. Practically all the university-educated Chinese I met could speak, or at least read, English. When a language problem arose in any public place, and my English and French failed me, it was only temporary. The problem was buzzed around and in minutes or even seconds, someone, usually a secondary school student with a smattering of English, would come to my aid. Others able to speak a variety of European tongues – mainly Russian – would voluntarily approach and ask if they could help in any way.

The Chinese were then making a huge, and seemingly successful, effort to reduce the many Chinese language dialects to one or two official dialects. Even more useful to the stranger was a program to express Chinese letters and numerals in European lettering. This was most helpful since I could syllabilize the Chinese words into pronouncable sounds usually understood by the Chinese.

The month of August, when I visited China, is, unfortunately, perhaps the wettest and hottest of the year there. August was also the holiday period for university staff; many academics had fled their universities for cooler areas. As well, the weather interrupted flying schedules and when we were aloft I had a good view of the ground only about half of the time.

My visit to China was too short, due to my business commitments in Tokyo, and this was particularly galling since no time limit had been imposed by Chinese authorities on my stay in their country. I would very much have enjoyed visiting some of their mining areas, but the schedule I had set for myself did not permit this.

From Shumchun to Canton

I entered the People's Republic of China at the border crossing of Shumchun. Shumchun is at the north end of a bridge crossing the narrow river which marks the boundary between China and the New Territories area it has leased to the British colony of Hong Kong. The village on the British-occupied side of the bridge is Lowu. The differences between Shumchun and Lowu – which are only one hundred yards apart – and in my treatment in each of them, reflected in miniature the differences I observed between Hong Kong and China.

In contrast to the brisk, immaculate, and impersonal soldiers who had processed me out of the colony of Hong Kong at Lowu, I was confronted at Shumchun by two khaki-clad figures in charge of China's entry formalities. They stood on the footpath between the train rails, in the centre of the bridge. There was no counter or desk, no handy telephone, no briefcase or papers, and no air of officiousness. Their uniforms, unadorned and worn with the indifference of fatigue suits, had long trousers and long-sleeved tunics with tight collars which, as opposed to the open-neck shirts and shorts of the Hong Kong military police, seemed out of place in the hot wet weather. They were unarmed; every Hong Kong border official had worn an impressive black leather Sam Browne belt supporting his holstered revolver.

One of the Chinese officials was tall, thin, placid, middle-aged, and apparently the senior man. The other was short, stocky, and young. These men took my documents without comment. The senior man examined my passport, the junior my medical certificate. I felt certain that neither could read English and that this had to be a well-rehearsed act.

To my astonishment, the young officer suddenly pointed to a date on my medical certificate and said, "This date is meaningless, sir." I looked and noted with shock that it was indeed meaningless! I looked at my certificate again. It took me a few seconds to think clearly.

"Ah," I said, "there is a correction on the last page."

The officer looked, and then said, "Yes, thanks, everything is now in order." He handed the certificate to the senior man who, to that point, had said nothing, as he looked at my passport photograph. Now for the first time in the three-minute performance, the senior man looked me straight in the eye, his face crinkling into a smile, and said, unhurriedly and with a gentle wave of his hand, "You are welcome." (Later, the British equivalent upon my re-entry to Hong Kong was: "You are processed, sir.")

Despite the informal and unimpressive appearance of these Chinese officers, they nevertheless convinced me of their efficiency. To my surprise, I discovered on several occasions in the ten days that followed that in China "efficiency" does not always come dressed in a pair of neatly creased trousers, polished shoes, and a white shirt.

Lowu was small and compact, consisting of a few well-built, white-washed, and impersonal offices. Smartly-dressed, armed Hong Kong Chinese police staffed the entire place. The only non-military corner was the bar and restaurant where the principal adornment on the wall was an advertisement displaying with equal artistry the curvaceous beauty of a large bottle of Coca Cola alongside a buxom white girl in a tight-fitting red and white bathing suit.

Across the bridge, Shumchun was a hive of activity, noise, music, and seeming disorganization amidst great heaps of bricks, lumber, reinforced steel, and large buildings freshly completed or in the process of construction. There were a lot of new buildings, mainly two- and three-storey brick and reinforced concrete affairs rising out of rice paddies, sugar cane, and papaya gardens. They seemed out of place somehow, a paradox I became used to all over China. Civilians were everywhere, mostly under cover the day I arrived because of rain. I saw no armed Red Chinese border guards (or even any barracks) although they must certainly have been nearby. I looked for my first glimpse of a Chinese flag and finally found one forlornly draped about its pole in a sodden mass.

There was a great din at the Shumchun railroad station where about three hundred Chinese were waiting to board the train. High-pitched Chinese music with a lively rhythm (too loud for my taste) blared out over the loudspeaker system, competing with the babble of voices. I was the only European in sight as the crowd bustled and hurried toward the doors of three or four passenger carriages. I clutched my tickets in my hand with some concern until I saw a small group of travellers who seemed certain of the carriage they should board, so I followed them. We settled into plain but clean seats. Before we could introduce ourselves, the train whistle blew, the carriages began to move, and we were on our way. Clearly we were in a better carriage, which was perhaps three-quarters full. Except for a group with airline-tagged hand luggage, the others in the carriage, practically all male, were neatly dressed, obviously resident Chinese, and, I assumed, probably civilian officials of some kind. Several of them carried folding fans in their hands and briefcases. As I sat by the window in a seat for two, I looked over my fellow passengers.

I identified from their dress and airline flight bags, a group of a dozen young Cambodian men. There was also a Ceylonese diplomat. Only he responded to my English greeting, so we sat together from Shumchun to Canton.

During my journey on this train I became acquainted with the Chinese emphasis on tea. Tea is everywhere, served from a teapot, thermos bottle, or an individual mug with cover which is both your private teapot and drinking cup. It is often poured into ordinary drinking glasses. The tea is green, made very weak, and served tepidly warm, without sugar or milk. Sipping a cup or glass of tea is as natural – and apparently as necessary – in China as breathing. I became an addict after the first three hours, or, in quantitative terms, after the first three quarts. The act of sipping and refilling became a psychological and chronic tug of war between me and a dimpled Chinese girl determined that I should never empty my glass. This contest turned into a physical ordeal for me until I learned to recognize the word for *Men* in Chinese and Russian.

The train from Shumchun to Canton also introduced me to the Chinese dove. The white dove, as the symbol of peace, is a common sight in China. It appears in the more ornate indoor plaster sculpture of public buildings, in outdoor stone sculpture, and often as an indoor alabaster ornament – supporting lamps, for example. The first of these to catch my eye was a large white plaster one mounted above the headlight of a passing locomotive.

The countryside through which we passed was the flat agricultural land of the Pearl River delta. It was cut into rectangular blocks with irrigation canals and elevated pathways alongside. A few workers with hand tools were busy in the gardens despite the drizzle and the sodden condition of the soil. The train engineer seemed to enjoy using his steam whistle to occasionally toot "hello" to clusters of people in the fields.

In perhaps less than a half-hour the extensive fields of the delta were left behind as we approached the river and then continued beside it towards Canton. The river water was an ugly brown-grey colour and flowed with a fair current. An astonishing variety of motor and sail boats and cargo scows plied the river in both directions. Most of them moved slowly and appeared unpainted or dull in colour. They seemed to be mainly smaller cargo boats and practically all had flimsy living accommodation on the rear deck area. Sometimes there were women, children, and small animals, such as pigs, chickens, or ducks on board. The vessels in unusual shapes and sizes, low clouds, drizzle, and generally drab colours of the boats and the river water all combined to produce in my mind a fascinating scene.

I had read before my journey began, that all flies had been eliminated in China, that no dogs or cats prowled the streets, that virtually all rodents and other vermin carriers had been eliminated, and that all milk was now pasteurized. Realizing that control measures would be difficult in any country not equipped with up-to-date sanitation, and simply impossible among nearly 700 million people, I looked somewhat skeptically for evidence of such conditions. I saw no dogs or cats or rodents anywhere in China and heard only one dog bark when I wandered back into a darkened hotel building at midnight and had trouble finding my room. (The dog served as an invisible nightwatchman.) And I saw only one cockroach!

Cleanliness, I soon learned, is an important facet of the ideology of the new China. While I saw no spitting on the streets, and no garbage other than in containers or small heaps awaiting prompt removal, spittoons were everywhere. Many are designed (as were the under-the-bed potties of our own pioneer period) with a lavish floral pattern and cover. I was baffled at discovering these attractive receptacles coyly tucked under the edges of well-upholstered chesterfields in large and sometimes crowded airport lobbies, train stations and hotels, until I learned their true purpose.

As our train approached Canton, buildings of all descriptions, mainly of ancient vintage, crowded in on both sides. The track on which our train was running soon became one of an increasing number of parallel rails. Then the train slowed to a crawl, during which the "tea maiden" in our carriage led in a male guide. He was young, bright, spoke French and English, and had documentation for all the foreigners in the carriage. We were to be taken to two different hotels by taxis, he announced, while an embassy car awaited the arrival of two others.

The hotel to which I was taken had been built in the mid 1930s on the bank of the Pearl River. It was clean but in a threadbare and tattletale-grey state and had an odour of mildew throughout. I was somewhat depressed until I looked down on the Pearl River from my eighth-storey window. It was a fascinating sight. The Pearl, an important artery of commerce, is a wide, brown, soupy-looking river moving at appreciable speed. Travelling with it and against it were myriads of boats of all descriptions, all of archaic design. I felt certain that a biblical scholar could recognize a facsimile of the original ark among this river traffic.

Inspired by this bustling scene, I decided to stroll the streets, alleys, and waterfront of Canton. The city core was about three thousand years old and looked it, with cobble lanes rather than streets, open sewers, and many tiny shop fronts, originally two or three stories in height on top of which two or three more had been subsequently added. Cast-iron lamps and hitching posts; roughly made, semi-opaque glass window panes; well-cracked, hand-made wall and floor tile; baked clay tiles for roofing and some gutters completed the scene. All of this was in sharp contrast to the city's periphery, where post-liberation construction of apartment blocks, government buildings, parks, and sports fields had been built. I spent an hour in a large state-owned department store where I had a guide-interpreter to help me. Later I walked through and exmined a partially completed three-storey walk-up apartment block.

From my hotel window I secured a fair view of the city, a view which, at night, seemed highly unusual to my western eyes. There were no neon or coloured lights (in fact, no bright lights anywhere), but rather thousands of small white lights, stationary or moving like fireflies. The city was ringed with the silhouettes of newly built factory smokestacks, rising, it seemed, directly out of the rice paddies. The streets were often wide, and some were newly paved, often bordered with recently planted eucalyptus trees and lined with scores of curious little factory workshops, all very crowded, primitively equipped, but buzzing with activity.

Adults and children and countless bicycles were everywhere; it seemed just as well that there were very few automobiles in the city. There were, however, numerous modern trucks and buses. Pedicars – a pedalled tricycle capable of carrying two passengers or five hundred pounds of goods – appeared to be popular. Wagons were drawn by individual men and pushed by three women, the latter occasionally singing in chorus. Porters shouldering traditional bamboo poles with cargo on each end, reminded me of China's historic means for the transport of materials. A few people were barefoot. Nearly all were dressed drably, sometimes in threadbare or tattered garments. But all seemed clean. And perhaps 10 per cent wore cheap wristwatches – one of my indices of wealth.

The populace clearly moved around in family groups. Few very old people were on the streets. Often I saw a mother carrying a tiny baby strapped in a shoulder-fitting hammock, sometimes with two to five other tots straggling along, single-file, like a long tail, each cling-ing to the other's shirt tail. (This was, of course, before China set out to control its population growth.) And girls of seven to ten years of age could often be seen carrying their one- or two-year-old brother or sister in a shoulder saddle.

One of the things that struck me (and which was later corroborated by other Europeans) was that, although I certainly saw thousands of Chinese babies, some under physical conditions that could not have been comfortable, I never heard one cry. Perhaps crying infants are a mark of the affluent society! Children of all ages appeared invariably well-disciplined. They generally appeared jolly and physically busy with games, including kite-flying, ball games, and tag.

Sports seemed popular among adults, principally basketball, swimming, weight-lifting, wrestling, and, during the winter in the north, I was told, ice-skating. Cultural hobbies included painting and sketching in public parks, stamp- and coin-collecting, dramatic clubs, ballet, and opera. Chinese youngsters, like their western counterparts, devoted considerable energy to simple pranks: trees in the parks seemed to be populated by numerous whistling and shouting small boys. Later, in Peking, I saw a broken water pipe by the roadside being put to use by some boys who had learned the universal trick of applying a thumb to a jet of water in such a way as to direct it by request upon those they liked, and by surprise upon those they did not.

I saw no particular evidence of poor health among the adults or the children. The only recognizable physical defect among the very young – up to about three years of age – was small patches of baldness. This was not common but its presence was made very obvious by the application of a white ointment to cover the affected spots. White ointment on universally black hair is eye-catching.

The Chinese, young and old alike, have a deep-seated and robust sense of humour. While not always immediately apparent, it is always lurking just below the surface. I found this to be true from the coolie on the street right up to "the leadership." The sense of humour varies only in degree of subtlety but is always easy to arouse. Thus it did not surprise me to learn that the circus has a place in the new China alongside ballet and opera.

An Evening at the Canton Opera House

Poor flying weather made it necessary for me to remain an extra evening in Canton and I asked to go to a public gathering. The opera was suggested and I agreed.

The site of the Canton opera house – by accident or design – was in a unique location which western architects could well apply to advantage. Instead of being on the curb of a busy thoroughfare, it was almost in the centre of a city block. Access was by a half-dozen wide walkways, perhaps one hundred feet long, connected with four streets. Certainly there would be no traffic congestion problems here, I thought, when the private automobile arrived in Canton.

Canton alone, I learned, supports over twenty opera companies which rotate between city and "outside" opera houses, usually for two-week runs. These companies are graded according to talent. Admission prices varied.

While I have attended occasional performances, I am not a connoisseur of opera, and must admit that I feel ill at ease in the high-society, fashion-plate environment of North American and much European opera, where audiences seem to attend to be seen and heard rather than to see and hear. Thus, I had a mild sense of my usual unease when I went to the opera in Canton.

The evening was hot and humid. Since Canton is semi-tropical, and this was the height of the summer rain season, I decided to wear a white shirt and tie, dispensing with a jacket. I arrived at the opera dressed in this manner and took my seat – fourth row centre in the orchestra – and my worst fears were suddenly realized: I was again sartorially out of place. To my amazement, most of the men around me sat in trousers, sandals, undershirts, and nothing else! Everywhere I looked, there was an amazing informality. And it was far more casual than any North American "come-as-you-are" party; here was the smell of humanity.

The jam-packed opera house was wildly noisy and I was certain the hordes of children could never be quieted. The aisles were full of moving, standing, and sitting people. Apparently this was quite normal. The audience ranged in age from three months to ninety years. Probably one-fifth of the women present had babies under a year old in shoulder hammocks. The aisles were alive with little girls between three and seven years of age. Large numbers of these girls stood, packed between the front-row seats and the edge of the stage, their little noses literally pressed against the edge of the platform.

The opera house, which held twelve hundred, was simple and undecorated, yet functional, with a large cafeteria just off the main lobby. It had been rebuilt three years earlier on the same site where opera houses have stood in Canton "for centuries." Ventilation was helped by a number of large fans hung like chandeliers from the high ceiling and the stage lighting was excellent. A moving ribbon of script was projected on a screen to one side of the stage, providing the dialogue as the play progressed.

I was told there would be two operas, one modern and the other classical. The program was to run for three hours with just one intermission. This, combined with the fact that the seats in the theatre were made of wood, made me feel that they were carrying the spartan aspect of communism too far!

Suddenly, the music began. The orchestra is hidden from view in the wings, behind the curtain, so the music comes forth without warning. When the first performers appeared on stage, total silence, except for the quiet shuffle of bodies, fell over the audience and continued throughout the performance.

I watched both operas with fascination, and had no difficulty following the plots, thanks to the brilliant pantomime of the actors. I was also interested in the music and sound effects which, to western ears, were unusual. As well, the costuming and scenery were spectacular. Somehow, as I followed the heroic exploits of Wu Sun, a lengendary Chinese Robin Hood, I was also kept entertained by the audience. Altogether it was a wonderful party for everyone! I can no longer listen politely to the wails of North American impresarios claiming they "cannot sell opera to the masses."

An Ivory Sculpture Factory

I have always had an interest in art, being particularly attracted to Eskimo or Inuit carvings. I was, therefore, delighted to be able to go to a Chinese ivory sculpture factory in Canton.

Between 1950 and 1960, this particular factory had been reorganized and enlarged from 43 employees to 450 employees. The premises were cluttered with work benches, supplies, tools, and weak electric bulbs dangling from the ceiling. In fact, it resembled the studio of a hive of artists more than a factory.

The employees, always called "workers" or "colleagues" in China (perhaps because the word *employees* cannotes capitalistic exploitation, and Russia has pre-empted the word *comrade*) worked in rooms of up to fifty people. They carved industriously, shoulders hunched and heads bent over the individual benches. Each seemed oblivious to his or her surroundings and concentrated completely on the exquisitely delicate artistry involved. I actually startled several of them when, sometimes after several seconds, they suddenly became aware that I was standing beside them. These artists, men, women, and children ranging in age from twelve to perhaps fifty years, were quite obviously utterly devoted to their work.

I looked for evidence of ill-health, undernourishment, or occupational disease, and wondered about the environment of ivory chips and dust, the poor light, eyestrain, and the quality of the air. To my great surprise, only a few of the older workers wore glasses. Also, only a very few of the men, and none of the women, smoked cigarettes. I was told there were frequent breaks during the day, when groups would leave their benches for a stroll and some fresh air. I saw no food and was told that all workers went to a cafeteria about two blocks away. The ubiquitous Chinese tea, however, was at everybody's elbow, served warm in glasses by roving attendants. Occasionally, as work progressed, the public address system (which is everywhere in China) broke, harshly to my ears, into an announcement. At intervals, a girl reads from the latest newspaper or music would be played.

The personnel of such a factory conformed in general to the structure of all "industrial workers' groups." There were the apprentices: a number of artistically promising youngsters aged twelve to sixteen, recommended by their schools and their artist parents, who often worked in the same factory. During their three-year training period, apprentices were provided with all the necessities of life and paid six to nine dollars per month.

The principal group of workers was divided into eight grades. The lower-skilled and least adept were largely technicians, the others were the artists. The eight grades were provided with all the necessities of life and paid from fourteen to forty-three dollars per month. Ranking above these eight grades was a small group – about five in the factory I visited – who were masters. They were responsible for the artistic standards of the personnel and the product. They received all the necessities of life and were paid, in addition, up to eighty-seven dollars a month.

Above these was a small administrative staff, always surprisingly young, perhaps averaging twenty-five years of age. The top official and head of the administrative department might be either a man or woman. To a westerner of that time there was a surprisingly widespread acceptance of leadership from women. Those employed in each of these factories worked eight hours a day, six days a week, with about two weeks' annual holidays. The techniques of ivory carving which I saw these workers employing called for a high degree of skill in a difficult – and probably fast-disappearing – medium. I certainly gained a new appreciation for ivory sculpture after watching these artists at work.

Like all industrial workers in China, men working in these factories were eligible for a retirement pension at sixty and the women at fifty-five. The conditions of work and the remuneration enjoyed by industrial workers were, however, not shared by agricultural workers, and no secret was made of it. The leadership stressed that the elimination of this disparity was a principal economic aim of the nation.

Ideology and Communication in the New China

The first time I noticed any ideological propaganda in China was at this industrial arts factory. It was quite low-key and entirely from the administrative staff. Its general theme was that in pre-liberation days, artists had been cruelly exploited or ignored and left to starve. The new society now offered them real security for the first time in history.

The single red flag at Shumchun and a simple, life-sized, untitled plaster bust of Chairman Mao Tse-tung in the lobby of the international airport in Canton were the only evidences of nationalism I had seen to this point. The bust was white against the light-coloured plaster of the lobby wall and was supported by a single column without drapes or other ornamentation. It was in good taste and not unlike our own custom of displaying the portrait of the Queen in foyers of public buildings. Public displays of nationalistic or ideological symbols always seemed discreetly done in those sections of China which I visited. There were only a few flags, perhaps on the whole less than in our own country.

Aside from the store windows, I saw no commercial advertising signs or billboards as we know them in America. This was in striking contrast, of course, to Tokyo and Hong Kong, where outdoor advertising is an extensively developed art. Occasionally in China a billboard did appear. I saw three in Canton and noted that each carried a message of social or political appeal. Since 70 per cent of the population was illiterate in 1961, the billboards and other signs were necessarily well-illustrated to convey a pictorial rather than a written message.

One of the billboards I saw consisted of a picture of a family group with a young boy holding a large open book and pointing at a page. Brothers, sisters, parents, and grandparents were all grouped around, and from some distance away, Chairman Mao looked on with a beneficent smile. The message was clear. The leadership wanted everyone, young and old, to study and become literate. A critic might well say, "Fine, but why Mao in the picture?" to which the Chinese would reply, "Chairman Mao is more than a political leader to us. He is a figure not unlike Abraham Lincoln and what boy has not been told of Lincoln's personal struggle to become educated?" Mao was also a teacher by profession, serving as a librarian's assistant at Peking University and later as principal of a school before he embarked on his long career as a professional revolutionary and political leader.

The few other posters and billboards which I saw dwelt on such subjects as sanitation, elimination of drug habits, and the need for unity between agricultural and industrial workers. I found these pictorial murals interesting and much less offensive that the ever-present barrage of billboard advertising in the west, with its strange suggestion that shapely women, in various degrees of undress, are the best judges of everything from automobile tires to life insurance.

An effective means of social and political communication, common to most public buildings in China, is the dedication plaque found in the foyer on the most prominent wall in a building. The message usually embodies a moral principal or motto such as "A great nation is built on unity, work, and loyalty." I found such messages inspirational and informative. What did disturb me however was that practically all such sage advice was ascribed to only one source – Chairman Mao. This seemed monotonous to me: there certainly were and had been other great and wise men in China in addition to Mao. In recent years, of course, the Chinese leadership has indicated clearly that it understands the dangers not only of the "personality cult" but also of undue regard for doctrinaire Marxism.

Several years after my visit and less than twenty years after the establishment of the New China, Chairman Mao and his colleagues decided that the Chinese Communist Party as a whole had to be disciplined and remoulded, and that the intransigent and ingrained rigidity of Marxist bureaucracy had to be rooted out. The Cultural Revolution was introduced to replace the old and to rejuvenate the new generation. The astonishing policy of allowing secondary school and university students time away from their studies to "smoke out" entrenched governmental rigidity, irregularities, and corruption was probably effective, but its eventual extremism forced Mao to dampen the ardour and rein in the excesses of his Red Guards of "the new generation."

This revolutionary policy was an interesting historical and perhaps important social experiment. Clearly, at twenty-year intervals, a new generation, consciously or unconsciously, can have grounds for being "restless" and "reacting" to a complacent bureaucracy – thus prompting rebellion, subtle or agressive, unless some manner of release is provided. Perhaps Mao's socio-political experiment is worthy of closer study by the world at large. It would not be the first great historical, technical, or cultural contribution made by China toward world progress.

These events, of course, all lay in the future when I visited Canton in 1961.

Domestic Aspects of Life in Canton

During my visit to Canton, I was shocked at the almost total lack of the fine buildings, streets, shops, and crowds of well-dressed people so evident in the prosperous colony of Hong Kong. Canton, of course, was a prime target in 1937 of Japanese bombing, and was occupied by them until 1945. The city's economic recovery did not begin until 1949, when Mao and his colleagues gained control. The advances made in Canton during the first decade of the New China, although important, were not yet clearly obvious to the newcomer on a brief visit in 1961. The new construction (mainly factories) was located toward the outer fringes of the city and scattered in a manner that hid its extent.

Quite frankly, the general standard of living was low. However, I saw no signs of starvation, nor evidence (more difficult to perceive) of hunger. Unlike in Hong Kong, there was no begging in China – either for food or money. Quite abundant quantities of foodstuffs – flour, beans, and garden produce – were piled on the Pearl River docks or were being moved about the city openly on trucks or push-carts. Ducks, a few chickens, and an occasional pig wandered freely about the countryside and suburbs. It was hard to conceive of starvation, even hunger, under such conditions. Food *was* rationed, however, and I felt certain that the variety was probably quite limited.

In 1961, the great mass of people in Canton were dressed monotonously. I saw little variety of colour and almost no evidence of style. The women and girls paid little attention to their appearance, and make-up was not used. The girls' hair was simply done up in two long braids down their backs.

Despite Canton's low standard of living and its general dilapidation at the time of my visit, the cleanliness, both physical and moral of the city was its greatest achievement, as I saw it. Everyone worked vigorously, no idlers were visible, and there seemed to be time and inclination to relax – as evidenced by the evening or holiday crowds of families on the streets, in the shops, in the parks, and at the opera and movie houses.

From Canton to Peking by Air

As I moved north through China some thirteen hundred miles to Peking, I saw a gradual but consistent improvement in the general well-being and appearance of the people and their cities. Canton, the capital of a fertile, sub-tropical, agricultural region – three crops a year barring floods – is the bottom rung on the ladder to Peking in many ways.

I left Canton by air. The drive to the airport was made soon after dawn and the sights and smells provided an interesting kaleidoscope that seemed to epitomize the great struggle and paradox of China's re-awakening. Hundreds of push-carts laden high with every imaginable kind of farm produce, but mainly spinach, cucumber, onions, and squash at that season, were crawling toward the city, passing, crawling in the opposite direction, an equal number of push-carts laden with tubs of "night-soil" from the city's millions, to be used as garden fertilizer. Darting between the counter-current of push-carts were a few modern diesel buses. Hundreds of people were moving here and there on foot. This slow stream of laborious human activity travelled through the mists of dawn along the main North Road, then under vigorous mechanized construction to emerge as a magnificent, wide, paved, and tree-lined avenue.

The plane I boarded was a Russian-built Ilyushin-14 aircraft, closely resembling our DC-3. Its departure was delayed for an hour because of weather. The Chinese airline is particularly cautious: both Chinese and European technicians within China assured me of the accuracy of the almost unbelievable claim that China's air safety record is perfect. To that time, it was said, they had never had a single civilian airplane crash with loss of life. The volume of passenger air traffic was not large compared to our own, but in a country of nearly 700 million (seemingly well-equipped with modern airports), it was still considerable.

I was curious about military aircraft; although I landed in five of China's largest western airports and flew over others, I saw only two small mono-jet fighter aircraft. They were on the ground and without obvious armament, although they were guarded by one of the only two armed men I saw in all my travelling in China.

The Ilyushin I boarded was the regular once-daily flight to Peking. It was about half-full with a score of passengers, but there was no empty space. Unoccupied seats and every available corner were packed with air-express and mail bags. We had a stewardess who plied us with the usual tea in a glass, along with additional gimmicks more characteristic of capitalist airlines, such as magazines, cards, candy, and bamboo fans. She even put sugar in the tea!

I had a window seat offering a good general view of the ground, and asked if I might take photographs from the air. This is a practice frowned on in several countries, and it was, indeed, the only restriction on photography that I encountered anywhere in China, other than the blanket requirement that all film exposed in that country must be developed there.

At the first stop, a young man reboarded the plane with an enormous watermelon, and the stewardess ruled that it should be weighed as it might prove to be excess baggage. The problem was quickly resolved by the stab of a knife. Each of the passengers, including myself and the stewardess, received a welcome slice. It is not hard to like the Chinese; they can be very practical philosophers.

Overnight in Changsha

Our aircraft came down at Changsha for a planned three-hour stop
for fuel and lunch, as no food (save for the unofficial and quickly
consumed watermelon) was served on the plane. Many Chinese take
a long lunch period almost akin to the Latin siesta. However, since
thunderheads were gathering over the Changsha airport, it was announced that we'd spend the afternoon and night there and continue
the next morning.

I was pleased to have this unexpected extra time in Changsha, the
capital of the important province of Hunan, since it is the town where
Chairman Mao Tse-tung was educated. This was recognized in an
appropriately modest way at the airport by a life-size statue of Chairman Mao, standing before a plain but beautiful, purple velvet drape
that hung in folds from ceiling to floor. As usual, the statue and drape
were untitled and without flag or any other adornment. There was a
large coloured map of China on one wall and several large Chinese
water-colour paintings on other walls of the airport waiting rooms.

I walked around the city for several hours. The standard of public
works, the amount of new construction, the quality of the people's
clothes, the scarcity of human-propelled push-carts, more fresh paint,
more flower gardens and landscaping, a few bobbed hairdos on the
girls – and a higher percentage of wristwatches – all indicated a generally higher standard of living than in Canton.

I was tired and hungry when I returned to the hotel. Unknown
to me, a corner of the dining room had been discreetly screened off
for my use and a place set for me at a small table with a rare knife
and fork. As I walked through the still-crowded public dining room,
a Chinese stranger, unaware perhaps, as I was, that provision had
been made for me, caught my eye and motioned to the empty chair
beside him. He was at a large table with seven or eight male companions. His hospitality was so spontaneous and heart-warming I
couldn't decline, and so I slipped into the chair. Not one of them
knew a word of English or French. The dishes were all totally strange
to me, and I had to work with chopsticks before a panel of experts.
At last, I was really in China!

I ordered beer for all of us since I had noted that it was the popular
drink of the south and one of the people's few "indulgences." We all
enjoyed ourselves as my erratic chopsticks and curious eating habits
made me the unwitting clown of the company. I even started the meal

with soup instead of finishing with it! When the meal and our "conversation" were over we spent as much time again shaking hands, bowing, and saying good-bye as we had eating the meal, which I had found most interesting in itself.

The main courses, served in large china "dish-up" bowls, included steamed rice, a green vegetable resembling spinach or cabbage, but with a salty taste as if mixed with seaweed, and steamed fish. The soup was clear with some chopped green onions. What I enjoyed most was the "bread." This consisted of roll-sized lumps of wheat dough that had been steamed, served hot. They tasted like old-fashioned stew dumplings. I encountered more of this steamed bread, and always enjoyed it, as we travelled from "the rice country" of south China northerly into the "wheat country." No butter, margarine, or oil were served. I do not remember tea being available but the clear soup was there throughout the meal, available by dipper from its large bowl. We served ourselves from platters set on round tables with well-scrubbed wooden tops. There were neither tablecloths nor napkins in the large room of twenty or more tables.

As our plane continued north the next morning, we paused at Wuhan, again beyond the normal time required for refueling and transfer of passengers, to await further weather reports. I took advantage of this stop to make a two-hour tour of the city.

Wuhan, on the famous (and often infamous, because of its rampaging floods) Yangtze River, was already at that time a fast-developing, totally integrated, industrial complex. It embraced four earlier cities on both sides of the river. Numerous new factories and plants could be seen from the air. First we saw the cluster of high brick smokestacks and then, as we approached closer, we saw new factories and nearby integrated apartment house developments, and, radiating out from the city new highways, railroad spur and marshalling yards, and connecting canal systems to the Yangtze.

Meandering through its great flood plains, the Yangtze reminded me of the Mississippi River. It rises in the west of China and flows about thirty-five hundred miles to the East China Sea. The river's huge volume of murky water, 1.2 million cubic feet per second at its mouth, is laden with silt that annually deposits a thin layer of fresh topsoil over the flat cultivated delta lands. Often, the deposition of this silt causes the course of the river to shift and continue the development of the braided system of natural channels. The costly solution to this uncontrolled flooding is to dredge one or more deeper channels to control the water flow and to cover the channel banks with stone or concrete to reduce erosion. Side channels and dams are often constructed to receive the deposition of the sand and silt. Much evidence of these control steps could be seen. A major structural problem in controlling the course of such rivers is that a strong bedrock foundation is often not available for dam or embankment construction and/or the building of bridges. This was the major challenge in the erection of the first "permanent" bridge across the Yangtze River by the government of China after Mao and his colleagues came to power.

A source of great pride to the Chinese is the truly remarkable mile-long Wuhan Yangtze River bridge which was completed in 1956, joining north and south China for the first time in that country's long history. Their bridge gives them all the more pleasure because, contrary to the views of foreign "experts," who regarded building it as virtually impossible, they built it in record time.

Unfortunately I did not see the bridge on the ground, but when the stewardess first pointed it out to me from the air, I saw in a single glance this obviously remarkable conquest of the Yangtze. I learned that not many miles from Wuhan a recent meander of the wild river had cut a fresh, vicious swath across an intensely developed agricultural area, spewing mud and stones over highways and precious fertile gardens. Having learned of this recent event, as well as the efforts of many generations of farmers struggling against the results of the Yangtze flooding, I appreciated more fully the endless patience and persistence of the Chinese.

The general pattern of improvement and the increasing tempo of activity continued as I travelled northward. There was more construction, more evidence of industrialization, more mechanically powered transport. This new construction was, for me, the most dramatic visual impression I gained. Rising suddenly in otherwise vacant fields, it seemed to have dropped from the skies.

As I flew from Wuhan to Chengchow in the unpressurized plane, I had a good view of the country below. We appeared to fly between 6,000 and 9,000 feet. The physiography and development of the land changes markedly in the general region between Wuhan and Chengchow. The south-to-north 1,350-mile section between Canton and Peking consists, in general, of relatively flat to gently rolling country so low in the south that it is still struggling to emerge above sea level. It then gradually becomes more elevated towards the north.

From the air, the region around Canton resembles Holland. The land appears to be half water both by accident and design. Where there is too much water, it is dyked out. Where there is too little, it is brought in. The pattern of mud and water plots that compose the fertile, sub-tropical land of the Shumchun to Canton region are coloured in tones of yellow, grey, and brown, with green where crops are advanced.

As one proceeds north and the land rises, the water-rich areas become less extensive and are confined to river valleys bordered by low hills, coloured red, suggesting intensive laterization of the rock formations, which easily excite the interest of the prospector. Between the hills, the valleys are intensively cultivated and the pattern of repeated, gently curving, valley-crossing dykes give the entire winding valley the appearance of a great twisting, segmented centipede.

North of Wuhan, the geometry of land cultivation takes another form. The land is higher, drier, and with rolling hills. The cultivated areas occur as large rectangular blocks, not unlike the cleared farming townships of southern Ontario. The "red earth" has given way to a predominantly grey land colour.

In Chengchow I experienced the first of many exhibitions of Chinese honesty. Because the snap-lock on my briefcase had failed earlier, and I could not quickly locate the key, I had transferred my passport and other important travel documents, plus all the currency in my possession, into my jacket pocket. I had then taken off my jacket and hung it on a clothes tree beside me in the public lounge while I drank a cup of tea. For some reason I forgot it as I left for the city by car.

We arrived in Chengchow for a leisurely lunch of generous proportions. To my surprise, when I politely waved away various courses, both the waiter and those at the table refused to return the food to the kitchen. Several times I was plied with food beyond my capacity to consume and despite my protests.

It was not until three hours later, when I reached for some money to pay for my lunch, that I realized to my great alarm that I had left my jacket at the airport. In a somewhat agitated state, I returned to the airport with my companions where I found my jacket in the public lobby, just as I had left it.

I left Chengchow with the highest regard for the honesty of its citizens.

My Visit to Peking

I was met at the Peking airport by a capable young English-language agent of the China Travel Bureau. The drive from Peking airport to the city was in mid-morning, so traffic into the city consisted largely of trucks, wagons, and countless bicycles moving in single file along each shoulder of the road. At dawn and sunset, as crowds go to and from the city to work, the scene was not unlike that in Canton. Swarms of people (the population of Peking grew from 2 million to 7 million between 1949 and 1966), on foot, on bicycles, and on over-loaded trucks travelled into the city to work. In the opposite direction there was a continuous parade of hand-drawn carts, wagons, and trucks carrying night-soil from the city to the countryside.

We drove through the suburbs over impressive, tree-lined, wide, newly built avenues, past many large brick and stone masonry buildings, recently built or still under construction. I asked about the identity of various buildings and a jumble of answers followed: radio-electronic factories, apartments, technical institutes, shops of all sorts, more apartments, schools, post-offices, medical clinics, and more apartments. We passed several outstanding public buildings, an occasional park, and several basketball courts. Finally we passed through the ancient city gate and arrived at the hotel where I was to stay.

The city gate of Peking is one of several entrances through the Great Wall that surrounds the old city. Most of the wall was being torn down to make room for modern structures but some gates and sentry towers were being retained as historic sites. With few exceptions, most of the new building construction was peripheral to the core of the old city. The older buildings of Peking were built of clay brick which resembled the low-temperature sun-dried adobe in the south-western United States. Red tile roofs in various degrees of disrepair were common, as were gutters in the cobble lanes. However, redeeming the deterioration of age was the occasional presence of a wrought-iron or brass door or window screen of exquisite pattern.

My hotel was predominately European in style and I noticed twenty-five to seventy-five Europeans present in the dining room. They were practically all male technicians staying in Peking or in transit. My rough estimate was that about two-thirds were Soviet citizens, the remainder being Czechs, Hungarians, Poles, Germans, or Swedes. I later learned that there were several fine hotels in Peking, each catering to a specific group. These hotels are identified, for example, as the "diplomats' " hotel, the "visiting conventions' " hotel, and the "minority groups' " hotel, among others.

After dinner I left the hotel alone for a stroll along the city streets. The weather that evening was cool and dry, a pleasant change from the south. The streets were well-lighted, clean, and teeming with people moving about in family groups. The standard of clothing and appearance were the best I saw in China. My alert eye caught sight of a few cheongsam, split-to-the-hip skirts, but on the whole the style for younger women remained the dark pleated skirts worn calf-length with tuck-in white blouses, white bobby socks, and dark flat shoes. Despite the puritanical cut and length of their dresses, some of the younger girls used them for practical purposes. When the weather was warm, men would sometimes roll up their trousers to their knees. Occasionally, a girl would have an even more picturesque solution. She would sit down in a relatively quiet corner, gather her skirt onto her lap and use the front edge as a vigorous and effective two-handed fan. This exercise always seemed to fascinate any men who were around. While the girl's temperature may have dropped, the men's certainly rose! For older women, blue pantaloons with white or blue blouses hanging over the pants were favoured. Men wore baggy blue trousers with a variety of shirts over the trousers.

In Peking people were everywhere, on foot or bicycle. Indeed, the streets of Peking always appeared to be crowded. However, despite differences in the colour of the clothing, in the buzzing of conversation, and the odours, the crowds in Peking were really not very different from those in London, Paris, or New York. I was surprised at the efficiency of the bus system, the equipment being mainly of European origin and consisting of numerous modern, articulated, electric trolley buses, clean, fast, comfortable, and always crowded. While bicycles and pedi-cabs were numerous I saw no rickshaws and very few push-carts. There were many sturdily built trucks.

The people of Peking did not seem to be as thin as those further south. This, I was told, was because of the wheat diet in northern China as opposed to rice in the south.

In Peking I saw the first public symbols of communism among the Chinese. In the parks and museums a notable number of young girls, and fewer boys, wore the red scout-like kerchief of the Communist youth groups.

After gazing for a time into shop windows and at people, I followed a gathering crowd moving toward the sound of band music. It led to a square where a western-style circus complete with canvas tents was in full swing. It was late, so, regretfully, I did not go in. It was just as well, since next morning I was awakened at 5:00 A.M. by a knock on my door. When I opened it, I found that I had been mistaken for a Soviet technician who had wanted a "call" at that hour. I grumbled that I was a Canadian capitalist who was never to be awakened before 7:30 in the morning.

My hotel was comfortable and interesting, offering all the conveniences of a western hotel. The view through the dining room windows, which overlooked the roof of a large modern hospital across the street, provided an interesting diversion at breakfast time. Small groups of health-conscious nurses out on the hospital roof performed calisthenics like a ballet class while we flabby foreign male technicians looked on.

Each floor of the hotel had a service department and several small conference rooms which were constantly in use by small groups of either European or Chinese technicians. Some of the meetings of the Chinese appeared to be Communist Party weekly gatherings. I observed several of these through windows or doors left open during the warmer hours of the day, and they always seemed to be lively and businesslike. Debate was general and copious notes appeared to be taken. Occasionally, the chairman exercised direct control over the debate or embarked on a harangue of his own.

I was told that such meetings were a vital part of China's social-political organization. Small groups, usually under the chairmanship of a Communist Party member, met regularly for an hour each week. The group might be an elected "block committee," the hotel staff, or the shopkeepers of that city block, for example. The leader encouraged comment, debate, and suggestions on almost any relevant subject an individual might wish to raise. Simultaneously, the leader had a wonderful opportunity to explain and develop the "party line" in terms of every-day problems.

This amazingly effective "grass-roots" liaison between leaders and workers permitted the leaders to state blandly that theirs was the world's most democratic social-political system. The leadership argued that every move they made had been initiated by the workers and that only a minimum of persuasion from the "top" had ever been necessary. Regardless of "who persuades whom" the workers were certainly vocal and made to feel they played an important role in government. I was asked at least a score of times what I thought of some new innovation, or if I had suggestions to offer toward improving some service. I was told by several enquirers, many in humble office, that they would like to discuss my suggestions at their next committee meeting.

I visited several of the more prominent public buildings in Peking, attempting to strike a balance between the pre-liberation era – Imperial Palace, Imperial Summer Palace, Peking University, a Buddhist temple – and the post-liberation period – People's Great Hall, the Historical Museum, the Agricultural Exhibition Hall, the Geological Museum, and a large industrial arts factory. The government of China is clearly committed to the preservation of the architectural and artistic treasures of the Chinese people.

The People's Great Hall, which serves as the national congress centre, is a truly remarkable structure both inside and out. It provides every conceivable comfort for the seating of ten thousand delegates in the assembly hall, a remarkable banquet hall for five thousand and also contains twenty-nine large lounges, one for each of the delegations of each of the twenty-two provinces, the five autonomous regions and the two federal cities, Peking and Shanghai. Each of the lounges is beautifully decorated with the handicraft arts of a particular province. Consequently, it is one of the capital's outstanding show places of exquisite art in many forms – marble, ivory-carving, wood-carving and inlay, lacquer, porcelain, carpets, carved jade, *cloisonné*, crystal glassware, embroidery, lace, silver and gold filigree, painting, and ceramics. The huge structure, designed by a group of Chinese architects, was reportedly erected in ten months by a corps of fourteen thousand workmen.

The architectural style of the People's Great Hall is western European, along the lines of the great town halls of the Scandinavian countries but with some of the interior glitter of Versailles. The dominant colours are cream, gold, and red, a pleasant modification of the traditional Chinese combination of red, gold, and blue. It is the annual meeting place of the national assembly but is also frequently used for conventions and large conferences. It faces a large city square, the Square of Heavenly Peace. Directly across from it, on the opposite side of the square, is the equally impressive Historical Museum, and on the third side is the restored Imperial Palace. It was at the front entrance of the People's Great Hall that a police guard carried the second firearm I saw in all my travels in China – a revolver in a belt holster.

I also enjoyed the ornate architecture of the four-hundred-year-old Imperial Palaces and their luxurious furnishings. But, like the baroque style of Europe, I found it too rich in exotic detail to "take" in large quantities.

Professional Leaders in Peking

In Peking I met a number of Chinese leaders who were at that time (1961) prominent in government, trade, science, and university teaching. They had received letters about me from equally prominent Canadian friends of mine who had visited China in the preceding year or two. My meetings were informal, relaxed, and the subject matter was wide-ranging. The questions I posed were all answered, some logically, some plausibly, and some in what I considered an amusingly simplified manner.

The leading political figure I met, Kuo Mo-jou, the chairman of the Chinese Peace Committee, had distinguished himself in archaeology, drama, medicine, and as one of China's policy-makers in the field of international relations.

The trade expert I met was vice-chairman of the International Trade Department and general manager of the Bank of China. He was fluent in English and had travelled widely.

The most senior scientist I met was the director of research, Institute of Geology, Academy of Science. He spoke little English but apparently read it proficiently since there was scarcely a British or American scientific journal I mentioned with which he did not appear to be familiar. He was a typical, likeable "long-haired egghead" whose love for scientific discussion led him into talking about research in isotope-ratios even before the tea was poured – a cardinal sin in China. His absent-mindedness verged on the tragic. He had even overlooked removing a bust plaque of Stalin from his office wall and the former Soviet dictator had been rejected by the Chinese leadership two years earlier!

The professors I met included one who was then a professor of geodesy at Peking Institute of Geology. He was young, fluent in English, had travelled extensively in the United States, Sweden, and Switzerland, and appeared very able. The senior geologist I met was with China's Geological Survey and served as director of the Geological Museum of Peking. We discussed China's foreign policy. It was described as non-aggressive co-existence. The subject of international peace was constantly laboured and was their greatest concern. I am convinced that they were and still are sincere in their attitude as: they had then not yet developed the capability to fight a modern war; they are determinedly and successfully committed to the domestic development of their vast country without interruption and co-incident military waste attached to preparedness or fighting; as Marxists, they believe in the inevitability of communism as an inescapable socio-political evolutionary step; and China, as in the past, is not an expansionist power.

Subjects like Taiwan, Korea, the India-China frontier, and Tibet were all touched upon. I sensed both tenacity of purpose and great tolerance in their attitude toward Taiwan and other problems generally. Several times I was told, "The Chinese people can wait; time is in our favour."

During my discussions in Peking, emphasis was placed on China's "Five Principles" of foreign relations:

(1) mutual respect for state sovereignty and territorial integrity;
(2) mutual non-aggression;
(3) non-interference in each other's internal affairs;
(4) to develop, strengthen, and safeguard the security of the nation,
(5) to safeguard and consolidate the peace of Asia and the world.

The subject of China's place in the United Nations was also discussed. I was told again what I knew and many westerners forget, that China was one of the founding nations of the United Nations and, accordingly, was given both assembly representation and a permanent seat on the Security Council. I was told that China had asked only for what she had earned and was given years ago and was then being deprived of by an imposter (Taiwan) more acceptable to those in control of UN policy.

In my discussions with senior Chinese officials, the United States was talked about in a curiously naïve manner. The American people, or "workers," were held in high regard for their tremendous technical skills, but it was regrettable that they were still being so terribly misled by a president and small clique of industrialists and militarists bent on developing economic, military, and political spheres of influence all over the world. I pointed out that I thought the American people were actually very close in their thinking to that of their government and vice-versa. The Chinese foreign policy officials with whom I discussed these issues, looked at me – an erstwhile American – and exclaimed reprimandingly, "But you slander the American people!"

I was told repeatedly that China would like to become friends with Canada and was reminded of physical similarities and certain historical links between our two countries. Dr. Norman Bethune's name, among others, was mentioned. He had died while attending to the medical needs of Mao's soldiers and became a Chinese national hero, being honoured, in fact, by becoming one of the very few Caucasians to be depicted on Chinese postage stamps.

The subjects of education, sanitation, and peace had gripped China with the crusading force of a religion. The Chinese civil war had been led by Communist intellectuals, many from universities. Perhaps this, together with the basic need for large numbers of educated technicians required for a modern mechanized and industrialized society (and which received tremendous help from Soviet technical assistance between 1957 and 1960), had provided the impetus to move about 200 million people into schools during the years 1949–61. I was deluged with statistics on educational performance, and there was much physical evidence of progress in new school buildings.

The Chinese understand the value and the power of education. The city bookstores were packed with crowds of all ages. More than once I saw older adults totally preoccupied in reading publicly displayed newspapers or titles of museum exhibits. The new government of China had introduced measures to greatly simplify the whole process of education, including officially encouraging the use of only one dialect – Pekingese – in place of the many dialects spoken in different sections of the country, and an attempt to break away from the complicated Chinese script and to use Roman lettering as we do in the west.

I discussed, in most general terms, China's mineral development. Evidently, the country was making great progress in this field and at a constantly accelerating rate. Their techniques then appeared to be as modern as ours in America although, of course, not yet as extensively applied. There seemed to be no reason why they could not remain essentially self-sufficient in the minerals their burgeoning economy needed. They were particularly pleased with results from their oil and gas exploration and development.

Re-birth of a Great Nation: Socio-political Evolution

My most lasting impression of China was of the spirit of the people. The Chinese people are on the move. They appear to know where they are going, are optimistic about their prospects, and very proud of their striking progress.

My considered judgement is that no other form of government could have accomplished in China as much in so short a time. China's 670 million people had been exploited and divided, ravaged with starvation and disease, and torn apart by decades of fighting, both internally and against invaders. They were largely illiterate. They needed an ideology to build morale and unity and they needed leadership that could and would impose tough discipline in order to effect change. In the late 1940s, the time was propitious for such a development. The man who emerged as China's leader was an intellectual and a politician of great organizing ability who had spent the previous twenty-five years in a persistent, unwavering campaign of spreading the Communist ideology throughout China.

I have travelled and worked in many countries over much of the world. As a result I have seen many forms of social-political organization first-hand. My great interest in people is, perhaps, not so much that of the humanist stirred by emotion, as that of the engineer faced with solving a problem of social organization in the interests of maximum well-being. In my view, each country on our planet has its own unique problems. The ideal social-political system for each particular country is dependent on many factors. Among these are geographic location in terms of climate, topography, and neighbours; size; history; temperament of the race; literacy; natural wealth of the country; and degree of industrialization. These factors combine to produce unique national characteristics at any given period of development. As the factors, which are all variable, change, so does the character, and so, therefore, do national needs in terms of an optimum socio-political system.

In our world there are countries at various stages of development covering a wide range of extremes. It follows that we should expect a wide variety of socio-political systems and there is probably a useful place and purpose and time for most soci-political systems that are in operation today. It is also my contention that we must seek to understand and accept this immutable law of socio-political evolution, or our rigid and egotistical beliefs will destroy us.

I have no doubt that China will emerge as a dominant world power. The size of China's population and the exensive land mass of China itself – but above all, the resilience, determination, and accumulated social wisdom and discipline of the Chinese people – would appear to make this inevitable.

I returned to Canada profoundly impressed by what I had seen and learned in China.

XV

Assisting "Third World" Countries by Exploration Programs

When I went to China in the late summer of 1961, I had been working for more than a quarter of a century in the private sector of the mining industry. Through my own efforts, and those of my family and colleagues, I had gained financial independence and all the physical comforts which my family and I could reasonably enjoy. But I was determined to avoid being trapped by materialistic pursuits. Money had never squeezed me into its mould and I resolved that it never would.

The successful amalgamation of the Bralorne and Pioneer mines had brought me special satisfaction, and the commencement of development of Sogepet and its exploration for oil and gas in Hudson Bay was a stimulating and ongoing opportunity. But I was still searching for a comprehensive challenge through which I could give wider scope to my scientific imagination and social ideals. Such a challenge emerged not long after I celebrated my fiftieth birthday.

In the early spring of 1962, I accepted an invitation to participate in a conference on Canada's overseas aid program sponsored by the Canadian Institute of International Affairs. It was to be held in London, Ontario, in May 1962; John W. Holmes of the institute, several senior federal officials, and several academics would deliver papers and lead the discussions.

The information I gained at the conference came as a considerable revelation to me. While I had had a good deal of comprehensive experience in mineral exploration overseas, it had always been on behalf of the private sector. I had only limited knowledge of the bilateral external aid activities of Canada and the foreign aid activities of the United Nations.

Like most Canadians I had vaguely heard of the Colombo Plan. This had been established in the early 1950s by some of the wealthier Commonwealth countries, to provide co-operative economic development for some of the less well-developed sectors of the earlier British Empire. At the London conference I learned that Canada's participation in this plan had developed in part through the initiative of C. D. Howe, who, as Canada's wartime Minister of Munitions and Supply and later as Minister of Reconstruction and Minister of Trade and Commerce, was concerned with the post-war employment of returning Canadians and at the same time with accelerated industrial development. Mr. Howe had supported the proposal that Canada should contribute to the development of the hydro-electric generating capacity of northern India, where there was major natural hydro-electric potential.

C. D. Howe knew that there would be a variety of advantages if Canada were to manufacture and to provide the steel pipe, the turbines, the generators, the cable, the cement, the structural steel, and to make available the engineering services necessary to develop the potential hydro power in northern India. This would provide what was regarded as a vital service to India while contributing to employment and economic development in Canada. In net terms, relatively little of the large capital funds necessary for carrying through the project would leave Canada.

The development of India's hydro-electric potential became an important element in Canada's early post-war external aid contribution to the Colombo Plan. It set the pattern for the subsequent "high" Canadian content arrangements which continue to prevail in the work of Canada's principal national bilateral aid agency, the Canadian International Development Agency (CIDA), and through our contributions to the agencies of the United Nations which Canada supports.

Upon my arrival at the conference I had been delighted to find that Dr. G. C. Monture was among its participants. Slim Monture, an Indian of the Mohawk tribe, was a descendent of the Iroquois Chief, Joseph Brant, after whom the city of Brantford, Ontario, was named. He interrupted his studies in mining and metallurgy at Queen's University to serve with distinction in the Royal Canadian Engineers during the First World War, becoming a commissioned officer. The war over, he returned to Queen's, graduated and then advanced to a number of senior administrative positions in the mines and technical surveys branches of the federal civil service. I had first met Slim when I was exploring for strategic minerals in British Columbia. During the Second World War, Monture was one of Canada's appointees to the Joint Production Resources Board in Washington, D.C. Later, he was involved in the work of several post-war United Nations projects. He was well qualified to discuss international issues.

At the conference, Monture was critical of Canada's almost total pre-occupation, to that time, with its contribution to the Colombo Plan program, practically limited to sending hydro power-generating facilities to India. His vigorous criticism surprised, and appeared to confuse, some of the senior bureaucrats present who regarded Canada's external aid program as being nearly ideal. When Monture was asked what he thought could be more constructively done he argued that external aid programs should have as their primary, not secondary objective, the provision of direct assistance to developing countries. External aid programs should be designed, above all else, Monture argued, to help any developing country to help itself.

Recognizing the wisdom inherent in what Monture said, I spoke in support of his point of view, referring to the rich natural resources, not only of former British colonies, but also of countries in Central America and on the Pacific rim. Monture's arguments and my intervention in support of those arguments had certainly stirred things up.

Not long after the London conference, as I was still weighing the differences between bilateral aid versus universal aid services, the Hon. Paul Martin asked me to meet with him to discuss Canada's external aid programs. He suggested that if I were interested, a senior post in the federal international development agency, CIDA, would be open to me. Despite that complimentary gesture, my final choice was the United Nations service. When I indicated this decision to Monture, he advised me to contact John Carman at UN headquarters in New York.

My First United Nations Assignment

When I spoke with John Carman on the telephone, he remembered me well from the time both of us had been involved in the Athabaska uranium rush in the late 1940s. When he suggested that I visit him in New York anytime, I said I would fly down the following day.

Carman's ability had been recognized by the senior officials of the United Nations, where he had become the senior technical officer of the Minerals Section of the UN Technical Assistance program, then under the administrative directorship of Dr. Roberto Arce and his capable assistant, Joseph Barnea. Carman understood my mood and was aware of my ability.

My meeting with Carman had hardly begun when he said, "We can use a guy like you, but where?"

"Timbuktu?" I prompted.

"Oh, so you're that flexible. That makes it easier."

"Speak Spanish?" Carman asked.

"A few lessons many years ago," I replied, "but no practise. Still, it would probably come easy. I speak French."

"Okay," he replied, "I can think of one slot we've been trying to fill for a couple of years but no 'gringo' has been crazy enough to take it as yet," he said. "The place is Patagonia. Are you interested?"

"Perhaps," I replied. "But where is Patagonia? Tierra del Fuego?"

"Not quite," replied Carman, "but close. The project area involves the southern-most one-third of Chile, all hellish rain forest and mountains you wouldn't believe; up to the top from 'el Pacifico' and overlapping the edge of the Argentinian pampas. It's all empty. The Chilean government wants it explored to establish a geological data base and to determine if there is any mineral potential. We figure it'll take a year. They have a good National Geological Survey and a topnotch director, Carlos Ruiz, but they devote all their time and energies to the sunny north. Smart people, the Chileans. Think about it."

I returned to Toronto and "slept on it" for a night to secure a dependable organic computer printout, as is my custom. When I told my wife Mary of my plans, promising that I would either return to Canada at intervals of two or three months or arrange for her to visit me, she agreed to the proposal but reluctantly! After twenty-five years of marriage, Mary had grown to expect the unpredictable from me.

A day or two later, I telephoned my acceptance to Carman. His reply, so characteristic of him, was: "We'll have to get you there fast, by November, before we involve the UN Personnel Recruitment – it takes them two years to process an applicant."

On November 7, 1962, in Santiago, Chile, I presented myself to Señor Adriano Garcia, UN Resident Representative ("Ambassador") to Chile, and to Dr. Carlos Ruiz. I was about to embark on my second major career. It would prove to be the most creative and rewarding period of my entire life.

However, I did have a sense of apprehension concerning my new assignment. Aptly perhaps, I learned on arrival that my first address in Santiago was to be on the Avenida Huerfanos – Street of the Orphans. There were some lonely moments when I felt like one!

I spent my first few days learning about my new responsibilities.

I also arranged for Mary, Marion, and an artist friend of Mary's, Phyllis Janes, to spend the approaching Christmas season with me in my Chilean "exile." It seemed desirable to reassure my family – and myself – that my voluntary exile was not entirely a form of martyrdom!

My UN colleague for the Chilean project, Dr. Valto Veltheim, a Finnish geologist from the Geological Survey of Finland, arrived two weeks later. He spoke only Finnish and German, no English, French, or Spanish. Later on, when we organized ourselves as a working party, with four young Chilean geologists as trainees, we had to communicate in at least three, and sometimes four, languages – Spanish, English, German, and French. To deal with the language problem, I organized the field work on the basis of two and sometimes three field parties, each on its own exploratory (and linguistic!) journeys.

When our entire working group periodically gathered to assess the progress of our work there was a babel of languages and translations. I thoroughly enjoyed these multilingual reunions, but the variety of languages we used added immeasurably to my problems in preparing the final reports, with fieldbooks and notes in three languages, including Finnish!

As I organized the work program for Director Ruiz's approval, I was dismayed at the almost total lack of background data for the Patagonian region from Puerto Aisen southward. Practically no maps existed, save for the coastline, sections of which had been brought to the attention of the reading public through the publication in 1839 of Charles Darwin's journal of his voyage on the British naval vessel *Beagle*, on which he had served as a naturalist.

A century and a quarter later my colleagues and I travelled and searched for minerals along and inland from the same Patagonian coastline that Darwin had explored. It had probably not changed much in the interval. There were few roads and trails in the region and only isolated communities. The coastline and climate were very reminiscent of Alaska, also a sub-polar region. Rugged rock cliffs loomed up out of the rough sea, occasionally indented with fiords into which glacial ice or rivers emptied.

Central Patagonia, inland from the region bordered by the rivers Exploradores, Baker, and Lago Buenos Aires, includes the largest, non-polar glacial icefield in the world. The lower section, down to the edge of the ocean, is covered with dense brush and thick forests of small conifers, flanking the canyonous valley slopes and covering the occasional delta.

The coastline was alive with seals, walrus, and some penguins.

The rocky shoreline waters were rich in shellfish, including *erizos*, sea urchins, a national delicacy.

While there appeared to be no fish near the coast, they were present a few miles seaward, where the undersea Cordilleran fault zone and earthquake belt, with upswelling warm water currents, formed the continental edge of that land mass (just as the same fault zone does along the Alaskan Pacific coastline).

The very few settlers lived in the small coastal coves or river deltas where there are small patches of arable land. There they trapped for saleable pelts and had small cereal or vegetable gardens. They cleared their land patches with frequent uncontrolled burning of the forest growth rather than using implements. This centuries-old practice had given the name Tierra del Fuego – Land of Fire – to the coast and the entire island archipelago to the immediate south.

While the coastline of Patagonia teems with life, the mountainous, rain-forested slopes above it lack practically all animate life. Darwin had made one or two major inland traverses and had written in detail of them. My companions and I would traverse on foot all seven major rivers in our geological study of Patagonia.

Some limited side-scanning aerial photography had been attempted to assist in the determination of possible hydro-electric potential from the wild rivers that ripped through the canyonous slopes of the rain forest, but the quality of the resulting photography was poor owing to almost constant layers of low cloud. Side-scanning photography is an early technique in which pictures were taken of the ground by cameras attached to the side of an aircraft instead of pointed straight down. The resulting photographs viewed the ground at an angle rather than from the vertical, and the latter is much more accurate. Even the better side-scan photos available to us presented a distorted perspective of the area photographed and were of little use for ground location control.

Despite these problems, I identified a single fault feature in the photographs which we located later on the ground as a stream-occupied valley. Following its course made the very difficult Rio Pascua traverse considerably easier for us. A second "plus" was that we discovered copper-zinc mineralization in the same structure.

Our general work plan involved, in the absence of other travel routes, using the major river systems as our access corridors. Following the rivers either up- or down-stream we maximized our opportunities to study rock outcrops. Since my colleague, Veltheim, was less robust and less experienced in rugged terrain than I, it was arranged that he would make those few traverses where vehicles, boats, or pack-horses could be used. The more rugged traverses were usually a mix of pack-horse and/or back-packing on foot.

In carrying out our geological exploration in Patagonia we made nine major traverses right across Chile from the edge of the Pacific Ocean to the crest of the Andes and the border with Argentina. We also explored the watershed dividing the Pacific and Atlantic oceans along the crest peaks of the Cordillera and back down along the river valleys to the Pacific shore.

The area in which we worked includes, as I have noted, the largest non-polar icefield in the world. The North and South poles are covered with polar ice caps up to two or more miles thick, as those axial areas are very rarely exposed to sunlight and solar energy. Since the Earth tumbles or rolls unpredictably, the shady polar patches and their polar icefields in effect actually move around from the human point of view. Greenland is one such polar patch in the northern hemisphere; central Patagonia is a corresponding mate in the southern hemisphere. Such non-polar icefields slowly melt and disappear as new ones slowly form.

On our most difficult traverses, in terms of rugged terrain and the absence of roads or trails, I took along a single Chilean trainee, Erik Klohn, a keen and strongly built young geologist with mountaineering experience. With us we had two Chilean settlers, wiry, tough, "bush-wise" individuals who were extremely resourceful. This team performed remarkably well.

There was no apparent wildlife in the rain forest, or as it is sometimes called, the "rain jungle" in which we traversed. These forests or jungles occur along mountain slopes which form the crumpled edges of continental collision "plates" such as the Pacific edge in North, Central and South America, where large volumes of water from the ocean are evaporated and dropped on the nearest mountain chain by prevailing off-ocean winds.

Such slopes are covered with the great forests of the world, if they have not already been despoiled by man or burnt through natural fires caused by lightning, vulcanism, or meteoric impact, or killed by drought. Sometimes rain forests occur in the low basinal areas of large river systems, usually in the equatorial zones. The lower elevation edges of such forests can be swampy and in most cases there is a dense tangle of underbrush, which gradually lessens up the slopes. In the Cordilleran rain forest slopes the middle slopes can be beautiful parklands of huge trees, centuries old, with no underbrush since the tree canopy "soaks up" all the solar energy. Well known North American samples of these are the Cathedral Grove on Vancouver Island, the Redwood Forest Park in California, and several forest reserves in Alaska.

During the several months I worked inland in Patagonia I cannot recall hearing or seeing any animals other than a few large domesticated horses in the rare native settlements in the river delta areas. We were grateful for the horses since there were no bridges across the swift, turbulent, and icy rivers on the bouldery delta plains. We crossed these raging rivers safely on the backs of these rugged horses, as they stumbled and swam.

Bush Fare in Patagonia

Lacking wildlife, even fish, for food on the overland traverses, we occasionally did as the settlers did, and drove a few sheep ahead of us along the trail. Each two or three days, an animal was slaughtered and spit-roasted over a campfire. We washed the roasted meat down with liberal quantities of maté tea, drunk directly from a communal bowl. This strong tea, I learned later, probably spared me from chronic hepatitis.

The Patagonia-Pacific coastline and the high elevation edge of the Argentinian pampas were very different from the rain forests. The coastline teemed with fowl, mammalian life, and shellfish. Among the shellfish was the *erizo*. Although under normal circumstances I would never have chosen sea urchin from a menu, I ate it with some relish after a week-long diet of campfire mutton.

On the Argentinian border there were more culinary delicacies to recompense us for our spartan diet "on traverse." Among these were two of note, both of which gave me some initial difficulty. The first was ostrich eggs.

After weeks in the rain forest without seeing or hearing a bird, I was delighted on my first walk on the dry arid slopes of the Argentine pampas to find on the ground a lovely large bird feather. I held it up for my companions to see. "Let's be careful" one said. "If we are close to the nest, the ostrich will attack us."

"An ostrich?" I exclaimed, "a real ostrich in this country!"

"Yes," was the answer. After a pause, he continued, "I see the nest and no bird around. Let's look at it."

In the cradle of sand and boulders there was one large egg about five or six inches in diameter. One of my companions picked it up, shook it, tucked it into his blouse, and broke into a fast walk, muttering, "*Vamos, muy pronto!*"

Some distance away we halted, pierced the tough shell with two small holes, and took turns sucking at the contents. One short suck was adequate for a lifetime in my case! But my companions finished the pint of liquid with the same relish as others would drink Coca Cola. Later, from a safe distance of about two hundred yards, we saw the ungainly form of the ostrich to give credence to the whole episode.

I encountered my second culinary delicacy on the Patagonian pampas when two gauchos, who were branding calves, invited us to make camp with them one night. There is only a narrow strip of this pampas in Chile itself but great expanses of it spread out from the Andes height of land into the Argentine. The height of land divides the heavy rain forest and icefields of the Pacific slope from the strikingly different unforested, open, dry, grasslands of the eastern slope of the Andes. This Argentinian slope is range land not unlike the foothills of the Canadian Rocky Mountains. It forms the great cattle ranges that introduced the world to canned "bully beef."

That night as we sat around the crackling fire, tasty, bite-sized portions of meat roasted with green peppers were the principal dish. I asked about the meat and was promptly given the Spanish name which only served to puzzle me. Nonetheless, I enjoyed a hearty meal. The next day, when opportunity allowed, I glanced at my Spanish-English dictionary and, sure enough, the name *ostrea de los cerros* – mountain oysters – was there and defined. It was a shock to discover that they were the testicles of bull calves that had been castrated – a prized delicacy to some!

Completion and Results of Our Patagonia Mission

After eight months, our mission to the Patagonian region of Chile was completed. Velthiem, with an ailing stomach, departed for Finland. I remained a further month in Santiago to prepare our group's reports with detailed conclusions and recommendations. In the meantime I was entertained by various government ministers and honoured by being appointed an honorary member of Chile's National Geological Research Institute.

The net result of this Chilean mission was that I had satisfied the government officials concerned and had a sense of work well done. Certainly Dr. Carlos Ruiz was highly pleased with our work. In addition, I had established my reliability and technical competency with the UN Mineral Section agency and had found a new and challenging professional niche for social service. None of this had apparently escaped the notice of Director Roberto Arce, who now suggested that I join his headquarters staff in New York. While I declined his invitation, we agreed on a compromise. I was to be posted to an important UN regional office in Port of Spain, Trinidad, for one year. My primary responsibility was to advise the newly independent government of Trinidad and Tobago on the formation of a Ministry of Petroleum and Mines. Moreover I was to serve under the administrative direction of the UN Regional Resident Representative, James Keen, in evaluating additional requests for technical assistance from various Central American or Caribbean basin countries.

Keen was on outstanding administrator who had been a senior wartime staff officer with Val Duncan of the Rio Tinto Company when Val was a Colonel during the Second World War. Keen and I co-operated very successfully.

Port of Spain, Trinidad – A Creative Period

The year I spent with Keen, during which our Central American activities were initiated, was perhaps the most creative period of my entire professional career with the UN. I visited and studied with care the needs and mineral potential of every Central American country except British Honduras. I also familarized myself with the geology of British Guiana, Colombia, and several West Indian islands. Happily, Trinidad and Tobago were much more accessible to Canada and Jamaica than was Chile, and Mary was able to enjoy long visits with me while I was based there.

My responsibilities were determined by signals from UN headquarters in New York to James Keen. These messages were the result of national requests for technical assistance made through formal diplomatic channels in New York by any country in Central America or the Carribean region. Such referrals implied approval of a UN assistance program and acceptance of its cost, on some shared basis. It was my responsibility to visit the applicant country and then identify whether projects were feasible and economically possible. Following that, I would prepare a technical plan of operations. Keen would then handle the related diplomatic negotiations between the government of the country and the UN agency concerned.

In the meantime, my specific task in Trinidad itself was to be an advisor in the organization of the mines section of the newly formed Ministry of Petroleum and Mines. I was also to serve as a resource person for an international commission appointed by the United Nations. Its members were Dr. Jean Charbonnel of France, Dr. Charles Heller of the U.S.A., and Bogliar Mostafi of Iran.

This commission had been invited to assist the newly independent nation of Trinidad and Tobago in the development of its national policy for the management of its highly important petroleum industry. This industry, which accounted for about 75 per cent of the new nation's exports and thus was essential to its economy, was part of Trinidad and Tobago's colonial heritage from earlier British developments in which various multi-national companies had been involved. The British Colonial Office had trained, and left in place, a competent group of Trinidadian civil servants who were completely qualified to administer the earlier colonial regulations, *vis à vis* Great Britain. Independence now required many revisions which would be the task of the International Commission to advise upon and myself to assist in the broader administrative sense.

The major oil companies, led by British Petroleum and Shell as co-ordinators, had already compiled all the geological data obtainable for Trinidad and Tobago on a single informative map. A Swiss geologist, Dr. H. Kugler, who had been a pioneer in that petroleum geology study of Trinidad had made important contributions in the compilation of this map and had been allowed to copyright it personally. Amazingly, when Kugler retired to live in Switzerland, he had had this map reproduced commercially and all who wished to secure copies of it, including even the government of Trinidad and Tobago, were obliged to purchase their copies from him in Switzerland. This was a most unorthodox situation, which led me to urge the government of Trinidad and Tobago to repossess the map and the right to reproduce it, which they subsequently did.

All land title records and operational regulations applicable to the petroleum lands in Trinidad and Tobago had been introduced by the United Kingdom. Thus there were no problems in this connection for the commission. Later, however, after the commission departed, I was asked to draft new regulations covering all future applied-for off-shore lands, in general and specifically, to protect the interests of the now independent nation, to the hitherto unexplored off-shore North Basin between Trinidad and Tobago, which I helped to discover.

Since there were as yet no mineral mines worthy of the name, other than numerous small aggregate rock quarries, there was little I could do to help the mines section as such. Accordingly, with one practical field assistant, whom I trained, I set about evaluating what evidence of minerals was present and, if possible, to find other deposits. There was much to be done in this regard, and both Trinidad and Tobago, for a prospector, were delightful to explore.

Both islands are beautiful: mountains, beaches, trees, flowers, bird life, exotic colours and perfumes are everywhere. Such an environment influences the populace and the mixed races there are natural, friendly, and fun-loving. Along with Jamaica, they rule the Kingdom of Calypso with their music and dance. The steel drum bands reportedly had their origin in Trinidad when some of the men of the islands recognized the musical potential of the oil drums discarded at the oil refineries where they were employed. This is typical of the natural creativity and musical sensitivity of the people of Trinidad and Tobago.

Port of Spain is a very busy and prosperous international port, not only for the considerable export of Trinidad-produced oil, but also as a transit port for northern South America (which lacks suitable deep-sea ports), as well as for Panama Canal traffic.

Trinidad is a roughly rectangular island about fifty miles by forty miles. To guide my prospecting I needed a companion who would also serve as an interpreter of the pidgin English of the rural people. Fortunately, I was blessed in finding a most capable individual named Albert. At least that's what I called him until a momentous day when, together, we made a significant discovery on Tobago's Robinson Crusoe Bay. From that time on I called him Friday. Albert was quite proud of his change of name after I had outlined for him the essence of Daniel Defoe's novel *Robinson Crusoe* and the great trust that Crusoe had placed upon his faithful native companion Friday.

Albert had introduced himself to me soon after my arrival in Port of Spain. He had come to the ministry office with small pieces of rock he had collected and wondered if they were of any mineral importance. Albert was brought to my office and I spent perhaps an hour with him and his rock collection. He appeared to be intelligent, observant, and energetic; and he was a natural prospector with evidence to prove it. He lived and worked in, and had travelled over, the Cadbury cocoa plantation, North Mountain area, where the best potential for minerals theoretically existed. Among his specimens were two of an iron ore mineral, hematite, and I felt their source could be important. I arranged that he guide me to their location a week later.

My impression was that Albert, who was about my height but slighter in build, (though just as muscular), was perhaps older than me or had aged more quickly. He was happily married and had a grown family. While he had little money, he was rich in common sense, as well as being literate. His church meant a great deal to him and he worshipped there faithfully. He was sociable, temperate, extremely patient, and, though physically tough, gentle of spirit. When I once chided him as the model man, he simply replied, "I come from a lovin' family." When, on several occasions, we passed near his modest home, he invited me in for tea. I met his wife, grandchildren, and neighbours and readily understood his affection for his family and theirs for him.

Albert and I soon visited all the known small quarries on Trinidad. While there were not many of them, nonetheless they provided the required materials – shale for cement and clay for ceramic ware, bricks, and roofing tile. There were also a few small gypsum and limestone quarries, known as "evaporite sediments" to geologists.

I was fascinated by the evaporite beds, formed by ancient sediment, which had been carried from higher elevations to become layers on the bottom of a lagoonal sea and subsequently evaporated when the shallow ocean cover disappeared through crustal uplift. I sensed that perhaps these could yield large-volume deposits, probably in exportable quantities, as is the case in Jamaica. I questioned a geologist of the Canadian Dominion Oil Company concerning the presence of evaporite sections encountered in oil-field drilling. To my delight he knew of such a section, which was several thousand feet deep, in an off-shore wildcat well in the northern section of the Gulf of Paria, on the west coast of Trinidad, known as the Boca Raton Channel.

To whet my appetite further, the geologist mentioned that the same section contained fluorspar, a salt rich in fluorine, another potentially important industrial mineral. He added, jokingly, that the large upthrusting Pilares Fault that cut across Trinidad may bring it, or portions of it, into view on the land mass "somewhere."

Later, Albert and I established that this was indeed the case. Unfortunately the outcropping of fluorspar we found along the coastline of Gaspar Grande was of only marginally economic size.

The only metallic mineral known to be present on Trinidad or Tobago was magnetic iron on Trinidad. It, too, was known to be present only as "float" blocks. Nonetheless Albert and I examined them. They were in a small valley in a rain jungle corner of the northern mountains. This area had been, for almost a century, part of the cocoa-coffee plantation lands of the British Cadbury family. We prospected the area carefully for larger iron masses, but without success. The only memorable events of our prospecting in that sector were some frightening experiences with venomous snakes!

Geologists call a range such as Trinidad's northern mountains a *horst*. This is a large rectangular block of more ancient rock which has been thrust upward as a result of the faulting or breaking of the outer portion of the Earth's crust. In tropical zones these elevated areas are cooler at night and more dew is deposited on them. They are excellent sites for growing certain crops, such as coffee and cocoa.

Except for the small area cleared for cultivation, the rest of the plantation was a tangle of jungle growth without road or trail. This meant a criss-cross tangle of fast-growing and fast-rotting shrubbery, trees, huge ferns, and much shadow from larger trees – a mini-rain forest. This is an ideal habitat for snakes, and in the tropics many of these are poisonous. Albert and I travelled over this terrain with machetes in our hands to cut the underbrush and if need be, to kill snakes. We encountered and killed several, removing the poison sacs from them so that it might serve as an antidote for us or others suffering from snakebite. Fortunately, we were never bitten.

We prospected all around the island of Trinidad and the lesser islands in the Gulf of Paria and Boca Raton – the Rat's Mouth, despite learning, belatedly, that the only occupants of some of the smaller islands were horribly maimed lepers isolated there from social contact by the authorities. We were surprised and initially alarmed to find that the lepers, who lived in their own self-made thatch dwellings, roamed around freely and were not confined. I did not know at that time if that terrifying disease was contagious.

We had landed on one occasion at a roughly built pier and, lacking any guide, had taken a foot trail that led directly to the leper community. There we became the subject of great interest to them, and they, a frightening picture of hideously deformed humans, to us. Only later did we locate the clinic compound and modern residential building where a few Trinidadians and a European medical researcher worked. Paradoxically, the same smaller islands were shared by beautifully feathered songbirds. As proof of our efficient prospecting, we found, on the high point of one island where, probably centuries earlier, a cannon had been positioned, a nest of ancient iron cannon balls.

Since Albert and I could find no significant minerals on Trinidad, I pondered other development opportunities. I thought the island might become a ship-transit point. Smaller low-draft freighters, loading in nearby shallow-water ports along the Caribbean coast of South America, could conceivably bring their cargoes to Trinidad and transfer them there into larger "deep-sea" cargo vessels plying the mid-Atlantic and Panama Canal shipping routes. Some upgrading of mineral ores might also be done during such a trans-shipment stage by using Trinidad's abundant natural gas. For this, however, a larger deep-water port than Port of Spain would be necessary. My subsequent questioning of a parliamentary secretary produced, hesitatingly, the information that the Point Gourde Naval Base in south-westerly Trinidad – "where the Americans are" – was the only such port-site they had. Despite this apparent obstacle, I set out my ideas in writing for the government. After completion of our work on Trinidad, Albert and I commenced work on Tobago.

Tanker Spill or Oil Seep?

Tobago, which lies about 20 miles north-east of Trinidad, has an area of only 116 square miles. It is a slender island, measuring only about 7 miles at its widest point. Beside Tobago is the tiny island of Little Tobago, also known as Bird of Paradise Island. It was to this island that the birds of that name were introduced from New Guinea in the South Pacific Ocean.

In sharp contrast to Trinidad, which is highly industrialized, Tobago was, in 1963–64, almost totally natural with its many beautiful "white sand" or coral beaches along the west coast. A score of these had attracted a number of elegant and exclusive resort establishments for international clienteles. The east coast was exposed to the Atlantic Ocean and rougher seas and storms. There were a few lovely beaches there also, including Robinson Crusoe Bay, made famous by Robert Louis Stevenson.

The northern half of Tobago is rugged and hilly and largely composed of granitic rocks. It supports a typical, tropical "hill country agriculture" of coffee, cocoa, and tree fruits. The southern half of the island is entirely unlike the north, a flat plain of modern coral limestone, averaging probably two hundred feet or less above the sea. This section of the island supported extensive coconut plantations producing copra for export.

The entire island, particularly in the north, was dotted with colourful, small shantytown communities engaged in agriculture. Like northern Trinidad, Tobago is a year-round fantasy of coloured shrubs and vines, and the colourful scenery is not limited to the land. Coral reefs with their exotically beautiful fish and shellfish attract tourists from many countries.

Albert and I knew that exploring Tobago would not be easy. I had read the limited information available concerning its geology. The northern half of the island was easier to evaluate since it was all elevated rock and the geology had been mapped. Only the year before my arrival, two British geologists had made a coastal sand-sampling survey that revealed nothing of importance. On the other hand, the southern half of Tobago was an enigma. It was entirely covered by coral limestone of relatively recent age. Water wells dug in the limestone produced brackish water suitable for agriculture irrigation. There was, however, no information concerning the rock below the limestone capping save for one well-drilling which was reported to have been attempted in 1907, at a point called Petit Trou.

This well had been abandoned at a depth of about one hundred feet when quicksand was encountered. Its drilling had been directed by Cunningham Craig, a British Colonial Office geologist who had wished to confirm, if possible, an earlier sailing-ship captain's report of green slime issuing from a crack in the sea bottom. Craig had found nothing in his well, but he did report the presence of tarry oil staining on a coastal rock cliff nearby.

Our prospecting of Tobago was based on a procedure similar to the one we had employed along the north and north-east coastline of Trinidad. Albert and I, each clad only in swim shorts and with a packsack on our back and a pick in hand, walked, preferably at low tide, along the beach at the bottom edge of the rocky shore to examine any rock outcrop present. Where there was only the limestone reef capping, we tried to peer beneath the coral. As the days passed, we saw nothing of interest. Still we continued our search.

Then, one day, after we had almost totally encircled the island and were practically at the end of the island airport runway, the monotonous tramping at the surf edge ended. There was still much coral reef in evidence, but here the pores of the rocks contained a tar-like material.

I asked Albert to scrape some of the tar carefully into a sample sack while I looked in detail at the nearby base of the cliff, half afraid that I would find some oil or grease drums discarded from the airport. I climbed between large angular blocks of the coral rock fallen from the cliff face. Peering between two blocks, I could dimly see an arched cavern with a floor of beach sand. I realized that the solid arched roof was the base of the coral reef. It was inside this cavern that we might find the answer to the riddle of the nature of the rock below the capping. When I called Albert over to look into the cavern, he became uneasy. "Must we crawl in there, Doc?" he asked.

"Yes," I replied. "Not now, but tomorrow. We'll need a flashlight, ropes probably, and other gear."

Next mid-morning at low tide, we returned to the cove, called Robinson Crusoe Bay. Using my flashlight, I could see that the cavern extended inwards more than twenty feet, and that its roof was cracked and some blocks had fallen off. I fastened the end of a rope to my belt and left the coiled remainder with Albert. "I'll crawl in," I said. "I want to take some rock samples, but I mustn't hammer too hard. You watch the light of my flashlight even if you can't see me. If anything goes wrong, try to drag me out with the rope. If everything goes okay, I won't be long." With that I began crawling in under the rock roof about three to five feet above me.

As I crawled froward, the roof gradually lowered. Soon I was in complete darkness and bumping my head, on which I had taken the precaution of putting a cloth cap as protection against the rocky surface. I pried off small pieces of rock to examine them under my flashlight and was disappointed to see no change. It was still part of the coral limestone and to my alarm it broke off easily. The possibility of a collapsing roof was very real, and the cavern in which I was groping my way was becoming narrower; if I kept moving ahead, I would soon be unable to turn around and would have to back out on my knees in darkness.

As fear produces fear I wondered about snakes and venomous lizards clinging to the roof of the cavern. However, my flashlight indicated I was probably only five feet from where it ended. This reassured me. I crawled onward over sodden sand which appeared to become coarser and more jagged to the touch. With my pick I raked two or three pounds of the material into a sample sack. Then I crawled back out safely into the daylight.

Later, in the hotel, I dried a portion of the sand and found it contained much crushed fossil material but no limestone particles. Whether that was good or bad I did not know. Two or three days later, I gave a sample of the tarry surface material taken from limestone above the cavern and my sample of sand from the cavern floor to an acquaintance, an oil company geologist. I asked if he would have an analysis made of the tar to determine if it was a crude or refined material, and also arrange for a paleontologist to determine the nature and age of the sand.

A few days later, the geologist reported that the tarry material was of natural oil origin. It was not a refined product. The sand contained much broken fossil material of indeterminable Tertiary age – the third geological age that lasted from about 65 million years ago until about 2.5 million years ago. This information was exactly what I had hoped for – some evidence of Tertiary age sediment below the modern reef capping. I knew that the oil and gas reservoirs of Trinidad occurred in sediment of that age. The same type of material, I reasoned, when water-soaked, could have been the "quicksand" encountered in the drilling done in 1907, a mile or two away by Cunningham Craig.

With this evidence in hand, my course of action was clear. I began to prepare a formal proposal for my senior colleagues in the UN. I recommended that the UN finance a seismic line to be surveyed across Tobago Island from Robinson Crusoe Bay and westerly along a west-side reef for a total distance of three miles. If that offered encouragement, I recommended a follow-up aerial magnetometer survey of the reef-covered south half of Tobago and seaward westerly for several square miles over the ocean. Such surveys would indicate the thickness of the rocks and whether at depth they were layered sediments, as opposed to inhospitable granite.

When these ideas, and my entire research project, were outlined to the minister's chief technical officer in Port of Spain, Trinidad, he promptly disappeared for about three days. When he reappeared, he told me that my theory was totally without foundation. During his absence he had gone to Tobago, persuaded friends to take him by boat, and had searched for an oil seep in the sea bottom such as an earlier sea captain was reported to have seen, but he had seen nothing. He and his friends had noticed some tarry residue on the reefal rocks on the beach, but they were certain it was spillage from oil tankers passing nearby. He explained that he was from Tobago and would be delighted if oil could be found nearby, but he had no faith in my theory. My own faith, however, was not so easily shaken. I knew that the dried crude oil on the beach reef, first reported by the British geologist in 1907, pre-dated oil tanker traffic by many years.

And so I went ahead and recommended to Director Arce that the UN become involved in some initial exploration of the theory that a Tertiary-age sedimentary basin existed, in part beneath southern Tobago and westerly under the ocean between Tobago and Trinidad. Support for my theory came from Wilhelm Groeneveldt-Meijer and Marcel Schwob, both senior offcals of the United Nations Special Fund. While Groeneveldt-Meijer, a very able geophysicist, counselled against a land-based seismic survey, he supported my suggestion for the large-scale aeromagnetic survey. The result was a striking success. A large, late-age sedimentary basin was identified between Tobago and Trinidad, with a thickness exceeding fifteen thousand feet.

After considerable delay, discussion, and continued lobbying on my part, the UN authorized marine seismic surveying over a portion of the same sea area. This provided additional confirmation of the presence of a desirable basin for hydrocarbon exploration. Then there occurred an intriguing interlude.

The UN project manager, a petroleum geologist who had supervised the seismic survey contract, was still in Trinidad and reported to UN headquarters that a Soviet oceanographic research vessel, having completed a work program off Cuba, would visit Port of Spain in Trinidad for a day. Interested persons had been invited by the Soviets to visit "on board." The Trinidad government, however, had directed all its officials to avoid the vessel. The UN representative posted there was anxious to learn if the Soviet vessel had taken any sea-bottom rock samples which might be of interest to us. He was not certain as to what action he should take.

"What should I do?" he asked me by long-distance telephone call to my UN office.

"Get on the vessel and learn all you can," I replied.

To his and our delight the Soviets were co-operative. They showed him a sea-bottom sample taken from our area of interest. It was a late-age Tertiary rock specimen. So now we were ready for drill-testing. We had a large sedimentary "basin" of great thickness and correct age and preliminary seismic evidence of promising reservoir structures. However, before drilling could commence, regulations should be in place to outline, encourage, and control all aspects of private hydrocarbon exploration in the interests of the newly independent government of Trinidad and Tobago. Up to this time all such authority had been administered from the Colonial Office in England.

The government of Trinidad and Tobago requested that the UN again make my services available to assist in formulating the procedures for the granting of exploration concessions for well drilling. This was agreed upon and the necessary arrangements were made.

Back in Port of Spain, Trinidad, working with the same chief technical officer, I presented proposals for the division of the larger area into more than a score of concession areas for tender to the private-sector oil industry. I set out my recommendations concerning the desirable exploration obligations for each area and the prior financial deposits to be posted to ensure work performance and the royalty payable to the government in the event of success. In addition, I attempted to include the unique Canadian "checkerboard" system of redistribution of productive lands between the discoverer and the government.

Under the checkerboard system the entire area to be explored is divided into a grid of equal-sized squares like those on checkerboards. If a discovery is made in a white square, then the concession to develop all of the white squares is granted to the discoverer. The concession for all the black squares reverts to the government, which may resell by auction or keep its black squares for national development.

While officials in the UN headquarters rejected this checkerboard proposal, they accepted the other recommendations I made. These included that the concessions be put up for the world-wide public bidding; that the bidders be required to accept certain defined conditions; and that they make provision for various forms of voluntary bonuses. These bonuses would largely determine the winning bids.

Since the UN had spent almost one-half a million dollars for the aeromagnetic survey and the seismic survey, with separate interpretations of each, I felt this sum should be recovered from the interested bidders.

I also proposed a "sales kit" which would provide comprehensive information on all aspects of the exploration concessions. To recover all of the UN's expenses and to discourage the "simply curious" I recommended that the "sales kits" be sold for "about $3,000 each" and that every bidder be required to purchase a kit.

With all this accomplished and approved in general in one week by the chief technical officer and parliamentary secretary, we shook hands and parted. I was to return shortly to UN headquarters in New York to report on the progress we had made.

But as I was preparing to leave for the airport, the chief technical officer suddenly reappeared at my hotel. He reported that within minutes of our earlier "good-bye" he had encountered, by chance, the senior official of one of the island's major oil companies who, also by chance, was a friend of his who could be completely trusted. This friend, when told, confidentially of course, of our exploration concession plans, had said, "Look, we can save you a lot of trouble and time. My company will buy six sets of your sales kits at $25,000 each, and you won't have to bother with any auction sale!"

My immediate response to this was a resounding "No! This would defeat the whole purpose of the exercise. We want global competition and widespread bidding for several good reasons. But," I added, "you've given me an idea. Perhaps my $3,000 for the 'sales kit' is too low. Think about it!" With that, I departed for the airport and my return flight to New York.

From reports given to me in 1969 and 1970 I learned that the chief technical officer had redeemed himself handsomely. He had persuaded his superiors to price my "sales kit" at $50,000 each and twenty-six international bidders had each paid that sum. The $1.3 million so realized was much more than the total cost of the entire UN program as planned and implemented.

This "windfall" proved a very serious embarrassment to the United Nations as several high-level officials privately and earnestly confided to me. It contravened a key clause of the UN Charter: the UN could not accept a profit for its services. During the course of months of internal debate over how to resolve this predicament, the funds were quietly transferred from the joint UN–Trinidad project account to Trinidad. This was also contrary to established policy but apparently was the simplest way to accommodate the UN's super-bureaucrats.

By July 1971, exploratory well drilling commenced and proceeded intermittently but successfully. In August 1976, the *World Oil Journal* summed up progress to that date as follows:

> Several large gas fields have been discovered north of Trinidad. One recent giant-size discovery by Dimenex on an Occidental farm-out flowed between 32-37 million cubic feet per day from two zones. Between 1970-73 the government . . . discussed a liquified natural gas project which would ship 400 million cubic feet of gas per day to the U.S.A. but no price could be agreed to. . . . The government made it clear that it will export natural gas only after it has been assured that there will be enough to supply the growing domestic market.

This Trinidad project, which had resulted from the exploration I carried out with my colleague Albert, scored several "firsts" in the UN record book. It was the first oil and gas exploration project the UN had ever undertaken, the first to prove a striking success, and the one and only project of any kind to return more than its cost, even before the program was completed.

This success story has given rise to a question in my mind. As the years have passed since gentle Albert and I worked together I have wondered how I would respond if we were ever to meet again and he were to ask: "But Doc, weren't we looking for oil . . . ?"

Panama and Porphyry Copper Concept Successfully Developed

My next project was in the Republic of Panama where a single UN technical assistance expert had been based for about a year, unfortunately without significant results. The government of Panama was eager to improve that situation and to have the UN assist in the discovery of mineral deposits there if possible.

When I went to Panama early in 1964 no mining activity of any kind was being conducted in the country, although many small relatively insignificant mineral indications were known. There had been considerable mineral prospecting and assessment of the country's hydrocarbon potential over the years, but with only modest success. There were a number of obvious reasons for this.

Large portions of Panama are covered by late volcanic lavas and ash which hide earlier rock formations and evidence of mineral deposits. Given these conditions it was understandable why there was only a small Geological Agency with a director and two or three European geologists, mainly employed in reconnaissance geological mapping of the country's more accessible western slopes.

With the co-operation of the Panamanian director, Dr. Jorge Luis Quiros, I secured an able guide-driver and a jeep. We toured the Pacific western slope of the Panamanian Cordillera for two weeks, and examined many of the mineral indications known to both the Geological Agency and a geologist attached to the American-staffed Panama Canal Zone Administration. None of these indications appeared to be of great interest. For the following two days I travelled with two Italian geologists attached to the Geological Agency, who, like me, had spent time re-examining older known mineral occurrences.

During my conversation with them we had before us a large road map of Panama to aid me in locating various areas they had visited. I pointed with a pencil to a place on the map named Cerro Colorado (Red Mountain).

"What's that? A town? Have you been there yet?" I asked.

"Yes," said the senior geologist, who had the nervous and distracting habit of suddenly using his hands to simulate a bongo drum player. "I've been there. No town. Just a hill, but much iron oxidation. I took samples but found nothing in them. Probably a volcanic cone, and a waste of your time to visit."

Little did he, or I, realize then that he was dismissing from his mind, and from mine also, a landmark which would, within a few years, prove to be a billion-ton porphyry copper deposit!

As my questioning of the two geologists revealed nothing encouraging, I spent my final few days in Panama City examining what sketchy geological records were available in the Geological Agency office. The most voluminous records dealt with a jungle sector of south Panama where a small but rich gold mine had earlier been exploited and exhausted.

The next most complete records were reports of field surveys made by an American petroleum geologist, Dr. Robert R. Terry. Prior to 1948, he had spent about twenty years traversing the whole of Panama on behalf of Gulf, Sinclair, and Union Oil Companies, searching for

sedimentary basins with hydrocarbon potential. Terry was a meticulous geologist, so I read his notes and field sketches with much care.
One of his field-note entries caught my attention.

He described a copper-speckled boulder engulfed in a volcanic
flow rock which outcropped on the Divide of the Azuero Peninsula.
This was simply an oddity to Terry but a clue for me. I set out to
track the source of "Terry's boulder." From other documents I came
upon the description of sparse lead-zinc mineralization at the same
Divide elevation. Some pitting had been done on the lead-zinc but
the showing was abandoned because there was so little mineral. No
other geological detail was available. Nonetheless, I sent the UN's sole
technical adviser to the Geological Agency scurrying up the long trail
to the old lead-zinc showing, simply to bring me back a sample of
the host rock.

To my delight it was intrusive granitic material, often the parental
source of mineral-bearing porphyry. So there was a "window" in the
volcanic capping and a suitable host rock in view! I asked about the
coastline on the Caribbean side of the mountain slope. "Was there
any outcropping rock there that I could see or that had been mapped?
Any "granite" or mineral occurrence?"

"We know of no rock outcrops," was the answer. "But there are
stories that many years ago small quantities of gold were found in the
ocean beach sands at that point."

That was sufficient evidence for me to base a plausible exploration
proposal. Granitic rocks were present in the area and some protruded
through the volcanic rock capping; there was evidence that some of
the associated hydrothermal "juices" of those granitic rocks contained
copper ("Terry's boulder"), lead and zinc (the pitted showing), and
possibly gold (the beach placer). I defined an area and outlined a
program entitled the "Azuero Project" after the most prominent geographic feature nearby. Initially, I proposed a reconnaissance geo-
chemical survey of the drainage systems on the eastern slope of the
Azuero Peninsula.

That reconnaissance effort, followed by much difficult fieldwork,
proved encouraging. By 1969, after much more work and drilling,
the Cerro Petaquilla and Botija copper porphyry ore bodies had been
defined. Not far from these two discoveries and just outside the UN's
Azuero Project area, the giant Cerro Colorado mine was developed.
This was the big one that we had ignored because a "bongo-playing"
geologist had told me it was a worthless hill – and I had believed him!

From 1969 to 1975, various official statements were made indicating the importance of this group of major copper discoveries – the first porphyry discoveries identified in Central America. On September 6, 1969, *International Outlook* stated: "Panama this week called for bids on sizeable copper deposits found by a United Nations exploration team. At least a dozen companies, American, British, French, Italian and Japanese plan to bid."

On November 19, 1970, the *Northern Miner* reported: "President Demetrio Lakas announced that the Panamanian–United Nations copper discoveries, Botija-Petaquilla, had developed between 375 and 500 million tons of ore to a drilled depth of 400 feet."

The Cerro Colorado copper ore body, identified in 1969 and established as having proven importance by 1974, was developed by an aggressive, colourful, controversial yet creative Canadian promoter, John C. Doyle, head of the Canadian Javelin Company, with the technical guidance of a highly capable geologist, Paul Kents. Doyle, characteristically, had hastened to Panama upon the first disclosure of the UN success with the Petaquilla and Botija discoveries. He had sought authorization from the government of Panama to develop those discoveries but the government elected to allow the UN to complete their originally planned program. Thus he settled for a "second best," an adjoining concession centred on the Cerro Colorado.

Although the government's initial refusal to grant the UN discoveries to him was a great disappointment, Doyle graciously sent a letter congratulating me on the technical judgement I had shown in preparing the program for the initial discoveries. This congratulatory letter was one of the very few I received from any source concerning this successful program.

On July 17, 1975, the *Northern Miner* reported on Doyle's company, Canadian Javelin, and its activities in Panama's new Azuero copper district. "Canadian Javelin, after extensive diamond drilling and other development work, reports that feasibility studies contemplate bringing the property into production at a rate of 88,000 tons per day." Javelin subsequently lost control of the Cerro Colorado discovery by indemnified expropriation.

Other Projects in Central and South America

During 1964, I was involved in field surveys in British Guiana, St. Lucia, Costa Rica, Guatemala, El Salvador, Honduras, Peru, and Bolivia. My work as a geologist in these countries was necessarily followed by considerable subsequent research and some additional ground studies for supportive evidence, before the UN programs were drawn up. Some years of persistent efforts by others were usually necessary before success was achieved in these various undertakings. Success, of course, was not always attained in the short or long term. Often, in the type of work in which I was engaged, different individuals and/or groups made specific contributions at different times, and occasionally break-throughs occurred. Let me give you an example.

While I was based in Trinidad I contributed to the technical groundwork and conceptual development for programs through which the UN Special Fund and the Canadian International Development Agency (CIDA) established beyond doubt that the inland Takutu Basin of British Guiana was a structural rift, or great crack in the Earth's crust, which was later filled with marine sediments that hosted hydrocarbon potential. Confirmation of this scientific concept and its economic significance were assisted by other Canadian contributors. Dr. Peter Hood of the Geological Survey of Canada subsequently concluded that the Takutu Rift formed a segment of the probable proto-historic course of the Amazon River which, in earlier times, may have had its delta in the Caribbean Sea. Later, Home Oil Company of Canada led a group which drilled and proved the presence of modest oil reserves in that sedimentary trough. I was delighted to learn of Home Oil's participation for it gave the development there an added Canadian flavour.

From 1962 to 1964, I worked in a dozen countries in the Caribbean and Central and South America for the United Nations Technical Assistance Agency. When that work was completed (and crowned with the glory of having a calypso lyric composed and dedicated in my honour!) the director of the UN group for which I worked, Roberto Arce, invited me, for a second time, to accept a post in the headquarters in New York as one of his senior advisers. It was a flattering offer.

My two years of absence from the "pressure cooker" of big-city life, however, had made me doubt the wisdom of taking a desk job in New York City. Still, the prospects of an exciting new challenge and closer promixity to my family were most appealing. It meant I could commute by plane on weekends to our family farm, Franmar, which Mary and I greatly enjoyed, and which was not far from Toronto's airport. Also, I would have a comfortable apartment in New

York City where Mary could stay with me. And so I agreed to the New York posting "for a short period."

Project and Progress Adviser to Director, U.N. Headquarters, N.Y.

In New York, I worked with the director, Roberto Arce, his assistant, Joseph Barnea, and four or five other officials, including a Catholic monsignor, all of whom we were expected to "keep informed." My immediate co-worker was James (Hamish) Brown, a British geophysicist with a thorough knowledge of Africa based on his personal experience there. He was a fine person and an excellent professional colleague.

Hamish and I were the two senior advisers, temporarily replacing John Carman. All planned and ongoing Mineral Section programs were passed to us for technical evaluation and comment. These same programs were similarly "vetted" for financial, economic, personnel, and policy aspects by other specialists in the UN. Our office was in the large UN Secretariat building where the Assembly and Security Council and related commissions meet.

When I went to New York in early 1965, the UN's Technical Assistance Programs, including those of the Mineral Section in which I worked, were relatively simple. Gradually, however, we were immersed in the much larger and complex Special Fund Programs introduced in 1959.

The earliest Technical Assistance and Expanded Assistance Programs drew on the abilities of individual technical specialists, recruited from developed UN member countries and dispatched on the request of less-developed countries, primarily to evaluate and advise upon technical problems. When the initial Technical Assistance Programs were expanded, such specialists were expected not only to advise but also, when minimal equipment and/or personnel support were required, to remain, usually for a year at a time, to perform the limited amount of field work possible. My first mission to Chile in 1962–63 was a model of the Expanded Technical Program approach.

The Special Fund Programs evolved from the expanded programs and became substantial team-effort exercises. In 1965, a typical Special Fund Program operated for three to five years, involved three to six foreign experts, and required from $.5 to $2 million (U.S.) in equipment with a gross cost of about $1 million (U.S.) a year. Such programs compared in cost, and resembled to a degree, a mineral exploration program by a private-sector mining company in Canada or the United States.

A UN Special Fund Program had several aims, including, in probable order of importance: compilation of a data base of technical information concerning large areas of the country in question, such as the production of geological, geo-chemical and geo-physical maps; training of nationals of the beneficiary country in all of the specialities involved in the program up to, and for certain individuals, full professional level; organization of at least the nucleus of a national geology-mining-metallurgy agency with equipped basic laboratories and trained technologists to operate them. Most of these activities involved extensive and intensive field work.

If a Special Fund Program led to the discovery of a prospect which, after preliminary development, indicated the probability of a profitable mine or oil-gas deposit, as occurred in six of the programs I prepared, this was regarded as an added benefit and the Special Fund's duties were viewed as completed. In such a case, the national government concerned would repossess the National Mineral Reserve – the area set aside for exclusive UN study for up to five years – and retain it as a national asset or lease it in whole or in part to the national or foreign private sector. Other UN agencies which were developed later, such as the Revolving Fund or World Bank, might become involved in financing the relatively large capital development and/or production phases.

All forms of technical assistance, up to and including the Special Fund level, were financed through the voluntary pledges of member countries and not through any form of obligatory assessment. The formal, public, and ceremonial pledging procedure conducted annually by the UN General Assembly was effective; probably in large part because that procedure provided a rare opportunity for favourable public relations efforts on the basis of political rivalry. The United States almost always led, substantially, as a generous donor to technical assistance programs.

My earlier criticism of bilateral aid, given its "national content," may also be applied to UN technical assistance. When a proposed program was reduced to a plan of operations, all cost factors were scrutinized by sharp-eyed bureaucrats to ensure that, if the over-all pledging contribution of a country was say 22.4 per cent of the gross sum realized, that country would receive (that is, retain) approximately that same proportion of all equipment and supply purchases required for the program. I had been troubled by the way in which Canada acted to ensure that its bilateral aid programs, such as the Colombo Plan, aided mainly Canadians. Thus I was also troubled by this aspect of the financing of the UN technical assistance efforts. As justice should not only be done but also be seen to be done, aid should be aid and be seen to be aid, not a disguised form of self-help.

My colleague Hamish Brown and I were involved primarily in four activities. We studied technical progress reports concerning the many mineral projects underway in various parts of the world; we counselled the field project managers on technical problems that arose; we evaluated the progress of projects for the guidance of funding officers; and we prepared precise plans for specific projects, often from vague requests or proposals.

The initial requests for assistance often involved meetings, usually chaired by our director, with various permanent or visiting delegates to the UN of diplomatic rank, from the applicant countries concerned. In such meetings we attempted to reduce their requests for assistance into practical terms and programs. It was certainly refreshing when we were asked to simply send a field adviser to visit a country in order to determine what project would be most beneficial to that country. On the other hand there were a few representatives of certain countries who felt they knew exactly what they needed. Usually it was "an iron-ore mine and a steel industry"! After all, had not most economists described steel as the basic "sinew of industrial power and development"?

The U.N. Negotiation Circuit

On one occasion when I was working at UN headquarters, a policy issue in which I became involved required early resolution. Another UN agency, the Vienna-based International Atomic Energy Agency (IAEA), established in 1956–57 through the advocacy of President Dwight Eisenhower, wished to broaden its range of activities. The establishment of this agency had occasioned much debate between spokesmen of the Soviet Union and the United States. The general aim was to have the IAEA function as an effective international atomic energy inspectorate. In June 1963, the Soviet Union had accepted the principle of safeguards as set by the IAEA. But disagreements continued as to the form and control of the inspection arrangements which, it should be noted, did not cover reactors used for military purposes.

In 1965, the IAEA concluded that it should be involved in various aspects of the development, and have first-hand inventory knowledge of the uranium reserves of all UN member countries. At that time the Technical Assistance and Special Fund agencies, to which I was attached, were actively involved in uranium exploration. Two or three of our projects appeared to be economically viable given certain reserves of uranium identified.

Hamish Brown and I were asked by Director Arce, along with staff adviser N. Varlamoff, to attend a conference at IAEA headquarters in Vienna and to report back to Arce with recommendations as to what our agency's relationship to the IAEA should be in regard to uranium exploration. Subsequently, we recommended that we should vacate that field in favour of the IAEA, a step that was taken. This was quite noteworthy because it involved reducing the size and authority of a public bureaucracy, which is most unusual.

During the time I served under Roberto Arce, I participated as an observer in a number of international conferences organized by the World Bank, the International Monetary Fund (IMF) and the Economic Commission for Asia and the Far East (ECAFE). The ECAFE conference (which was the most stimulating for me as a professional geologist) was held in Tokyo in June 1968. It was attended by twenty or so of the world's leading earth scientists who were employed by government research agencies, several of the world's largest multinational private-sector corporations, and teaching institutions. They came from a number of the developed countries.

The purpose of the Tokyo conference was to establish guidelines and priorities and to seek agreement on the techniques to be used in various coastal reconnaissance surveys. These were to provide data baselines for the western rim of the Pacific Ocean, from Korea and Japan in the north, southward to China and Taiwan, and the southeast Asian coast to Indonesia. The objective was to develop an inventory of information on the near-offshore and onshore coastal strip of the Pacific Ocean western rim. It was hoped that such information would be secured through co-ordinated programs involving international agencies, mainly those based in the United States, national agencies of the coastal countries, and private companies with interests or operations in that area.

The research oceanographers and the economically oriented hydrocarbon mineral explorationists, who were present, agreed that the first regional activity initiated should be ship-borne seismic surveys. Subsequent events have confirmed the wisdom of this view. New offshore hydrocarbon fields have been, and continue to be, identified and developed within this extensive coastal zone.

While my work for the UN was challenging, I concluded in 1965, after slightly more than two years of full-time service, not to continue on that basis. My resignation from the United Nations' service as a full-time employee was dictated entirely by my temperamental and physical inability to serve as an administrator in a vast bureaucracy. Only the strong bonds of technical respect for, and friendship with, my colleagues, Roberto Arce, Joseph Barnea, John Carman, Hamish Brown, and a few others, had held me there for over a year.

The immediate cause of my resignation was my physical collapse and hospitalization for treatment of "acute bronchial pneumonia." Early in my life I had decided that I did not want to work at an inside desk job. I knew that I would be far happier working outside in the world of nature. Suddenly I had dramatic medical evidence of the correctness of that decision.

My Appointment as a United Nations Consultant

My resignation from my post in the UN headquarters did not however spell the end of my UN service. A new niche opened up for me in the UN in which I served happily for an additional fifteen years, as consultant to the general administrator. In operational terms, I became a senior roving technical programmer. This involved personally visiting countries whose requests for assistance had been approved. Where I recognized potential, and I invariably did, I drafted the initial program of objectives, operations, and cost.

In my work as a UN consultant, I was offered specific assignments which I was free to accept or decline. I recall declining only one such request, one which I considered to be completely beyond the range of my ability and interest.

As a consultant to the Administrator of Technical Assistance Programs, I ultimately served the UN on missions to over thirty additional countries by 1980. I regarded my work as a much-needed service on behalf of the world's less-privileged people. My recompense, beyond an honorarium, came from an inner sense that I was doing something that was beneficial to others, that I was exercising to the full the professional ambitions my widowed mother held for me, and honouring the patience and ability of the many fine teachers, both formal and informal, who had helped me to develop my skills.

One of the UN projects which gave me satisfaction in this dual sense involved the important La Caridad deposit in Mexico.

In Mexico with Guillermo Salas

One of the world's largest copper deposits, which involves more than a billion tons of ore, is the La Caridad in Sonora County, Mexico. In mid-April 1965, I shared with Guillermo P. Salas in the original exploration planning that led to the development of this huge porphyry deposit. Prior to that time, the UN Special Fund had been very active in twelve separate areas of Mexico, mostly along the Pacific Ocean coastal zone. The primary objective, at that time, had been to discover and develop an iron-ore deposit.

No substantive mineral discovery had been made in any of these areas. As a result, and perhaps unfairly, the UN program had been criticized publicly during the national election held shortly before I arrived in Mexico. This criticism had been most regrettable because the UN had a versatile and energetic team of international experts at their disposal in the country. Still, the problem and the criticism were understandable, given Mexico's unique relationship to the UN and its technical assistance programs.

Mexicans had developed, justifiably, a strong sense of national pride in their very important mining industry. To my knowledge, Mexico was the only nation during the mid-1960s that insisted on paying most of the total cost for its UN Special Fund programs. At that time, the majority of such programs throughout the world were about 80 per cent financed from UN sources. The Mexican people, therefore, were in a sense, paying for the right to criticize. I was soon made aware of this uneasy situation during a pre-mission briefing.

However, any uncertainties I might have had concerning the Mexicans and their ability left me quickly when I met my national counterpart, Guillermo Salas, then the Director General of Non-Renewable Natural Resources for the government of Mexico. I soon realized that Salas was an exceptional person with great ability, drive, and determination.

A sturdily built man nearly six feet tall, Salas was dynamic in movement, gesture, and speech, and had all the drive and power of the boss of an oil-drilling crew – which he could well have become were he not more ambitious – but his workaday directness and efficiency quickly mellowed to an easy Latin charm after sundown.

As a youth, Salas had worked as a chore boy with a group of American oil-well drillers in Mexico. This group had recognized his intelligence and persuaded him to return with them to Oklahoma at the time of the Mexican Revolution when all "gringo" enterprise was ordered to leave the country.

In 1936, Salas graduated in geological engineering from Oklahoma State University, subsequently returning to Mexico. There his remarkable engineering and administrative skills won him professional respect and leadership opportunities in various academic, governmental, and technical agencies on the national level.

When we met to discuss my mission in Mexico, Salas came to the point immediately. He said the last vestiges of the previous program should be terminated quickly. Any new approach would require a very different image and objective. He argued forcefully that it should be oriented toward the search for copper, of which, at that time, Mexico produced very little.

"If copper is to be the objective," I replied, "we should plan on an area close to known copper deposits, of which the best are on the American side of the border in the state of Arizona." He readily agreed. At that point in our discussion, he produced a map related to the earlier Special Fund program. I noted that a small area situated well east of Nogales had been added as an afterthought. No earlier work had been done on this small, isolated, northern area.

Salas and I readily agreed that the earlier small original area should be increased in size tenfold and extended substantially westward and southerly to "cover" the trend extension into Mexico, if present, of the important Bisbee-to-Douglas copper-mine belt of Arizona. In a single conversation we agreed on the manner in which the search for minerals would be undertaken and carried out in this area.

"What about search techniques?" I asked.

"Don't mention aeromagnetic surveys to me," Salas replied. "We've had too many of those. But I'm excited about infrared photography, and plan to learn more about it."

"Still too theoretical," I replied. "What about visually identifiable soil colour anomalies? That sometimes works in bare tropical-zone arid soil. Oxidation or bleach patterns could perhaps be spotted by a keen geologist from a low flying fixed-wing aircraft operating on parallel line intervals."

"No!" countered Salas. "Not at low altitudes. But it should work well at higher altitudes. Let's give it a try!" We agreed that if soil colour anomalies could be identified by air, then soil geo-chemical surveying should follow.

"What about some practical on-foot tours to earlier important discovery sites by half-a-dozen of your bright young men?" I asked. "They could visit some of the larger porphyry copper operations in the south-western United States, particularly to see, pick at, and taste, as I do, what is left of the original mineral outcrop areas."

"Perfect," replied Salas, "I'll want to be with them."

Such was the essence of the "Sonora Area, Joint Mexico–UN Program" as agreed between Salas and myself in late April 1965.

Five months later, in October of that year, Salas wrote to me: "We are launching our copper project in Sonora. Eight of our men leave for Arizona today. I have the greatest hope we will find one or more deposits of commercial importance." His words were prophetic.

Some soil colour anomalies were identified through aerial observation, as Salas and I had hoped. Later, the ground geo-chemical survey of one of the colour anomalies near the village of Nacozari yielded assays so extraordinarily high that "salting, probably by lazy field technicians" was suspected. Still later, the high assays were found not to be of soil material but of a very old rock-dump from a long, small-dimension "tunnel" driven into a low ridge some sixty years earlier.

After a long silence, a comprehensive final report reached me in 1970 from my friend Salas. In it he quoted his president, Diaz Ordaz, as saying that drilling of the La Caridad mine was a success. It had economic reserves of a billion tons of economically mineable open-pit copper ore which would be placed in large-scale production by Asarco Mexicana, a corporation with two-thirds Mexican government and one-third American private-sector ownership. The Asarco Company, which had a long-standing involvement in mining in Mexico, completed development of the entire ore body first identified by the "Sonora Joint Mexico–UN Project" in which Salas and I had worked together.

Upon enquiry in late 1987, I learned from officials of the La Caridad operation that 28 million metric tons of ore would be processed in that year, producing 1.8 million metric tons of copper and substantial molybdenum. Such annual production is clear evidence of the important benefits which resulted form the project in which I worked with Guillermo Salas.

My work on the Sonora project in Mexico, as well as my 1964 involvement in the Panama Azuero project, provided a geological insight as to the nature of porphyry copper deposits in the Central American Cordilleran context. Thus when the UN Technical Assistance Program received a request in 1971 from the government of Colombia for help in the identification and development of sources of copper in that country, I was asked to undertake the assignment. I agreed to do so.

Searching for Copper in Colombia: The Mocoa Discovery

On my arrival in Bogota, Colombia, I discovered that, largely as a result of financial aid from the United States, their "Ingeominas" agency had developed into a modern institution with excellent mineral exploration facilities, equipment, and personnel, but little success in discovering new mineral deposits. To that time, however, mineral production of gold and emerald had been undertaken. And yet, even the country's emerald production was viewed by some regulatory officials as a very mixed blessing because of theft, smuggling, and general banditry.

In 1970 there was an optimistic attitude in Colombia. Foreign interest appeared to have been finally aroused by their obviously huge coal potential, together with their recently identified and apparently large, high-quality nickel laterite deposits – discovered through serendipity by petroleum geologists.

In Bogota, I read all the available reports which dealt with copper, particularly those which might offer some clue as to the presence of porphyry-type copper deposits. Then I set out by plane and jeep to examine as many of these clue areas deposits as possible, in the company of a capable geologist guide, Dr. Jaime Cruz, and a driver-helper.

Cruz had suggested to me, half jokingly, that locating copper showings in Colombia was not difficult. Every "hill person" had an awareness of the value of emeralds and was immediately attracted by any stone or outcrop of bright green colour, typical of emerald and also malachite and chrysocolla, both surface alteration minerals of copper. Several times Cruz had been shown non-economic indications of copper which the discoverer believed to be emerald.

My travels and mineral examinations with Cruz of such earlier reported indications did not result in our finding useful evidence of possible porphyry copper deposits. Thus I finally resorted to a mixture of theory, fact, and fantasy.

I was aware of a UN discovery of a copper-porphyry deposit in Ecuador, which borders Colombia on the south, where the Cordilleran zone is relatively uncomplicated. The Cordillera, the mountainous north-south trending complex, is the mineral-related spinal column of the western edge of South America, Central America, and also North America. At the border between Colombia and Ecuador there is a low-elevation, east-west valley which serves as an important river and travel corridor. To an explorer with an inclination to fantasy, this corridor could possibly indicate the presence of a favourable transverse structure. I also noted that in this most south-westerly corner of Colombia, the Cordillera appeared to be a single unit, or collision slice, whereas in the north it became a complicated pattern of several units, or slices, toward the Caribbean coastline.

In this south-westerly sector, the infra-structural economics were good. Save for the rain forest, sloping steeply on the west into the Pacific Ocean, the rest of the Cordilleran unit on the easterly slopes was open and reasonably well serviced by roads, and well settled. Another possible element of interest concerning this sector was the report that evidence of gold had been found at one point in the Pacific coastal area of this region.

My final choice for the project area involved a relatively narrow, seemingly uncomplicated, segment of the Colombian Cordillera. Initially, I sketched it out on one of the country's road maps issued by the Mobil Oil Company. The area chosen extended from Mocoa to Neiva to Ibague, on its easterly side, and from west of Pasto to Cali and beyond, on its westerly side.

The initial exploration technique which I recommended to the Colombians and the UN Special Fund in September 1971 was similar to that employed in Panama in 1965. It involved a reconnaissance soil geo-chemical survey of the drainage systems traversing the chosen area. The terrain proved difficult to cover on foot. Thus the survey proceeded slowly during the years 1973–76. By 1977, however, an eight-square-kilometre area of interest had been identified and was being developed patiently by diamond-drilling.

Finally, in September 1982, it was officially announced that, with 80 per cent of the development drilling completed, a deposit of more than 260 million metric tons of a little more than 1 per cent copper equivalent (copper plus molybdenum content) had been delineated. While the volume of these deposits was not as great as those discovered through the Sonora project in Mexico, they appeared to be richer. In any event, this news gave me a sense of considerable gratification as I reflected on the beginning of my work in Colombia over a decade earlier.

It also gave me a great sense of inner satisfaction in terms of my "technical batting average." It raised to three – Panama, Mexico, and now Colombia – the successful UN technical search missions for copper porphyry deposits of economic importance in Central America, in which I had served as the conceptual programmer, usually with a single associate from the nation involved. My work in Colombia was particularly satisfying to me because it had resolved a puzzle that had challenged me since my student days at UBC: "Why should the great copper-molybdenum porphyry deposits of the Cordillera, strung like a string of beads the length of the western United States, seem to end at the border of Mexico and not re-appear until the Cordillera of Peru and Chile was reached?" I had now solved the puzzle for myself and others to follow. They appeared to be absent because they had not been sought, or if sought, had not been found.

Dame Fortune's daughter Miss Fortune is indeed a capricious flirt! And in Colombia that flirtation was also marked by some moments of great anxiety.

Dangerous Episodes in Latin America

While working in Colombia, I went with Jaime Cruz to examine a copper prospect in a mountainous area east of the Caribbean port of

Barranquilla, an old and colourful city close to the Venezuelan border. The examination of this prospect was to take two or three days. Thus Cruz had reserved overnight accommodation at a small but very attractive resort hotel near Barranquilla.

Before I left the hotel the following morning, I took my usual precautions of locking my wallet, my UN and Canadian passports, and other valuable items in my metal suitcase, and leaving my room key with the hotel manager. I took with me my usual work kit of packsack, sample bags and tags, pick, compass, measuring tape, hand lens, watch, and engineering notebook. In addition, I had a small amount of local currency in bills, and my camera.

Colombia is a fascinating and beautiful country with its chains of mountains, its river valleys, gorges, lowlands, and hilly areas. After travelling in our jeep through this terrain for a couple of hours, we reached a steep mountain trail which we had to climb on foot. We parked the jeep and climbed about a mile or more to the work area.

During the hour or so we climbed, I stopped frequently to chip at rock outcrops on my path and to examine, in my usual manner, the fresh rock chip by eye, odour, and sometimes a lick if an odour encouraged me. Finally we reached the end of the trail and a small plateau on the mountain top. This was one of the many mountain tops of the complex range in north-east Colombia bordering on Venezuela. It was a cloudless yet cool day with a magnificent view of the Caribbean coastline in the distance. We prospected the top of the mountain carefully in the same manner as I had on the way up. When our work was done, we all started back down to the jeep.

Cruz and the helper raced quickly ahead while I proceeded slowly down the trail, chipping and examining rock types. At a more leisurely pace, I could also enjoy the remarkably beautiful panorama of the Caribbean coastline in the distance. Finally, I came to a rock ledge ideally suited for taking pictures of the magnificent landscape. I stopped, prepared my camera, walked out on the ledge and started to focus my camera. Suddenly, I was jolted from behind.

Whirling around, I confronted two soldiers in military camouflage uniforms. Each had a machine gun vaguely pointed toward me. I was totally surprised by their sudden appearance. One of the soldiers then pointed his gun at me. The other aimed in the air and fired two or three shots as a form of signal. The soldier aiming his gun at me indicated that I should look down the mountain-side. I looked and saw a small flag fluttering among the tree tops about a half-mile away. Belatedly, I realized I was near a military encampment, probably the base of an anti-guerilla border patrol or anti-gem-smuggling unit. They must have thought that I was photographing their military base.

At last one of them spoke. His rapid, blunt gutteral Spanish meant nothing to me. *"No entiendo,"* I murmured.

Irritated, the soldier barked at me again. He was asking for my identification papers. I had a sickening feeling and I knew that I was in trouble – I had none with me.

I explained that my papers were at the hotel, where I was staying, and that I was a foreign official travelling with a Colombian government officer who was waiting for me in a jeep at the foot of the trail. The soldiers exchanged glances but gave no sign of understanding my explanation. One triggered another shot into the air and both, with jabbing gestures of their guns, indicated I should lead them down the trail to the jeep. Stumbling nervously, as they both followed behind me with guns at the ready, I proceeded to do so. I hoped that the shots fired would bring Cruz on the run up the trail to assist me, but they did not.

As I neared the bottom of the trail, I became increasingly anxious. Would Cruz still be there? Why had he not rushed to my side on hearing the gunfire? At last, we broke out of the brush onto the road and my worst fear was realized. The jeep and my companions were nowhere in sight!

My captors stared at me, clearly expecting some explanation. I simply shook my head in bewilderment. They both stood with their guns now pointed at my legs. Evidently their last single shot had been a signal to the encampment. A military jeep soon screeched to a stop in front of us.

In the jeep was a young uniformed officer with a revolver at his belt. Beside him was an aide with a Tommy gun. In front were the driver and a soldier with a loud-hailer. The officer stepped out of the jeep and approached me. In clear, polished Spanish he asked for my story. I gave it to him. When he asked me for identification, where I stayed, the name of the hotel, and why my companion had fled, I could only nod negatively. Finally, he asked if I felt I could recognize my seaside hotel "near Barranquilla." I replied with some desperation, "I think so."

"Well then, come," he said, "we must get to the bottom of all this."

The drive to the coast along a narrow but relatively level and asphalted road was an adventure in itself. I sat in the front seat jammed between the driver and the soldier with the loud-hailer, while the officer and his aide occupied the rear seat. The driver seemed to be a frustrated Grand Prix race champion and literally flew along the straight sections and roared through the frequent small hamlets along our route. The driver never reduced his speed or stopped for anything. As we neared each hamlet, the soldier with the loud-hailer blew a path for us, screaming his way through and around every obstacle. People, chickens, goats, and pigs responded with flying alacrity. And, of course, the roadside was lined, but from a safe distance, by crowds of excited or frightened onlookers.

Given our frantic pace, it was not long before we were in the coastal zone and soon among city dwellings, so we slowed down – but only slightly! Two city police cars joined the cavalcade, orange lights flashing, a relief from the loud-hailer which, happily, at least for my ears, became silent. We came to a wide, busy, waterfront avenue crossing our path. At this point, the military officer behind me tapped me on the shoulder. "Which way?" he asked. I did not know, and hesitated. But our driver didn't. He turned to the right.

Soon we were among large wharves and warehouses. "Not this way!" I shouted. Quickly we made a sharp U-turn and retraced our tracks. This time we stayed on the waterfront highway. We left the industrial area and were soon among stores and occasional hotels.

"Slow down!" I shouted.

"Are we there?" the officer asked.

"Not yet, but I feel we're close. I'm looking for a wide, open stinking ditch that we must cross on a narrow bridge!" I replied.

"A stinking ditch?" the puzzled officer asked, and gave up his questioning.

Suddenly I saw the hotel. "There it is! Cross the bridge!" I shouted.

With twisting and turning, police lights flashing, and one police siren wailing, the cavalcade ground to a halt in the small parking area of the three-storey resort hotel. Much relieved, I tumbled out of the jeep. The officer beside me, I proceeded directly to the hotel.

To my surprise and probably the officer's, not a person was in sight. No manager or clerk stood at their usual post at the reception bureau, no bartender behind the open bar in the public reception area. Not a soul in sight! I was baffled.

I went behind the reception counter to remove my key from the others hanging on hooks on the wall. My room was on the ground floor, but now I couldn't remember its number! Frantically I seized a half-dozen ground-floor keys and, with the officer at my side, hastened around the counter and along the room corridor, attempting to recognize the door to my room. In an open cubbyhole, where mops and towels were stored, we discovered a frightened maid. Only then did I realize that our dramatic arrival had apparently terrified everyone. I asked if she remembered the "gringo's" room. She pointed at one of the keys in my hand.

The officer asked her to find the hotel manager. We went to my room, unlocked the door, and then my suitcase. I quickly found my UN diplomatic passport. The officer glanced at my photograph and flipped through half-a-dozen or so pages, all impressively embellished with the diplomatic seals of various countries I had visited, including Colombia.

By this time, an embarrassed hotel manager had appeared in my room. The officer, with an element of contempt for the frightened man, said rather sternly, "I have a number of questions to ask you. But first, find your bartender. My companion and I have a question for him too!"

The officer and I proceeded to the public reception area. There we each ordered a drink and slumped down on a sofa. After a few minutes he asked, "Where are your companions?"

Again I had to reply, "I don't know." Then I hastened to assure him: "They'll be here sooner or later, I hope!"

Perhaps two hours later, as dusk approached, Cruz and our jeep returned. He was delighted to find me and was full of questions. But before he could get started, the officer asked Cruz to explain where he had been. Soon we had the full story.

At the first sound of gunfire, Cruz and the driver had raced in the jeep to the nearest police station, secured armed assistance, and returned up the trail to try to find me – or recover my body. Finding nothing, they had returned to the police station to complete a lengthy report. They had then come back directly to the hotel and found me there – alive!

And the photograph I had taken from the trail? It turned out poorly! Lots of ocean and brush, but no sign at all of the troublesome flag indicating the military encampment. Indeed, I had no evidence whatsoever of my incident with Colombia's military police who, aside from their loud-hailer, had treated me quite well.

When Cruz and I returned to Bogota by plane we were quickly
surrounded at the airport by half-a-dozen senior government officials
who wrung my hand as if I had been resurrected from the dead. Only
then did I realize that a badly frightened Cruz had, unknown to me,
instantly alerted his office in Bogota that I had disappeared after shots
of unknown origin were fired.

A day or so later, I left Colombia. My project planning was acceptable to the Bogota government officials involved, and later to my
United Nations superiors. I elected, at the time, to downplay the
military incident. After all, no blood had been spilt. Forty years
before, I had had the opportunity to work on a construction job in
Colombia. While the type of work I did there in my UN capacity was
somewhat different, I had fulfilled that earlier dream. It had been far
more exciting than I had ever wished it would be, and rewarding also.
It resulted in an important technical success; the identification and
development of Colombia's first large porphyry copper-ore body, the
Mocoa. In September 1982 the government announced that, with
development still incomplete, its work had drill-indicated in excess
of 260 million metric tonnes of 1 per cent copper-equivalent ore.

Twinkling Ceiling Lights Spell "Murder" in Managua

My treatment by the Colombian military had been reasonably civil
compared with what I had observed or been subjected to on other
occasions. During the 1960s, I saw recurrent evidence throughout
Latin America of the overt power of the military. Invariably they
exercised or threatened force against their own nationals to impose
upon the recalcitrant majority the political will of a few, usually self-
proclaimed, leaders. I saw clear evidence of the use of such force in
Managua, Nicaragua.

On my first visit to Nicaragua in June 1967, I stayed in one of
the principal hotels in Managua before leaving for the bush and my
project area base. It was an old but architecturally attractive hotel,
centrally located not far from the government administration buildings. Tito Somoza's beautiful sprawling white residence could be seen
on a hillside nearby. I was told by the taxi driver that not many days
earlier there had been a minor military uprising which had been
quickly and ruthlessly put down. Some furious fighting had taken
place on the streets beside the hotel.

On registering at the hotel I asked for a room on one of the upper floors so that I might enjoy a better view of the new city. I was taken to a rather lavish penthouse apartment with an attractive balcony overlooking a busy avenue.

I retired quite early the first night, tired from the long air trip and conscious of the need to be up and ready for an early-morning conference. As I lay in the comfortable bed after I turned off the bedside lamp, I was surprised to see, in the darkness, some twinkles of light along two walls and the ceiling of my room. "Fireflies!" I thought to myself. "How interesting." I watched, but the spots of light didn't move or flicker on and off like insects. I turned the light on again and got up to investigate.

I climbed onto a chair to reach the ceiling and ran my fingers over the small areas where I had seen the spots of light. I turned the bedroom light off and the bathroom light on. More light spots appeared on that wall. Then I realized they were tiny holes, in some places completely perforating the ceiling or wall, and, in part, covered with whitewash. Even more frightening, there was a recognizable pattern to these streams of holes. They were whitewashed-over machine-gun bullet holes.

The next morning, I asked a UN office employee about the most recent abortive uprising, while mentioning the holes in my room. "Oh, yes," he said, "there was quite a bit of gunfire all along that avenue about a week or two ago."

Three weeks later when I had returned from the field and was staying overnight in the same hotel, a tourist with whom I was dining said to me, "You know a lot of the last fighting in town took place in front of, and in, this very hotel. In fact, the doorman told me that the ringleader was cornered by 'Tito's boys' and killed in one of the upstairs bathrooms!"

Evidence of social unrest and aggressiveness was not confined to urban areas. In at least three different Central American countries I was cautioned by the "Planning Ministers" – in one case, the "Planning and National Emergency Minister" – to avoid certain forested areas in any proposed program I was considering. Under no circumstances was I to venture near, or fly over, the areas indicated to me. They were vaguely described as "American anti-guerilla training camps" or "guerilla hamlets" from which "visitors" rarely returned.

One of these dangerous areas in Nicaragua was situated close to a very large United Fruit banana plantation. I had arranged to meet the resident administrator of the plantation, since he knew much about the local geography, including, perhaps, evidence of nearby mineral indications. A meeting was arranged and I found him to be a most friendly man who had been in that company's service for almost twenty years. I did not ask about his "training camp" neighbours, but rather, how recurrent political changes affected his position and business. To my surprise he said, "By actual count, since I've been here, we've been through fourteen or fifteen revolts or 'upsets,' whatever you call them. But as far as we are concerned, I don't think we've lost one stem of bananas yet!"

More Close Calls

Not all the frightening episodes I've experienced in Latin America have involved the military. On one occasion, I went with a fellow Canadian called Smitty to help in the evaluation of iron-ore deposits on the west coast of Mexico near Mazatlan. In Acapulco, Smitty hastily engaged a pilot and chartered a small single-engined plane regularly used to take tourists on short flights around that resort area. Unfortunately we learned about the regular usage of this aircraft too late. A small tourist aircraft without adequate engine power or fuel supply should not be used in Mexico's coastal rain forest. Blissfully ignorant of this, we took off. We stopped at the makeshift dirt airstrip of a coconut plantation to purchase fuel for the plane. Since this was done by hand pump from steel drums and required perhaps a half-hour or more, I left the pilot and Smitty in conversation with the white planter and went for a walk along a dirt lane toward the sea.

The lane was cut through a strip of thick natural forest separating the plantation from the sea. After walking about two hundred yards, I arrived at a lovely small sandy beach and sat down on a driftwood log to survey the scene. There was an attractive expanse of white sand dotted with large pieces of driftwood all beautifully sculpted and burnished by the surf and sand.

Hearing a faint sound I turned toward it. To my surprise, I saw a large, beautifully coloured, black and yellow cat, about a foot and a half long and a foot high. I sat still, admiring its colour and lithe beauty, as it fearlessly approached me. Soon it was standing beside my legs, so I gently reached out and began stroking its head and ears.

When it suddenly sprang into my lap, I realized it was probably the largest cat I had ever seen. It weighed perhaps twenty pounds.

As the cat seemed friendly, I gently stroked its side but to my great surprise – and pain – it playfully dug its claws into my thighs. Clearly this was no ordinary cat!

As I carefully tried to disengage the over-friendly creature from my lap it simply sank its claws deeper and more painfully into my thighs. Now I really was worried, but figured the best thing to do was grit my teeth and sit still. I knew that cats do what this cat was doing out of a sense of pleasure. The question was how long could I endure the pain the cat's pleasure was causing me.

Mercifully the plantation manager and Smitty soon came looking for me. As they approached, the manager, with his dog, broke into a run. At that moment, the cat withdrew its claws from my thighs and stood upright on my lap, eyes fixed on the dog. "My God!" exclaimed the plantation manager. "That's one of the jaguar cubs!" I stood upright, holding the fearful yet now quiet animal in my arms while we were given the story.

We were told that the uncultivated forest beside the plantation still sheltered some jaguar, native to that area of Mexico. They are known as *el tigre"* and *tigre Americano*. The numbers were much depleted because of the great value of the beautiful pelts. Hunting and trapping of jaguar were no longer permitted, but poaching continued and a mature female had been shot the day before. This was probably her cub which had been overlooked or escaped.

The plantation manager said he would take care of the cub. I agreed, provided he would take a picture with my camera of the friendly cat in my arms. Whenever I think of that cat I remember how beautiful it was and how painful for me was the pleasure I brought to it.

After another refuelling stop and one overnight stay, we reached the iron-ore site. We completed our task at the site in a few hours and commenced our return flight. The young pilot, although he lacked adequate maps for navigation, felt that following the coastline back would take too long and decided to fly a compass course and travel inland.

After about two hours, our gasoline supply began to run low. We were well into the high Cordillera mountains and had seen no habitation at all that could provide us with a "position fix." In this mountainous area there was, of course, absolutely no place to land. In fact, as the cloud layer thickened, there were uncomfortable intervals when we could not see the ground at all. I sat up front with the pilot and kept my eye on all the instruments, particularly the compass and fuel-tank gauge. Smitty sat behind us finding some measure of fortification from a bottle of tequila on his lap. Whenever I questioned the pilot, or drew his attention to the instrument panel, he said not a word, nor did he glance at the instruments. Instead, he promptly released his right hand from the stick and, being a good Catholic, devoutly made the sign of the cross.

Finally, at dusk, through a hole that had magically appeared in the clouds, and just as I heard the engine begin to sputter as the gasoline gauge approached "empty," I caught a glimpse of a transmission tower in the valley below us. Excitedly, I pointed it out to the pilot. He changed course to follow the line of towers and lowered the altitude of the plane. Soon I realized we were following the river valley upstream, but I dared not comment. Before long we came in sight of a water reservoir impounded behind a concrete and rock dam. I wondered where and how we could land, since we were flying "on wheels."

Then, in the shadows on the side of the reservoir, we saw a more or less flat area from which rock had been quarried to construct the dam. I quietly considered our only three options with rising concern.

If we landed in the quarry area, the rigid fixed-wheel undercarriage clearly would be either ripped off before the plane touched water or, if attached strongly enough to the body would trip the plane into a somersault – an even worse scenario. Either option was dangerous and so was the third: if we crash-landed on the water surface without broken bones, I still could not swim a stroke. A quarry bottom was a more familiar terrain to me. However it would not be littered with finely crushed rock, but in all likelihood with large angular blocks resulting from primary blasting. The near-darkness and shadows provided a mellowness to each surface that made the choice even more difficult.

During the few seconds I had to weigh these options, I said not a word but watched intensely as if I were some completely detached spectator. The pilot chose the quarry bottom and approached it on a good glide angle. We touched down with violent bumps, followed by a crunching noise. Suddenly we came to an abrupt stop on the plane's belly, the crushed undercarriage beneath it. We had landed, alive and without broken bones!

Smitty, the pilot, and I were drenched in nervous sweat. For several minutes we sat in shock in the aircraft cabin. Soon a plant watchman, who had heard the plane engine and our crash-landing, arrived in a jeep. He told us that we were about twelve miles from Guadalajara, our planned destination. The plant watchman then drove us to Guadalajara and took us to a modest rooming house. It was clean and simple, but crowded, and so all three of us had to share one room with three cots. We did not protest. Showered and exhausted, we dropped on our cots knowing we were lucky to be alive.

Early next morning after breakfast, I arranged for a flight from the nearby Guadalajara airport to Mexico City for Smitty and myself. I sought out the pilot to say goodbye. He wrung my hand with mixed relief and anguish. With tears in his eyes he mumbled, "Mistair Smitty – he does not seem to like me!" And on that unhappy note we parted.

Any list of frightening episodes from my time in Central America should include the occasion I was asked to serve in an emergency capacity during a volcanic eruption in Costa Rica early in June 1964.

While I was in Costa Rica organizing a mineral exploration program, a dormant volcano suddenly became active, showering the countryside near the capital of San Jose with clouds of volcanic ash. An emergency request from UN headquarters suggested that I assist the Costa Rican government in its efforts to deal with the crisis until the UN's team of expert volcanologists could get there from Japan.

To that time my only practical experience with erupting volcanoes had consisted primarily of peering into the craters of Waikiki and Lahaina on the Hawaiian Islands. On another occasion I had spent a Christmas Eve with Mary and Marion, then a teen-ager, seated on a nearby hill watching the dramatic molten birth of volcano Paracutin in Mexico. On these earlier occasions I had been merely a naïve tourist. This time I was to become involved directly.

I reported to the Costa Rican authorities for directions and was told simply, "Do anything you think best to help us." The effects of the disaster were already serious since the ash falling from the sky like snow was clogging the rivers and water reservoirs, polluting the drinking water, and ruining turbines in hydro-generating plants. It would destroy the all-important coffee crop for the year, as the flower pollenization process, then underway, would be disrupted. A very fine dust, like a choking fog, was everywhere.

My thoughts went back to my underground mining days when we had deep concern about silicosis from ingesting silica dust. Everyone in the region of the volcano in Costa Rica appeared to be gasping, sneezing, and choking, despite wearing handkerchief masks, wet or dry, covering the face and nostrils. I became increasingly concerned about possible respiratory effects caused by the dust. Since there were no sophisticated analytical laboratories in Costa Rica, I collected a sample of the ash "dust" and airmailed it by diplomatic pouch for transmittal to a Canadian laboratory with an urgent request that it be analysed quickly and that a biomedical report be telegraphed back to us in Costa Rica.

I then decided to visit the volcano to prepare a report on its appearance and stage of activity as a guide for the volcanologists *en route* to the country, and the other experts with whom Costa Rican officials were in touch. Despite the hilly terrain and narrow roads, I finally reached a point at the base of the volcano. There I enlisted the services of two local farm labourers. Removing much of our outer clothing because of the heat, we set out to climb the flank of the volcanic hill, or cone, which was perhaps six hundred feet high.

As we began our climb, the footing was firm and the layer of ash less than a foot thick for the first four hundred feet or so. No molten material was evident as we struggled upwards – only billows of hot, ash-laden air.

As we continued, the increasing heat, dust, poor footing, and the difficulty of breathing through the cloth covering our faces began to take its toll. One of the labourers complained of exhaustion, lagged behind, and then turned back. The other struggled on with me, but hesitatingly. We were then only two hundred feet or so down the slope from the edge of the crater. I was in the lead, perhaps ten feet ahead of my remaining companion. Suddenly, there was another tremor.

A dense burst of fresh ash followed. I could see nothing. We were completely lost in the suffocating darkness. A sense of falling weight-lessly and vertically downward swept over me. All at once my feet seemed to touch solid rock. I struggled to collect my senses.

As the ash slowly settled and the air became clearer, I found myself almost waist-deep in fresh ash. Down the slope, I saw my companion standing upright knee-deep in the warm ash. He was struggling to turn and go down the slope. With one arm he was waving frantically for me to follow. While the ash was light and dry and seemed to be quite fluid, I found it difficult to manoeuvre my body. It seemed impossible to walk.

Desperately, I flung myself forward onto my stomach. Flailing my arms and legs I half swam and half crawled down the slope. Finally

I gained firmer ground and at last was able to stand upright again. With my companion, I stumbled, as fast as my tired legs would carry me, to the bottom of the cone as if *El Diablo* was in hot pursuit.

Covered head to toe in ash, every pore filled with volcanic dust, and enormously weary, my companions and I were greatly relieved to be together again and safe at the base of the crater. I had learned another valuable lesson and survived another close brush with death.

I had rushed to the scene of the volcano to secure first-hand information which I had hoped would provide assistance to others, fully realizing that I was a total amateur in regard to erupting volcanoes. My efforts probably did not contribute one whit toward reducing the danger or damage of that natural disaster, but I had minor comfort on one point. The ash analysis from my sampling indicated no free silica – the dread of silicosis was unnecessary. The experience served another purpose. It reminded me, once more, of the realism of a statement by historian Will Durant: "Civilization exists by geological consent, subject to change without notice."

XVI

Global Prospecting – My Life as a Technical Missionary

I have always been fascinated, perhaps even enchanted, by the world, this amazing Earth on which we live. Our intriguing sphere of continents, oceans, mountains, and valleys revolving in the universe captured my interest early. Ships from faraway docking in Victoria, the arrival of aircraft, the stories I heard from men who sailed the seven seas, my brother Tibby sailing away as a cook in a "tramp" freighter's galley – all these stimulated my boyhood interest in distant places. That interest continues to this day.

My first two years of service in the Technical Assistance Program of the United Nations were devoted exclusively to work in the Caribbean and Central and South America. All of the UN projects I undertook in those years were in the Americas, on "our" side of the globe. From 1965 onwards, my work for the UN was increasingly on the "other" side of the globe – in Europe, Africa, the Middle East, and Asia. My colleagues in the UN service and I did not plan it that way – it just happened as a result of the procedure we followed in deciding on the projects I would undertake.

The nature of any specific mission on which I might embark as a consultant to the administrator of the UN's Technical Assistance Program could not be predicted in advance. Where I would go, and when, was determined by the nature of the requests received from the applicant countries and passed on to the administrator for implementation. If he felt I had the qualifications for the mission he would turn to me, among others, to learn if I was prepared to undertake the work. In all my years with the UN I never reacted negatively to any mission post offered me, save one for which I lacked the competency required. Once I had embarked upon a project, however, and I usually embarked upon it alone, by choice, I was given complete freedom in regard to all necessary technical decisions, subject only to the diplomatic counselling and assistance of the UN Resident Representative in the country concerned.

I regarded my initial assignments with the UN as a practical in-

troduction to the nature of their activities. Through my work in the
Patagonian region of Chile, and my other assignments in the Caribbean and Central and South America (particularly my work in Trinidad and Tobago) I had been able to recover fully from the psychological
exhaustion which I had experienced as a result of the dramas, tension,
and success of the preceding ten years, most notably during the Hirshhorn chapter of my life. I was now able to undertake and enjoy, at
my own pace, many fresh challenges. I re-discovered quietness and
peace, and could appreciate again the magnificent simplicity and beauty
of the world of nature, in the hills, plains, deserts, forests, or jungles
of many foreign lands.

When I returned from missions abroad into the high-pressure
world of the UN headquarters in New York, I would become aware,
once again, that in the highly mechanized culture of western man,
many things absolutely necessary for the maintenance of human and
social life were disappearing. Not only that, but the socio-economic
problems of the developed countries and the callousness of economic
imperialism were worsening rather than improving the fate of the less-
developed countries. The latter looked increasingly to UN agencies to
help – particularly with disease epidemics, agricultural assistance to
produce food, and the development of natural resources to provide
income for self-improvement. I could serve, I realized, as a technical
missionary of social conscience to help with the last need – that of
identifying and developing economically useful mineral deposits.

Thus I continued to serve the UN as a prospector and geologist
by undertaking assignments in a wide variety of countries during the
years 1965–79. To provide an overview of the geographical scope of
the activities in which I was engaged during those years, it may
be helpful if I list the countries in which I worked during that decade
and a half.

1965 – Poland, Israel, Turkey, Austria, Tunisia, Senegal, Togo,
       Liberia, Kenya, The Soviet Union
1966 – Yugoslavia, India, Cuba
1967 – Belgian Congo, Nicaragua, Rwanda
1968 – India, Japan, Somalia, Trinidad-Tobago
1969 – French Guinea, Trinidad-Tobago, Guyana
1970 – Guyana, Austria
1971 – Somalia, The Soviet Union, Honduras, Colombia
1972 – Indonesia, India, Iran, Nepal
1973 – Nepal, Afghanistan, Pakistan, India, Morocco

1974   – Afghanistan, Iran, Pakistan, Greece, Somalia, Honduras
1975-76 – Jamaica
1977   – Burma, Iran
1978   – Madagascar
1979   – Madagascar, Haiti

Each of the countries in which I worked during those fifteen years is a source of rich memories for me. Some are pleasant, some less so. I went to each country to learn, to understand, and, if possible, to contribute to its economic development. I was motivated by an insatiable curiosity, social concern, and technical challenge. To the fullest extent of which I am capable, I worked without ideological or political bias.

If I have been successful as a prospector, practising geologist, and scientist it is because of my continuing willingness to question, and to re-examine the "conventional wisdom" regarding people, ideas, and things. This has made my life a continuously fascinating adventure, uncomplicated and happy, without enemies or regrets.

I have travelled through life, when and where possible, with a notebook and a camera to observe, to attempt to understand, and to program my "organic computer." Since the world of nature and all animate and inanimate life fascinate me, my memories, written records, and photographs are, as my dear mother would have said, "*un bon ragout*" – a fine stew. In this chapter, I recount a few of the more memorable episodes, mainly of an amusing nature.

In all the countries I visited, whether "centrally planned" (the UN term for Marxist Communist) or "free," I enjoyed mutual trust and respect. I travelled and saw what I wished to see and learned what I wished to learn. One of the great tragedies of our world is that so few people seem to be aware that they do have opportunities each day to share in, and to contribute to, a climate of openness and generosity in human life. I have encountered these qualities nearly everywhere I travelled throughout the world. This was particularly true when I went to Poland in 1965.

In Poland to Develop Fertilizer Raw Materials

Poland was not the first of the six "centrally planned" countries to which I had travelled and in which I had worked. Earlier, I had visited the Peoples' Republic of China and the Soviet Union. My mission in Poland was to assist in the finding and development of mineral sources for agricultural fertilizer production such as potash, nitrates, phosphates, and related materials. After discussion with specialists and officials in Poland, it was agreed that I should concentrate my efforts on helping to improve Poland's supply of potash.

Prior to the Second World War, Poland possessed important potash deposits in both the eastern and western sections of the country. Having been deprived of these deposits on both sides when national borders were changed after the Second World War, the Poles were trying to find new sources. A most able geologist, Dr. Zbigniew Werner, a senior scientist in the Industrial Minerals Section of Poland's Geological Survey, was appointed my counterpart assistant to help me identify new or unexplored "evaporite" sub-basins and to test for potash content.

Evaporites are mineral deposits formed by the solution, evaporation, and precipitation of salts, (potassium, sodium, magnesium, and others) in restricted bodies of marine water such as tropical zone lagoons, inland seas, or semi-isolated coastal waters. The processes which resulted in the development of such deposits were well understood by the Poles. Our problem was to find a new, and sufficiently large, evaporite basin buried at adequate depth to insure its preservation and then to determine its potential for the production of potash.

Dr. Werner told me that Poland's Energy Fuels Trust had drilled many deep but widely scattered exploratory wells in search of coal, oil, and gas in Poland's huge northern sedimentary plains overlapping the Baltic pre-Cambrian Shield area. While they had not been notably successful in these hydro-carbon investigations, I assumed all geological and geophysical data resulting from those efforts would be made available to me. Thus a meeting was arranged for us with the senior technical personnel of the Energy Trust. Werner served as interpreter. He was fluent in English as well as the three languages of most educated Poles: Polish, German, and Russian.

At these meetings I learned that (as is customary in the western world) the exploratory wells had not only been drilled and cored and cuttings recovered for study, but in addition, several in-the-hole geophysical surveys had been completed and the records kept. Included among these were strata radiometric measurements.

I knew from my knowledge of the Esterhazy, Saskatchewan, potash deposits that radiometric data could prove useful in identifying the presence and concentration of potash salts. I also knew that the Canadian firm of C. A. Sproule and Associates of Calgary were experts in this technique of interpretation as applied to potash exploration. I telephoned Dr. Sproule from Warsaw. He agreed to immediately send over one of his senior geophysicists, Dr. Stanley Harding. Harding was to play a key role in the eventual success of this project. As it turned out he also had several personal eccentricities which added immeasurably to the excitement of our mission.

I was at an important conference when Harding arrived in Warsaw. About half a dozen senior Polish administrators were sitting rather stiffly around a boardroom table listening to the chairman question me on the project's progress, when a secretary entered and discreetly placed a written note beside him. The chairman glanced at it, looked up, and said with some alarm, "Dr. Joubin, you must go to Dr. Harding. He has arrived and there is an emergency at the hotel." I excused myself, rushed out to a waiting car, and was driven to my hotel. During the drive I prayed silently that Harding had not suffered a cardiac arrest.

Upon arrival at the hotel, one of the finest and most elegant in Warsaw, I hastened to the manager's desk to secure my room key and find Harding. The manager was greatly agitated. His broken English tumbled out in confusion. "Your friend Dr. Harding has been very difficult. He says his room is not satisfactory. He brought his own bed. He prefers to sleep in the bathroom. He says he may have to find another hotel. He has asked that furniture be moved out of his apartment into the corridor. This cannot be done. Can you control this man?"

Having received this discomforting information, I took the elevator to the floor on which my room was located. As I emerged from the elevator, I saw Harding seated on a stiff-back wooden chair where the hall porter normally sat. He sprang to his feet when he saw me, thrust out his hand and asked, "Are you Joubin?"

"Yes," I replied. "You have a problem?"

It turned out that Harding had several allergies. The worst involved certain wool dyes and feathers of any type. Soon after he arrived, it became obvious to him that he would have a major problem in this hotel with its feather-stuffed cushions and upholstery and its down-stuffed quilts. Because of his allergies he travelled with his own gear – a huge kapok sleeping bag, a canvas folding bed, and other bags of miscellaneous equipment. Besides, he added a bit apologetically, he wasn't sure if this was to be a bush or city project. So he had brought everything!

I returned to the hotel manager and told him about Harding's allergies. The manager seemed to partly understand what I had said and told me that he would change the troublesome furniture pieces. When Harding and I later examined his room, he concluded that it now seemed "Okay," save for one thing.

"What's that?" I asked, with some impatience.

He lowered his voice and said, "Bugs! Electronic bugs! Probably I've been watching too many of the wrong T.V. programs. But could this room be bugged? You know – eavesdropping!"

"But," I protested, "what difference does it make? We have no state secrets to reveal, no conspiracy to plan . . ." Then an idea occurred to me. "But if you really feel ill at ease about bugs we can fix them!"

Around the room I went, turning off lights by loosening bulbs and pulling out wall plugs. Then I disconnected a small table radio which Harding had turned on and from which pleasant music was coming. Harding protested "That was Chopin. I love Chopin!" Ignoring his protests, I shoved a round marble-topped table to the centre of the room below a small chandelier of about six bulbs which provided the only remaining light in the room.

"Hold this table while I climb up on it!" I said.

"Why?" Harding asked.

"Because," I replied, "that's where the bugs could be planted. I want you to feel at ease. But of course," I added, "with all the lights off there's still the telephone!"

At that point Harding relented. "This is all crazy! Maybe we've gone far enough."

"Yes," I said, reconnecting the lights and the music, "I quite agree."

Harding had gotten the point: I heard nothing more about bugs or eavesdropping during our time together in Poland.

To be sure, Harding, the scientist, was a no-nonsense man when finally he was settled in a quiet office – all wood, no pillows – and poring over the data from the radiometric logs which the technical staff of the Energy Trust had loaned to him. After three or four days, he confided to me that he could "see some stuff" in two general areas. One was in a south-west sector of Poland where a shallow exploratory shaft had been sunk to evaluate a "salt dome." Another was in the far north-east, close to Poland's Baltic Sea port of Gdansk – formerly Danzig. Harding was more optimistic about the latter.

"If the evaporite sheet is continuous between the two drill holes for which I have data," he said, "it could be an extensive and thick salt bed." And so Harding and I recommended drill exploration in this area, near Gdansk, with equipment and technology provided by the UN. Our Polish colleagues, led by Werner, were impressed with the technical theory developed and fully endorsed the recommendation of further specialized drilling.

When our mission was accomplished, the technical staff of the Industrial Minerals Department decided that a banquet celebration was essential. It was held in a small lecture hall, elegantly decorated for the occasion with beautiful table linen, cutlery, chinaware, glassware, and flowers. Fine antique champagne coolers were strategically distributed around the table. Clearly, the women scientists on staff, comprising half of the members, had made all the arrangements for the banquet. Their finest personal family treasures were on display for the occasion.

Two violinists played Chopin softly in a corner. (Perhaps in honour of Harding – and there wasn't a feather in sight!) The men were all attired in dark suits; the women beautiful in their evening dresses and accessories. The inimitable Polish sense of elegance was on full display that evening. It took some effort to remember that these were the same men and women who bustled so seriously around offices and laboratories during working hours, in their white gowns and white head scarves.

Harding and I were the guests of honour. After we were seated, there were many toasts with fine Russian champagne. Language was no barrier since two-thirds of those present spoke English and there was no lack of interpreters. Harding sat across the table from me, much of the time in deep conversation with a striking red-haired beauty whom I knew to be a geophysicist. Perhaps they were deep into radiometric formulae, but somehow I doubted it!

After the initial course of fresh caviar was served and enjoyed, the entree was placed before us. To my surprise I noted it was steak tartare, an elegant dish with raw high-quality beef laced with spices as its main ingredient. When everyone had been served I picked up my fork and glanced over at Harding. As honoured guests I felt we should start together and encourage the others to follow. As I caught his eye, he seized his fork and, still deep in conversation with the Titian-haired beauty beside him, began to eat. Suddenly he exclaimed loudly, "My God, it's raw!" Gales of laughter filled the room. Another Saskatchewan farm boy had discovered steak tartare!

Poland was the second "centrally planned" country which I had visited. My trip to China four years earlier had given me an introduction to these forcibly disciplined societies which comprise over one-third of the world's population. These societies are ideological, economic, and social entities which those of us who live in democratic countries must try to understand, not with suspicion, rivalry, and ignorance, but with intelligence and honesty. They are in part motivated by enviable social traits that the democracies lack.

Some centrally planned countries are rich in resources, but most are economically underdeveloped. Most of these societies have risen from almost totally bankrupt socio-economic bases, mainly corrupt oligarchies. Often their people are, for the most part, illiterate. Given their historical and cultural background it is not surprising that these countries are seriously lacking in industrial development. They must suffer grave austerity until a semblance of national strength emerges. Poland, of course, was one of the rare exceptions to this norm. For centuries it had enjoyed a national identity of great cultural, intellectual, and industrial development until afflicted during the Second World War with grievous war wounds. Then it suffered the severe pains and trials of ideological re-orientation.

As Werner and I travelled through the smaller Polish towns and villages in largely agricultural areas, I noticed countless tidy and thoroughly cultivated gardens. There were many rather "run-down" old family homes, but all with some frilly touch of woodwork or paint expressing the individuality of the owner. We saw hard-working people, plainly and warmly dressed, with scarves and shawls to protect them from the still-cool temperatures of early spring. All appeared to carry tools or bundles of farm produce in their hands. Some older women and youngsters hawked small bundles of radishes, green onions, or cucumbers wherever groups gathered at railroad stations or at entrances of large buildings.

By contrast, Warsaw was a city of fine, large, and older buildings interspersed with patches of new, starkly built apartment blocks of post-war construction, many still devoid of landscaping. Various attractive parks were situated in the central part of the city, with large pieces of sculpture, generally commemorating some war event. The streets of Warsaw were a bustle of activity during business hours as people hustled to and from work. There was more colour in the dress of the city dwellers. The Poles are artists in every respect, and this was evident wherever I looked and whenever I listened. Along some of the side streets and alleys a few painters, weavers, carvers, or musicians displayed their work on the sidewalks. Some of them shared the familiar style and deportment of "hippies." Others whom I encountered asked cautiously if I had American clothing for sale or American currency to exchange.

I was in Warsaw for the 1965 May Day celebration, and witnessed the enormous parade, or, more accurately, the crowds that watched the parade. Tens of thousands lined the parade route. I had great difficulty in securing a good view of the parade and felt frustrated because I had my camera ready for the occasion. Finally, I climbed up on a broad masonry windowsill where, over a sea of coloured balloons, I felt I could get a glimpse of the dignitaries on parade. However, a constable quickly appeared and ordered me down, to mumbled criticism directed at him by onlookers.

I left Poland with warm feelings towards its citizens, particularly those with whom Harding and I had worked, and with a sense of accomplishment and anticipation that successful results would follow, which, eventually, they did. It took three or four years of argument and delay, due mainly to American concern about revealing to the Poles certain aspects of "western technology," but wells were finally drilled, and huge potash fields successfully identified. Although the need to develop an efficient metallurgical recovery technique caused further delay, the Poles eventually succeeded. These new deposits have been worked on a substantial basis for some years as reports of the Polish government, sent to me from time to time by a justifiably proud Dr. Werner, testify.

In Israel to Update "King Solomon's" Mines

Among the countries in which I worked during 1964 and 1965, my mission to Israel was particularly interesting.

The Israelis had requested assistance in the resolution of problems stemming from the unduly low copper production at their only substantial metal mine, the Timma copper deposit. Situated near the southern port city of Elath, a modern resort and fishing centre of the

Gulf of Aqaba, the Timma copper deposits are at the southern-most tip of the state of Israel where the present borders of the mountainous Egyptian Sinai Desert to the west and the state of Jordan to the east converge. Elath is less that one hundred miles north of Mount Sinai, in what is now modern Egypt, where Moses is believed to have received the Ten Commandments. The mining area itself is known as "King Solomon's Mine." In the Old Testament there is a brief reference to that area.

> King Solomon equipped a fleet of Ezion-geber, which is near Elath on the shores of the Red Sea, in the land of Edom. For this fleet Hiram sent men of his, sailors who knew the sea, to serve with Solomon's men. They went to Ophir and from there they brought back four hundred and twenty talents of gold, which they delivered to King Solomon.

As a prospector, I am quite prepared to accept the accuracy of the Old Testament statement. But I must reject the suggestion that this biblical passage refers to the present Timma mine site. For one thing there is no appreciable gold in the Timma copper deposit. Nonetheless, the deposits, both for their content of the semi-precious copper gemstones of azurite, chrysocolla, malachite, and smelted copper, have a long history of exploitation. In the limestone cliffs of the nearby Sinai, I was shown the crude smelter sites and slag heaps regarded by archeologists as dating from the mid tenth century B.C.

When I addressed myself to the efficiency of modern copper production at the Timma mines, I was able to offer counsel on both metallurgical and mine-operating problems. The latter, quite surprisingly, had resulted in large part from the over-indulgence of West German and American bilateral aid. Generous but unthinking bureaucratic sources from those countries had provided oversized and overpowered underground equipment that was causing productive areas to be lost through uncontrollable rock collapse.

The mine plant was up to date, but the chemical procedure then employed was somewhat obsolete. I devoted considerable study to the development of means for retrieving underground ore that had collapsed and become diluted with waste rock through over-mechanization and through excessive use of explosives.

The mining and milling complex was not far away from an attractive cluster of small residences used by mine employees. I remember in particular how the supply of fresh water was a serious problem there and how it had to be secured from deep wells. (All surface water from the Jordan River, south of the Dead Sea, is salt-laden and undrinkable. It is, however, suitable to a degree for irrigation.)

As my work at the Timma mine drew to a close, I was approached by a senior physicist from Israel's Physics Research Institute. He asked me if I would tell him about the development and availability of geophysical intrumentation, particularly the new types of equipment being employed in America, for mineral and hydrocarbon exploration. In this regard, we had several interesting conversations, which continued later in Tel Aviv and Jerusalem. We considered the possibility of UN aid for the offshore exploration of oil and gas in the Israeli Mediterranean. I judged this area to be of promising potential since oil was already being produced in the nearby Gaza coastal area.

When the Israeli physicist visited me in Elath, he offered to drive me back to Jerusalem by jeep instead of my using the commercial airline. I accepted his offer with enthusiasm since it meant seeing more of Israel. I thoroughly enjoyed the scenic drive as we passed through hamlets and neatly arranged kibbutzim in well-developed, irrigated agricultural areas.

As we approached the historic town of Be'er Sheva (Beersheba) about forty or so miles south of Jerusalem in the Negev, my companion, who was a lively conversationalist and an excellent tour guide, became almost silent. Be'er Sheva had been settled by the ancient Jews following their return from exile in Babylon after 538 B.C. Not far from the town I spotted a most unusual building. It was a large concrete installation, standing in total isolation in an arid, completely uncultivated area. A winding gravel road led from the highway to this large facility, which appeared empty and desolate, with no sign or other clue indicating what it was used for.

"What's that large building?" I asked, and received only a mumbled reply.

"Looks like a factory – what kind?" I asked.

"A textile mill I think," was the simple answer which closed the subject. I remained unconvinced. Years later when I read the October 5, 1986, edition of London's *Sunday Times*, the front page carried the headline: "Revealed: The Secrets of Israel's Nuclear Arsenal." I now had a rather belated, but more comprehensive and convincing answer to my question of all those years ago.

What I had seen near Be'er Sheva that day in 1965, as the Israeli physicist drove me from Elath to Jerusalem, was the outside of Israel's nuclear research establishment. Known as "Dimona," it was secretly built for Israel by France between 1957 and 1964. Details of the development and its function became widely discussed after the *Sunday Times* gave extensive coverage to information made available to it by Mordechai Vanunu, a technician who had worked at Dimona from 1977 until 1985. He had suggested that the nuclear facility had been misused to build an atomic bomb.

Not long after the sensational reports were published, Vanunu was apparently seized in London, where he had fled, by agents of the Israeli government. Taken back to Israel he was charged with crimes against the state, tried in secret, and sentenced to eighteen years in prison.

In 1965 the Israelis had divided Jerusalem in the style of Berlin. I noted much concrete and steel. Armed sentries peered from behind barricades atop the "wall." What a tragic contrast, I thought to myself, between modern Jerusalem with all its military and political tensions, and the Jerusalem which is a holy city for hundreds of millions throughout the world – Christians, Jews, and Moslems. *Jerusalem* means *Place of Peace*. As my diplomatic passport allowed me freedom of movement through the wall, I accordingly explored both sides.

I took pains to visit the River Jordan, hoping to walk near the place where John the Baptist had baptized Jesus. In the only receptacle readily available at the river – an empty pop bottle – I collected some of its rather muddy and foul-smelling water for the baptism of my new grandson, David. Back home, this Jordan River water was rejected by the minister, probably with good reason: my good intentions might possibly have sickened the infant!

I was particularly fascinated by Old Jerusalem. In retrospect, I view it as one of the two or three most colourful sectors of any city I have seen in all my extensive travels. I was most impressed by the tiny market sector of "The Thirty-nine Steps," the route of Jesus Christ's tortuous climb carrying the cross upon which he would be crucified. The entire scene, as I climbed the same steps, was as vivid to me as if I were witnessing the original tragic events of nearly two thousand years before.

By contrast, the time I spent in nearby Jordan was brief. There, I was more of an observer and tourist than an authorized UN planner. My only UN directive with respect to Jordan had been: "See how we can help without undue risks to personnel." Regrettably, I did not see much of the countryside. What I did witness were the profoundly tragic refugee areas along Jordan's border with Israel. I was overwhelmed by the deplorable poverty, misery, and despair of the Palestinian refugees, rejected on the one hand by the Israelis from their newly created Israel, and refused admission by Jordan on the other.

There were tight rows upon rows of small square identical shanties, each with a packed dirt area in front which was totally bare and traversed by open-ditch sewers. Drinking water had to be carried from a single distant source. The dirt yards and paths teemed with people of all ages dressed in rags. Moslems, they were largely deprived of schools, training, and employment. They probably would have perished had world opinion not at least sponsored this refugee zone which was meant to be temporary but was still, at the time of my visit in 1965, an immoral human tragedy.

My exposure to all of this left me in a state of emotional distress and mental perplexity. How could such an evil brew of distrust and hatred ever have been concocted, given the professed beliefs and responsibilities of the three great religious groups of Christians, Jews, and Moslems – all founded in this tiny area?

The energy, imagination, and unity of the Israelis, and the material evidence of these qualities in the outstanding physical development of their country impressed me greatly. On the basis of the knowledge I had gained about the socio-political characteristics of countries, including five "centrally planned" societies, I see Israel as strikingly similar to them in terms of economic and social centralization and ideological fervency. I grant that there are substantial political differences in terms of what are known as "democratic freedoms," such as the rights of an individual to free speech, movement, and a political voice in the leadership elective process by secret ballot. But in reality, what do these individual freedoms mean? Not much to those starving millions. I note mounting evidence in some "free" societies of either near-total indifference to the value and use of such freedoms or, alternatively, such an obsession with individual power that the will of the majority is splintered, thwarted, and, in the end, overridden in many ways by assertive minorities.

My work in Israel gave me a glimpse into the awesome power and dangers of competing religious traditions. As I travelled and worked in Yugoslavia and then in India, I encountered other traditions. Through my travels and work in these countries I became increasingly aware of the need for both individuals and societies to be sensitive to the value of traditions, but not to be slavish captives of them.

In Yugoslavia

Yugoslavia had sought technical advice from the UN on how to reduce the high levels of acid pollution of its major waterways caused by industrial waste. Although I had majored in chemistry, both organic and inorganic, for my first university degree, I did not regard myself as an environmentalist and advised my UN superiors of this. Nonetheless, they insisted, "Give it a try; you have a certain style." (That phrase "a certain style" was repeated on several occasions during my UN service, usually when an apparently impossible task had to be undertaken. I never did quite understand its meaning.)

After I arrived in Yugoslavia, my scientific counterpart, who was also an interpreter, and I gradually moved up its major rivers like good prospectors. We discussed pollution problems with successive plant chemists or metallurgists, of whom about half were women (a hallmark of Communist societies). All of these officials were concerned about the source of their plant water being polluted by factories upstream. No simple and inexpensive remedial step was apparent to them, nor was it to me, until I had travelled through the north and returned to the country's Mediterranean coastal area in the south, where, possibly inspired by sharing with my companions a bottle or two of the region's fine wine, a possible and partial solution to the polluted river waters occurred to me.

I suggested that industries in northern Yugoslavia consider the practical experiment of constructing, in the more polluted sections of the river, submerged dams of carbonate – rich limestone and dolomite cast aside as waste from the marble quarries in the south of the country. The concept of this novel suggestion was sound, at least in chemical theory. The alkaline rock would neutralize the acidic waters and precipitate the dissolved pollutants. I was assured that they would experiment with the idea.

My mission to Yugoslavia was undertaken several years after the extremely powerful earthquake of 1963 had left 80 per cent of the city of Skopje in ruins, killing over a thousand people and leaving a hundred and twenty thousand homeless. Amazingly, the Yugoslavians were busily engaged in reconstruction (with a completely new "earthquake-proof" plan) along the same historic and well-recognized zone of crustal rupture and violence.

Throughout my travels in Yugoslavia, particularly in the northern mountains and the southern Adriatic coastal region, I was overwhelmed by the natural beauty of the country. The high mountainous inland area was reminiscent of sections of the Coast Range mountains of British Columbia, with dramatic valleys and deeply incised rivers. The Adriatic coastal plain, centered at Dubrovnik, was more reminiscent of the Riviera areas of Spain, France, and Italy, dotted by seaside communities with historic and colourful cultural traditions, some dating back many centuries. The residents had a strong sense of pride in their beautiful ancient architecture, much of it using the finest marbles from nearby deposits.

My work in Yugoslavia gave me a deep appreciation of its remarkable diversity of ethnic cultures, languages, and customs. Some of the historically troubled Balkan regions have, since the end of the Second World War, come under enforced centralization within a Yugoslav federation and now appear to be sharing common aspirations. It seemed to me that the earlier violent ethnic rivalries, of which I had read, have been softened.

India and Serendipity

During this same general period, I went on two missions to India. While I readily agreed to work in India, I did not go there with the same hope and enthusiasm which had characterized practically all my other UN missions. Given the scale of its problems, I reacted to India with mixed feelings of futility and near despair. Still, I had a sense of compulsion to help in any way I could.

My first mission in India was to find additional reserves of high-quality magnesite in Madras State (now Tamil Nadu). Magnesite is a source of the element magnesium. Known reserves of the mineral, which is used, among other purposes, to make high-temperature-resistant ceramic brick, appeared to be approaching exhaustion. While the search for magnesite may appear to have no connection whatsoever with the enormous problems which confront India, there is indeed one. Magnesite was an exportable product; it could produce foreign exchange to strengthen India's economic base, a necessity if the country's fundamental human and social problems are to be eased.

Before I went to India, I knew that it was the world's second-most populous country and the one with the greatest population density. India comprises an area of approximately 1.26 million square miles. In 1951, it had a population of 361 million, or about four hundred persons for every square mile, approximately four times the average population density throughout the rest of the world. By 1985, India's population had climbed to about 750 million. This huge population and its rapid growth are, of course, the primary sources of India's human and social problems.

India's tragic level of poverty stems directly from its vast population and its lack of central planning. There are far more people in India than can be gainfully employed or than a social welfare system can adequately provide for. Many Indians are vegetarians. Indeed, in many sections of the country, certain animals are revered and are allowed the same freedom of movement as the people, even in the largest cities. Thus millions of Indians live at near-starvation level, competing with the animal world for the meagre food supply.

One of India's main problems is its lack of an effective system to control population growth. A two-or three-generation family group is a form of social insurance. There is not only a lack of incentive to control population, there is, on the contrary, a major stimulus for the maintenance of a large family group.

I must confess that in terms of the overall problems which must be resolved, and the prospects for such resolution, I found India to be the most depressing of all of the countries in which I have worked and travelled. There appeared to be little hope for human and social improvement for the great majority. Still, Indians I met and worked with in other third-world countries where hope and opportunity seemed to be present despite national poverty, invariably seemed to be flourishing.

I worked with V. Gopal, the senior geologist of the State Geological Survey based in Madras City, the state capital. Gopal was a well-trained, energetic, highly motivated, imaginative professional. After he outlined the problem to me, we made field studies of the magnesite mining areas together. On other field excursions in the same general area, Gopal led me to magnetic iron formations on which surface trenching had been done. Small indications of copper were also present.

Later, after evaluating all our field days in the wider context of the known geology of Madras State and that of adjoining Kolar State to the west, I suggested that the UN would probably be justified in undertaking an extensive regional aerial magnetic survey. Such a survey, performed by specially equipped aircraft flown at low altitude on a pattern of closely parallel flight lines, would serve a number of purposes.

In the first place, it would produce all the information necessary for a complete map of all magnetic characteristics of the rocks at surface, even if covered by soil, and to depths of several thousands of feet. Second, it would outline quite accurately the irregular areas of basic intrusive rocks (diorite/gabbro) near the margins of which new and covered patches of magnesite could, theoretically, occur. Trenching of such areas should quickly prove if such were present. In the third place, this type of survey would accurately pinpoint magnetic iron formations, including the extent of their iron content and to what depths they extended below the surface. Such an aeromagnetic survey might do even more. It might identify and track the historic and still highly productive Kolar gold-producing belt across northern Madras State. This last possibility excited me considerably.

From published reports I knew the geology of the Kolar gold occurrences and of their association with basic and relatively magnetic rocks. Also, my study of the maps in the survey office indicated a long river with a relatively straight course that coincided closely with projections of the known direction and location of the Kolar belt easterly towards Madras State. Moreover, my questioning as to the existence of any alluvial gold in this river valley elicited the reply: "Yes, very old records show some gold."

Gopal was reasonably agreeable to my proposal that an extensive three-goal aerial survey be undertaken. But he was not as enthusiastic as I had hoped. He foresaw many of the bureaucratic and political problems which did indeed arise later on. Eventually, a much emasculated aerial survey was completed. Shortly before I left Madras, however, there was another significant development.

I had asked Gopal if I might visit the Geological Survey chemical laboratories to judge the quality of their facilities, and he readily agreed to show me these. For some reason, they were largely devoid of staff until we arrived at the "wet chemical" laboratory. This was clearly a colonial-era laboratory with its sturdy construction, high ceilings, slow-moving ceiling fans to "vent" the place, and fine old marble laboratory benches. At one of the benches a lone laboratory worker was engaged in some activity.

I approached the individual and saw he was grinding some rock chips with a hand pestle and mortar and placing the ground material on a piece of paper. He explained that his chief had given him a lump of rock and asked him to determine its economic value, if any. He had noted that the rock was largely composed of glistening yellow-coloured "scales" of mica. It might, he thought, if finely ground, produce a pigment which, with some form of solvent, could make an attractive paint.

I agreed with his rationale and then asked him if we could perform another test together. He agreed, and I asked him to turn on the Bunsen burner and to pass me a pair of tongs. When the rock particle was held in the flame by the tongs, it started to expand to several times its original volume. This surprised the others and delighted me. I dropped the roasted material from the tongs onto the marble bench where it disintegrated into a small heap of golden-coloured, paper-thin flakes. "Vermiculite mica," I exclaimed. "Keep trying to develop it as a paint pigment." Gopal and I returned to his office.

On the way, I asked Gopal where the original lump had come from, because it could be important. I told him it was a unique mica usually found in curious eruptive pipes or vents that often contained other minerals of greater economic value. I added as a happy after-thought: "They can also be identified by aerial magnetic surveys like those we have been discussing."

Late that afternoon, Gopal reported to me that he had located a person "who knew a person" who could lead us to the source of the mica. It could be readily reached by jeep. I suggested that we visit the site the next morning and that we take along a Geiger counter to measure radioactivity.

Next morning, Gopal, two others, and I were in a jeep and headed for the site. He had located four Geiger counters, of which none worked, and had also brought along several bottles of English lime cordial.

"By noon," he explained when I asked about the cordial, "it will be intolerably hot where we are going."

"But I never drink in the heat," I told him. "Too fatiguing. If I can suck on a lump of salt that's all I need. Otherwise, I do without."

The mica came from a large water well by the roadside. Because of the aridity and low precipitation of the area, such wells were of large dimensions. Usually they were square, about twelve feet on each side and from fifteen to twenty feet in depth. In one corner of the bottom of the well, there was usually an even deeper and much narrower waterhole accommodating a slow seep. The digging of such wells produced a large volume of waste rock which was piled around the edges to add to the storage capacity when rare cloudbursts occurred. Examining this waste rock I found much visible mica. Since the waste heap was about four feet above the flat, arid plain, I asked Gopal to climb up beside me to survey the terrain.

With some imagination and minimal evidence, I said, "See, we stand here on the rim of a circular structure. The fresh rock is grey-green in colour – over there the soil is brown. That's another ring. I can't see beyond that but we'll walk across. We should cross other bands of soil of different colours, even pink!" With that Gopal and I set out on foot. Two others followed with the lime cordial supply, which they proceeded to entirely consume while acting as our provisioners!

Soon Gopal and I were picking up from the soil large black, beautifully formed cubic crystals of a titanium-iron mineral. "More good evidence of a carbonatite!" I exclaimed, and told Gopal of my satisfaction with our field survey. Then we returned to Madras. To the draft proposal for the aerial magnetometer survey, I added a recommendation that particular attention be paid to the indicated "carbonatite" area – an exciting fourth dimension to the program.

A day or two later, I left Madras City and flew to Calcutta and New Delhi to pay my respects to the Central Government Geological Survey of India and the UN Resident Representative.

Problems in Calcutta

Calcutta, as I first encountered it in 1966 was amazing, shocking, and frightening. Teeming masses of people and countless stray animals (some of the latter decorated with holy artifacts or inscriptions) literally swamped the sidewalks. Honking cars, tooting cyclists, and ever-more animals jammed the streets. Garbage and litter were dropped anywhere and everywhere. The open drainage system clogged the air with an all-pervasive, stomach-turning stench. The rare open patches of pavement were splattered with small red patches, resembling blood clots, like spittle from numerous consumptives. Later, I discovered that it was the residue of passers-by chewing betel nuts and spitting their reddened saliva on the street.

I experienced a violent element among this mass of humanity. Although cautioned by the hotel doorman not to venture into the streets on foot, I did so once, but only after taking what I thought were adequate precautions. Stripped to my shirt, trousers and shoes, with empty pockets and, I thought, no jewelry or trinkets showing (and only a bit of paper money hidden within a shoe), I ventured forth.

I had scarcely jostled my way fifty feet through the crowds from the hotel entrance before I was in trouble. Suddenly bowled off balance by one or two persons from behind, I staggered and felt my glasses falling off. Instinctively, I reached up to seize them. But somebody else's hand also had a grip on them! I managed to wrench my glasses free, but in the scuffle they were broken. Quickly, I lunged through the crowd to the relative safety of a store doorway. A cheap plastic ballpoint pen, which I had retained in the breast pocket of my shirt as useful but expendable, had disappeared. A retreat was in order so I shoved my way back the short distance to my hotel, and retired, somewhat shaken, to my room.

As I explained the reason for the Band-Aid repairs to my glasses when I went to the Geological Survey director's office the following morning, profound shock was expressed. My Indian colleagues were absolutely horrified at my idiocy in venturing to walk alone on a Calcutta sidewalk!

Fortunately this was the only such incident I encountered in all my time in India. I visited five or six Indian states and possibly a dozen large cities, and everywhere but Calcutta, when I went for my customary leisurely walks, I did so without the slightest problem.

Although officers of the Indian Geological Survey were courteous, they conveyed a definite sense of displeasure to me, hinting that problems were in store for the Madras project. They were embarrassed that any geological survey at the state level in India could attract a UN project without the intercession of the central government. I was subtly reminded that India was still in a "state of war," the aftermath of the Chinese frontier forays just ended, and that the Indian military authorities, under control of the central government, also controlled all air traffic and would take a dim view of my aerial survey proposal.

The central government officials I met were curious about, but

down-played the possible discovery of any "new" carbonatite structure. They said that other discoveries had been made previously but
were of no economic consequence. When I expressed sincere interest
in seeing publications concerning these others, they could produce
none. However, a year or so later, an irate British geologist who had
worked in India sent a paper to the UN giving details of another
carbonatite deposit he had identified, claiming that his discovery had
preceded ours! To top it all, the Central Indian Government Survey
gave notice that it had several projects elsewhere in India which, in
its judgement, were more worthy of UN support than the one I had
recommended. To pacify them, I asked for a list of these projects
and assured them that if senior UN officials agreed, I would return
and evaluate them. This, in effect, I did later.

After several years of frustrating efforts, mainly due to Indian
government and military bureaucratic complications, the aerial survey
was partially completed. However, I was not fully informed by the
UN of the eventual completion of the program and the results achieved.

The only authorized public news releases from the UN and the
Indian state government stressed the value of the survey in the development of iron-ore reserves. Reference was not made to the development of additional magnesite reserves nor, to my dismay, to the
definition of the Kolar gold-mining belt within Madras State. No
public statement was made concerning our carbonatite structure discovery at Koratti until three years later. Only various reports of the
Indian government to the International Atomic Energy Agency, to
which I had access, referred to the economic importance of the Koratti
carbonatite discovery as an important producing source of rock phosphate, vermiculite, and uranium.

The complicated involvement of the Indian military in our aerial
survey in Madras State gave rise to several UN "family anecdotes." I
limit myself to recording only one of them here.

Our geological survey was to be flown at a low altitude, about
three hundred metres above ground, along a strict flight pattern of
closely spaced parallel flight lines. Direction changes at the ends of
these lines called for short, sharp, looping turns. We employed foreign
professional pilots who had the skill, experience, and courage required
to fly in this manner.

Senior Indian military officers insisted on their personal involvement in every step of the procedure – as flight observers, in the
development of film, its safekeeping, and in all other aspects. The

prestige of being involved in a UN project, the novelty of the exercise, and the change it afforded from military routine, were, no doubt, the primary factors which attracted some senior Indian air force officers to serve as flight observers. But their interest waned quickly.

The long, straight, low-altitude lines produced an uneasy mix of nervousness and boredom, while the sharp and sudden line changes, always done by the pilot with a flair for the dramatic, were unsettling. Nothing was said, but the UN project manager soon noticed that the number of gold-braided officers flying in the aircraft was decreasing. They were being replaced by much younger and more junior air force crewmen, which led to another dilemma.

After the flying program was completed, an unforeseen day of reckoning arrived. The project manager's records of personnel flight time was presented to the military. The senior command realized with shock that half a dozen junior officers had accumulated so much flight time that they were now automatically entitled to immediate and rapid promotion through several ranks!

These junior officers were not the only ones to whose success I made a modest contribution when I worked in India. Another was an older Indian geologist regarded as a "dreamer" by his skeptical colleagues.

After completion of the aerial survey and carbonatite discovery, I toured five other Indian states. I met state officials and their technical directors to review mineral development activities and to offer general advice. During this tour, I was approached by an older resident geologist of the Indian Geological Survey based in Madhya Pradesh, the largest of India's states.

This man had read some American technical papers describing huge open-pit copper-molybdenum mineral deposits in the United States which were of the unique eruptive type broadly described as "porphyry" deposits. His reading of these reports had convinced him that there was a porphyry-type copper deposit near Karamsara in Madhya Pradesh. His views were repeatedly communicated to his colleagues and superiors, many of whom viewed his interpretation with skepticism.

The physical appearance of the old geologist did not impress me. He seemed almost constantly semi-tranquilized due to his chewing of the widely used "soft drug," betel leaves. This habit appeared to be as common in India as cigarette smoking is in the western world.

Nevertheless, I listened patiently to his story and agreed to go with him on a day-long car ride to the site of his "porphyry copper mine."

When we arrived at our destination, beside a well-travelled road, I was surprised to see an ancient waste pile of broken rock from some very old mine excavation. When I asked about this, the old geologist replied, "A mad Welshman, many years ago, drove a tunnel into this hillside to pierce that large quartz vein over there on the ridge." This did not surprise me. On at least a dozen occasions in remote corners of Africa and Central and South America, I have been led to exploratory mine workings, usually dating from the second half of the 1800s, attributed to a "mad Cornishman" or "crazy Cousin Jack."

I cracked blocks of rock on the Welshman's dump and noted specks of copper and iron sulphides within the typical porphyry-type volcanic rock characteristic of such deposits. There was further evidence of copper in a green staining on rocks of the dump long exposed to weathering. The old geologist clearly had more than a fanciful theory.

When I revisited the state officials following our field visit, I expressed optimism about the prospect and advocated more testing. I outlined in writing an initial modest program of work. But the state officials wavered – a remarkably well-developed art in India. They suggested that probably the Central Government Survey should undertake some exploration or even that the rich and aggressive American aid "Hardrock" program should explore it. Besides, they were aware that the Indian government had undertaken a relatively small work program in the area and had left the district presumably for lack of encouragement.

Uneasy with this vacillation, I communicated my enthusiasm in a memorandum directly to two acquaintances, William Morgan and Dr. D. B. Sikka, both geologists, who were attached to the National Mineral Development Corporation, the Indian corporation responsible for the nation's meagre copper production. I heard no more about the project for some years.

In the late 1970s, however, I enquired about the project. Indian officials advised me that the deposit, now called the Malanjkhand mine, had been identified as meriting accelerated development by various Indian government agencies and Soviet consultants from 1967 onward. At the time of my enquiry, they were preparing the old Indian geologist's deposit for copper production on a major scale.

This news delighted me and my only remaining wish was that my elderly Indian colleague, in whom I had shown some faith, had lived to see his own faith realized.

Lobster for Breakfast in Somalia

In 1968, my UN travels led me to Somalia and it is a country that holds vivid memories for me.

This mainly agricultural country, which emerged with its present name in 1960, comprises the pre-Second World War areas of Italian and British Somaliland, south of the Gulf of Aden. It occupies about a quarter of a million square miles on the north-eastern corner of Africa – the "horn" of Africa – on the north-west edge of the Indian Ocean.

Save for two major rivers, the Juba and the Shebeli, rising in the Ethopian highlands and converging to a lowland delta region in the south of Somalia, the entire central part of the country is a sun-tortured plain with a scant pasturage of tufted grass. The southern river delta produces agricultural products such as bananas, cotton, and sugar cane, while the arid central plain supports only a limited number of nomadic Somalis who mainly breed and train camels for sale as beasts of burden.

The capital Mogadishu is on the Indian Ocean coastline, near the river Shebeli. It is an ocean port of sorts, in that vessels must anchor offshore and be lightered by smaller craft. Mogadishu is centuries old and shows its age. Established in Biblical times, its population is a blend of Negroid, Arab, Indian, and European minorities from the earlier English, French, and Italian colonies. Several languages are used, but the primary ones in economic and political life are French and Italian. The dominant religion is Islam in the Sunni tradition.

A striking monument of the modern Italian period is a well-engineered road, built by order of Mussolini, three metres wide and made from two-cubic-foot granite blocks with mileposts of Italian marble. The road extends from Mogadishu to Addis Ababa in Ethiopia, a distance of about 650 miles. Tragically, it had been allowed to fall into a ruinous state of disrepair when we followed part of it in the mid 1960s.

The economic state of Somalia is poor, although natural resources to improve it are present. The uranium reserves our UN program identified could be, but are not, profitably exported. A noteworthy resource is their fish and shellfish potential, still undeveloped when I was there, save for domestic use. Refrigeration was unreliable so eggs, meat, and dairy products were of uncertain quality. Nevertheless, I still lived well on a regular daily diet of fresh boiled lobster, bananas, and coffee three times a day, including breakfast.

I was impressed by the cabinet minister with whom I worked. He was a plump, constantly smiling individual dressed immaculately in white shorts and white short-sleeved shirt, the better to show off two or three gold bracelets and a heavy gold wristwatch worn on each arm. While he left the business side of his responsibilities – drafting mining laws for the country – to me and his very able Indian aide, the minister devoted much care and attention to the planning of accommodation for his female secretaries in the regional base towns of our field operations, which he assured me he would periodically visit.

I first went to Somalia when I was still on the full-time staff of the UN and Hamish Brown and I were temporarily co-managers of the senior technical desk under Director Roberto Arce in the Technical Assistance Program. At that time an urgent directive had come to Arce which he had passed on to Brown and myself. It requested that "a mineral exploration program be prepared for Somalia."

Although Hamish Brown, an able geophysicist, had had previous experience on the African continent, he, like myself, had no experience or knowledge of Somalia. So we enlisted the assistance of another UN staff member, Nicholas Varlamoff, a geologist who for many years had been a field officer of the French Bureau of Mines, which was active in French-speaking areas of Africa. Varlamoff had visited Somalia but knew of only meagre iron-ore deposits there. Nevertheless the three of us decided that an aerial magnetometer survey would be justified to fully appraise this iron-ore potential.

Experience I had gained through working in the Rhodesias, as they were still known at that time, had given me considerable respect for the Great African Rift structure. This great zone of crustal rupture extends almost the entire north-south length of the African continent and is related spacially to various eruptive centres of economic importance, such as diamond "pipes," carbonatites, and chrome and nickel-platinum deposits.

As I reflected on what we should do in Somalia, I came to the conclusion that we should add a radiation monitoring instrument to our magnetometer survey which might detect any eruptive "pipes," if such were present. My colleague, Hamish, reminded me that "for iron ore we like to fly high but for radiation we must fly low." He agreed to make enquiries about the type of combination survey we had discussed.

Soon he was back with a canny Scottish glint in his eye and a smile on his face. "The contractors," he said, "will compromise on flight altitude and will run both surveys simultaneously for only one dollar extra a line-mile if there are no radac (radioactive) anomalies to plot. If there should be any, and radac interpretation and mapping are necessary, it will cost more. So let's go for both."

Capricious "Dame Fortune," and her sister "Serendipity," both among the most popular of prospector's patronesses, again had their day. The magnetometer results were discouraging for iron, but the radiometric results were encouraging for radioactivity. To follow up on this work, our UN agency in New York assigned the project to the International Atomic Energy Agency (IAEA) in Vienna. I served as a consultant to the IAEA on this Somalia project.

The first drill-testing results of radiometric anomalies were inconclusive. A generally low grade of uranium ore was indicated. Nonetheless, my assistance was requested to draft legislation conveying exploitation rights to an Italian consortium.

In the meantime, the Soviet team of geologists and geophysicists, recruited by the UN to do the field work, were becoming restless with the indifferent results from the first exploration. On their own initiative they were pushing farther afield. Soon a signal came from them. They had found something much better and wished to have more aerial radiometric surveying done.

Hamish Brown flew to Somalia to ensure maximum co-operation and effective completion of the Soviet effort. With him he took good-quality instrumentation with which he, as a geophysicist, was familiar. On his arrival in Somalia, he found that the type of aircraft required for our planned low-cost aerial survey was not available. With members of the Soviet team he outfitted and equipped a small and quite old Soviet civilian aircraft for the project in which he worked as the principal flight instrument operator until the program was entirely completed. Soon after he returned to New York, totally exhausted, Hamish suffered a fatal heart attack. All of us were profoundly saddened by the death of our gifted and totally dedicated professional colleague.

Eighteen months later, I returned to Somalia to evaluate the ore reserves the Soviets had developed by pitting and sampling the radioactive areas defined by Hamish's survey. Several Soviet technicians who had worked with Hamish were still there. They were badly shaken by news of his death. One of these summed it up well in his limited English. "Brown," he said, "was a real man."

Thoughts of Hamish's death bring to mind another haunting memory of death in Somalia. I was travelling to our field operations base in Bur Akaba in the southern section of the country about one hundred miles west of Mogadishu. My Soviet companions and I had arrived in our jeeps at a small village where we hoped to stop for a brief rest and avoid a looming dust storm.

As we entered the village, an eerie silence greeted us. "Must be trouble," the Soviet driver said as he slowed the jeep to a crawl. "Look!" someone exclaimed and pointed to a pile of objects stacked like cordwood beside the road. "Corpses!" the driver shouted. "Fever! let's get out!" With that, he wheeled the jeep around and drove at high speed the way we had come. Not a word was spoken by any of us.

Soon we saw a dust cloud on the road; another vehicle was approaching us at top speed. Our jeep was brought to a sharp halt and we tumbled out. "Turn them back," shouted our driver. We spread across the road waving our arms. Two military or police jeeps containing about six men stopped in front of us. Before we could say a word, one of them said, "Cholera! Have you been in the village?"

We nodded, "Yes."

"Then this officer must take you to a medical clinic. You are under quarantine!"

With that, one of the strangers climbed into the back of the lead jeep I was in. He told us he was a doctor, trained in Italy, and asked about our innoculations. Since I always carry documents giving my identification, I removed my UN passport and attached medical certificates from my safari jacket pocket. The doctor examined them in the bouncing jeep but offered no comment. He addressed the same enquiries to the driver and the Soviet geophysicist in our jeep.

Upon arrival in a suburb of Mogadishu, he directed us to the medical clinic. There we were subjected to physical examinations. I was placed in a private room. I was told that although I was innoculated against cholera I could be a "carrier" and would have to remain there in isolation for several days. I was provided with writing materials and began to prepare my report. The sight of the roughly piled corpses by the Somalian roadside haunted me for several days.

After my release from quarantine and the completion of my mission in Somalia, I returned to UN headquarters in New York. There followed several missions in India, and two in northern and central Africa, when the administration of the UN Development Program asked me to undertake an assignment in Cuba. I accepted it with enthusiasm, not only out of curiosity but because I am strongly attached to the Caribbean Islands and am familiar with several of them.

With Comrades in Cuba

I went to Cuba to determine whether re-exploration of the old Mina Grande del Cobre copper mining district, near Santiago de Cuba, would be economically justified. It had been highly productive under foreign ownership from 1830 to 1918.

My base was in Havana, but I travelled over the entire island, guided either by an executive assistant to Raoul Castro, brother to Fidel Castro and then Cuba's foreign minister, or in the company of various Soviet engineers. They were in Cuba to train Cubans in the production of nickel, chrome, and manganese from earlier established American enterprises, or to provide technical advice for the conduct of major exploration programs such as the offshore search for hydrocarbons.

An aide to Raoul Castro was assigned to assist me in all my programming, scheduling, and travelling in Cuba. Like several other senior Cuban governmental officials at that time, he was a Spaniard who had fled Spain after an unsuccessful anti-Franco coup. He was a remarkably well-informed, intelligent, and energetic professional who helped me in my mission. I believe he had been a university teacher in Spain. He was deeply involved in, and justifiably proud of Cuba's highly imaginative and successful educational system.

The Soviet experts spoke Spanish and some English. Thus we were able to communicate directly between ourselves. The Russians were affable and appeared to be greatly enjoying the time they and their families were spending on the lovely island of Cuba. Since they were well trained, and the geologists and geophysicists imaginative, we enjoyed some lively technical discussions.

I was surprised by the extent and quality of Russia's cultural activities in Cuban life. When I was there in 1966, some of the world chess tournament games were conducted in Havana and were attended by several Soviet and other national chess masters. I watched some of these chess greats from a distance, and saw Fidel Castro socializing as he moved from table to table among the contestants. I was told that the Soviet Olympic basketball team was playing exhibition matches on the island. A squad of Soviet Olympic-level wrestlers was expected when the basketball players left. At that period, Soviet ballet, opera, and symphonic groups apparently visited Cuba regularly.

The physical appearance of the agricultural and animal husbandry sectors of the Cuban economy were quite impressive. The good "housekeeping" and superior efficiency of these activities compared to similar enterprises in Jamaica or Trinidad, with which I was familiar, were quite obvious. I was surprised, however, by the rattletrap and junky appearance of the trucks and buses. I could understand this, since spare parts were no longer obtainable for the numerous old American vehicles, but the almost total absence of Soviet vehicles surprised me greatly.

Havana's *Cuidad de los Beçados* or "City of Students" interested me. It occupied an area which included an eighteen-hole golf course, a yacht club, and scores of fine large residences dating from the "palmy" days from 1933 to 1959, when dictator Batista ruled Cuba. Havana then was another American mecca like Reno or Las Vegas. I was told that this "City of Students" was populated at the time of my visit by about three hundred thousand students of all grades from kindergarten to university level, brought in to the modern conveniences of the city from rural hamlets all over Cuba.

About half the teachers were professionals of western European origin, principally from Spain, then still under Franco's control. All the students lived on the campus during the school terms. Every weekend, however, busloads of parents arrived to visit their children. I was fascinated by this school complex and visited it on several occasions to see classes in operation and to talk with the teachers about cultural and technical subjects.

In all my travels, I have never, with the possible exception of China, seen such emphasis on well-organized education as I saw in Cuba. The school systems in these two countries appear to train literally thousands of young agriculturists, medical doctors, and teachers to travel abroad and, in turn, teach and practice in other third-world countries. They sought not only to contribute through their professions or trades but also to promote the gospel of Marx in the same way earlier imperial economic empires had been conditioned for commerce by Christian missionaries.

A considerable surprise to me was the number of Canadian sales-people and agricultural consultants I met throughout Cuba. It seemed to me that Canadian technicians and tradesmen were outnumbered only by the Spanish.

Some earlier pre-Castro Cuban traditions had survived. This be-came obvious to me when I addressed the traditional weekly noon-hour meeting of the cigar-maker's union. At the time, I did not realize the honour being extended to me when I was invited to speak. Nor did I appreciate the significance of the event.

The union hall was named after José Marti, one of the Caribbean area's great "liberators." More than one hundred years old, the build-ing had been and still remained a workshop where cigars were hand-rolled in the historic Cuban tradition. The working hall on the second floor was large and plain, containing about two hundred wooden tables on which each worker rolled cigars. To my relief the barn-like hall did not smell of tobacco but had the pleasant aroma of rum or mo-lasses, apparently used in the maturing of tobacco for cigar making.

At one end of the hall were a two-foot-high wooden platform, a small podium, and two or three wooden chairs. This platform was widely revered among Cuban nationalists as the place where great liberators of Central America from José Marti to Castro had spoken in the name of national independence. It was just as well that I knew none of this when I was told that I was to speak there. It was fortuitous also, perhaps, that I had spent the evening before with a convivial group of newly made Cuban friends discussing much the same subject.

They had "planted" me in one of "Papa Doc" Hemingway's fa-vourite upholstered chairs in a secluded corner of his favourite Havana bar and handed me his favourite rum drink, a Daiquiri. Seated in this huge chair among my new friends, I joined them in my increas-ingly fluent Spanish in examining with care and concern most of the world's and Cuba's social and political problems. We had agreed at midnight that we would direct our attention to the final solution of those same problems when we next met.

When I was introduced as the speaker in the cigar-makers' union hall, I was described as a worker in the UN service who had come to serve Cuba. I spoke extemporaneously, having had no time for prep-aration, on a subject close to my heart, *La Paz Mundiale* (world peace).

The phrases tumbled forth without conscious effort. Occasionally I heard the echo of my own voice in that huge but otherwise totally silent room.

When I was finished there wasn't a sound. Then, suddenly, a tremendous mechanical racket like machine-gun fire filled the hall, and, just as suddenly, stopped. Puzzled, I had looked out over the work benches during the tulmultuous noise and saw that the audience was slipping the small steel blades they used in making cigars in and out of slots in their work-benches. Many were smiling. Evidently, I assumed, this was their traditional manner of applause. This was, in fact, confirmed when my companion rose from his chair and whispered to me "*Magnifico!*" as the meeting ended and we left the hall.

I travelled all over the principal island of Cuba by car, truck, or on foot, usually with Soviet geologists and/or geophysicists to familiarize myself with the basic geology and known mineral deposits. I did not visit the smaller Isla de Pinos, or any of the many exotically named smaller islands that occur around Cuba proper, since I was told these were reserved for tourist development and were to remain unspoiled by industrial development such as mining.

Havana, the capital and centre of government, is situated near the north-west tip of Cuba, which is the largest of all the West Indian islands. The naval base Guantanamo, granted to the American government by Cuba at the start of this century for help in securing Cuban independence from Spain, was still occupied and in use by Americans. It is situated at the south-east tip of the island. Cuba is the only well-established Communist nation in the western hemisphere. Its economy, historically and currently, is agricultural. Cuba is often called "the sugar bowl of the world." It produces some minerals, notably nickel, chromium, iron, and manganese. Some copper has been produced in the past and it was to confer with the Soviet specialists based in Cuba concerning the further development of this metal that I served there as a UN consultant. When I completed my consultation with them I submitted my report with technical recommendations to both the government and my UN agency director.

The Soviet UN experts in Cuba were somewhat different from those I had met in Somalia, Afghanistan, or to a lesser degree, in India. In Cuba an extra element was apparent – the universal and exceptional sociability of the Soviet men, women, and children. Probably this resulted from the infectious influence of the Latin-American temperament and way of life. Everyone worked, to be sure, but after sundown, music, gaiety, sports, and abandon were the order of the day. The Russians, mostly from the northern U.S.S.R., were posted to Cuba for two- or three-year missions, they brought their families, acquired fluent Spanish, and mixed well. They appeared to view their stay in Cuba as a protracted holiday, and the Cubans seemed equally to enjoy their more boisterous guests and benefactors.

Musings: The Colonial Heritage in Africa

Following my mission to Cuba, I worked later on the African continent in the Bas Congo sector of the Belgian Congo, then called Kinshasa. It eventually became Zaire. I also worked in Rwanda and in French Guinea. As I travelled in these African countries and in other former colonies, particularly in Central and South America, India, and Indonesia, I wondered why sociologists, historians, geographers, and political scientists have not described and evaluated more thoroughly what I regard as the creative aspects of the "colonial heritage."

My observations of development in Africa have brought me to the conclusion that, in many cases, the social and economic improvements effected during the colonial era provided the essential foundation for the initiative and modernization of these countries. I view these creative aspects of the colonial heritage as being far more economically, socially, and politically appropriate, valuable, and lasting than the contributions of many modern multi-national corporations. These latter have exercised and, in many cases, are still exercising a profound yet subtle form of manipulative "economic" colonialism without leaving much of continuing social, political, or physical benefit.

My work on behalf of the United Nations in ten African countries made me acutely aware of the great natural potential of that continent, not only in minerals, hydrocarbons, forestry, coastal fishery, and waterpower, but more so in terms of its human potential. Black Africa has the strong human beings, native intelligence, and motivation required for lasting progress. Many of the modern African states are free from the leaden blankets of religious and social feudalism – the products of centuries of exploitive colonialism – that continue to plague Central and South America and India. When Black Africa learns the arts of self-discipline, of unity and humane leadership, it will undoubtedly emerge on the world scene as a great new powerful sector of the globe. Africa has been a slumbering giant. Now it is slowly awakening.

Sharks' Teeth in the Congo

The Bas (Low) Congo is that narrow land corridor in which the huge Congo River flows and empties into the Atlantic Ocean. It is bordered by the Brazzaville Congo on the one side and Angola on the other. I was there in 1967, and the tragic turmoil that followed its independence from Belgium on June 30, 1960, was still apparent. The United Nations continued to play an important advisory role in the country's administrative services.

One major public works project for the newly independent country, in which a UN affiliate, the World Bank, was playing an important role, was the simultaneous development of hydro-electric energy from the Congo River and the improvement of transportation facilities by building a railway and a highway along the river gorge in order to develop an Atlantic coastal port. Another element in this mega-project was to develop, if possible, new mineral deposits in this Bas Congo corridor region. My mission was to assist in the latter objective.

My examination of historical records had revealed that a German explorer at the turn of the twentieth century, had sent to Brussels a specimen of rock found in the Bas Congo jungle, which on analysis was found to contain phosphate, a mineral important in fertilizer production. This knowledge, together with the information that important deposits of phosphate existed in the adjoining Brazzaville Congo, led me to search for this mineral.

I organized a small expedition which included a Belgian geologist who had long experience in the Congo and some knowledge of the aborigines in the area; a Congolese driver-mechanic to take us by jeep to the point above the rapids where we would cross the Congo River to conduct our explorations; and a handyman to carry our gear. A senior UN administrative officer would also accompany us to the river crossing, or "edge of the jungle." Since this Bas Congo corridor was the active passageway for the north-south movement of irregular, armed Marxist guerilla groups between Brazzaville and Angola we were provided with an elaborate document by the Congo government which carried government, military, and police seals upon it testifying as to our UN identity and our "right to free movement." In effect, this would protect us from Congolese military patrols attempting to stop this traffic of guerilla forces.

We arrived safely at the river crossing and the Belgian and I spent several exciting days travelling in the swampy Congo jungle in a dugout canoe manned by natives. The growth of trees and vines was so dense we rarely saw the sky. Various creatures crawled, swam, and scrambled through the swampy water. Other creatures called and chattered in the trees. On two occasions, we saw the extraordinary spectacle of a large fish climbing the low overhanging berry-bearing branches of a tree with its flippers to feed on the olive-like fruit, and then, having gorged itself, dropping back into the water.

Small groups of aborigines inhabited floating "islands" of matted roots and peat in the swamp. Aware of our approach from signals transmitted by drum beats on hollowed logs, they greeted us with much curiosity. At one stop, my Belgian colleague took a Polaroid photo of one group and presented the print to the headman. He quickly recognized his native companions in the picture but was unbelieving when they pointed to his own image. Mirrors were unknown to them. They were fascinated when they looked at their own reflections in the mirror of my Brunton compass.

During our time in the jungle, I examined the natives' ingenious implements – signal log drums, reed spears, hooks, and crude nets for fish or game – and the trinkets adorning their persons. I noticed a tiny baby, clearly preoccupied with some shell-like objects in its hands. When I approached and looked more closely, I was electrified – they were one-half to one-inch-long sharks' teeth!

Sharks' teeth embedded in the sedimentary rocks that comprise the ancient lagoonal, living environment of the shark, can be good news to an economic geologist looking for phosphorite. They often occur together.

I drew aside my Belgian colleague, who could speak some of the primitive dialects, and suggested that he ask the headman about the origin of the sharks' teeth. The headman strode to a fishing net and pointed to a "float" on the net. I had noticed this float but concluded that it was probably a piece of tree bark, like natural cork, but now I examined it carefully and realized it was a porous rock in which I could see broken fragments of shells including sharks' teeth. "That's what we are looking for," I told my colleague. "Can we be led to where this material came from?"

After a couple of minutes of discussion with several of the men around him, my colleague replied, "Yes, they'll show us. It will take a couple of days by boat or raft."

Eventually, we were taken to two or three outcrops of phosphorite beds. The outcrops were of reddish-coloured, porous and crumbly rock, which rose in mounds about ten feet high and twenty feet in diameter from the brown muddy water of the swamp. We poled our canoe through the swamp amidst large leafy trees heavily draped with moss and hanging vines which grew out of the water. There were no flowers – all was a drab grey-green colour. I collected samples from each outcrop for analysis and made descriptive notes of the scene.

The reddish mounds were, I felt certain, of the same occurrence (or of the same type of source) as the specimen the German explorer had sent earlier this century to the Belgian Colonial Geological Survey in Brussels, and which I had seen there. With a sense of satisfaction about the success of the search itself, mixed with intuitive misgivings about its location – whether it was in the Bas Congo (in Belgium) or in Brazzaville Congo (French) – we began our return journey to Élisabethville.

I was uncertain not only about our precise location, but also about the problem of access, of working with drills to develop the deposits, and the physical difficulties of mining and removing the material through the jungle to a market. And I asked myself: "What if the UN sends me back into this frightening watery jungle to develop it?" Meanwhile, problems lay ahead of which we were mercifully unaware.

As soon as we were out of the jungle, we reached the Congo River and recrossed it by barge without major difficulty. On the other side we picked up our jeep. With our driver at the wheel, we set off down an asphalt highway.

Rounding a curve in the highway, we suddenly found ourselves confronted with a long, practically stationary line of vehicles, mostly trucks and buses, all overloaded with goods and people. It was obvious that a military roadblock lay ahead. It was mid-afternoon and we were impatient to complete our long drive before dark.

Our Belgian colleague unlocked the dashboard glove compartment and withdrew the specially prepared government *laissez-passer* document rolled up with a coloured ribbon, not unlike a diploma. He read it with care and mumbled something to the jeep's driver who promptly pulled out of the line-up. Passing the stationary vehicles, we drew up and double-parked at the head of the line.

We were at the top of a gentle incline where the road had been cut through a hill. A few large trees and short grass lined both sides of the road. On the right side a large army tarpaulin served as protection against the sun. Below the tarpaulin was a collapsible army table at which three or four army officers with much red and gold braid on their uniforms sat in a row. Two or three soldiers of junior rank hustled various drivers before the table where they were being questioned. Some sevicemen were searching trucks. Others were herding the many truck-riding passengers into groups under the larger trees. On both elevated shoulders of the road stood a number of partly concealed, tripod-mounted machine guns. The gunners crouched on their bellies, eyes on their sights, and fingers close to triggers. While the entire scene was menacing, I felt we were handling ourselves well to that point. It won't be long, I thought, before we are on our way again.

Two or three minutes passed. I was reassured to see a couple of the officers at the table glance in our direction. They were obviously aware of our presence. "All we need right now is a little more patience on our part," I thought.

But our jeep driver's self-restraint had run its course. Either the nervousness of looking down six machine-gun barrels, or over-confidence in the power of the diplomatic "Holy Writ" in the Belgian's hand caused our driver to blast hard, several times, on the raucous horn of our jeep. I cringed. All colour left the Belgian's normally ruddy face.

An infantryman, Tommy gun in his crooked arm "at the ready," sauntered over to our jeep, dragged our driver out, clubbed him with a single blow to the head and shoulder, and walked back to stand again beside the officers' table. Our driver fell to the pavement, mouth open, and lay very still. He appeared only semi-conscious. I watched him for a few moments and then glanced towards the officers' table to see if there was any sign of their readiness to attend to us. No one even glanced our way.

I pushed the Belgian in the front seat by the shoulder and said, "Let's go." With that we both got out of the jeep. We walked through the line of trucks and paused, in plain view, scroll in hand, about ten feet from the officers' table.

Finally, those being questioned at the table moved away and we moved forward. The Belgian quickly unrolled the document and handed it to one of the officers who seemed to be in a daze. He took the document, turned it on its side, then upside down. It appeared that the officers could not read French. I approached in order to read it for them, and understood, with fear, the source of our problem. The officers seated at the table reeked of liquor. It was pointless to try to convey to them all that was on the scroll, so I simply repeated half a dozen times . . . *"Nations Unies. Nations Unies."* Finally, with a wave of the hand from one of them, we were dismissed. We returned to our jeep, lifted our still limp driver into the back, and the Belgian drove like lightning for Élisabethville.

My mission to the Congo was completed successfully and, fortunately, safely as well, and I found that the experience I had gained had improved my ability to tolerate uncertainty, an ability that, happily, was not put to quite the same test during the years 1972 to 1977 when I served in Pakistan, Afghanistan, and Iran.

My work in Pakistan concerned uranium exploration and fell within the domain of the International Atomic Energy Agency, which I served as a consultant. Our project area was in the arid mountain country west of Dera Ghazi Khan, where I was reintroduced to that remarkably patient transporter of cargo and humans, the camel, whom I had grown to respect in Somalia and Morocco. On later assignments I travelled over other parts of the country, but it was in Iran, however, that I was more deeply involved in UN work.

For the Shah in Iran

I completed three assignments in Iran. The first two, in 1972 and 1974, were UN missions; the third, in 1977, was for an Iranian crown corporation. During this five-year period there was rising social unrest and violence in Iran. The Shah, Mohammad Reza Pahlavi, employed repressive measures through his secret police, the Savak, to deal with opposition to his policies.

While the Shah had appeared to western eyes to be a social reformer in the early 1960s, he had, in fact, concentrated all political power in his own hands. His social programs, including his nominal emancipation of women in 1963, brought him praise in the west, but had not gone far to eradicating poverty and illiteracy. Along with members of his family, the Shah became even more fabulously wealthy as the price of oil rose in the mid 1970s.

The Shah's most powerful opponent was the Iranian religious fundamentalist leader, Ayatollah Rouhollah Khomeini, who mercilessly condemned the Shah's total acceptance of "western moral and social decadence" in all its forms. Khomeini's call to the Iranian army to turn against the Shah and to establish an Islamic Republic, coupled with deteriorating social conditions and the fanaticism of Khomeini's followers, finally drove the Shah from Iran. However, that lay several years in the future as I prepared for my initial journey to Iran.

My first assignment in Iran came a year or so after the elaborate celebration of the 2,500th anniversary of the Iranian monarchy, which had attracted vast numbers of visitors and the rulers of many countries. During the celebrations the Shah extolled the extravagant notion (totally untrue) that he was a descendant of Cyrus and Darius, who had established the monarchy. The spectacular Iranian architecture, the new arches, monuments, and buildings that lined the wide avenues from the Teheran airport to my hotel were breathtakingly beautiful as were many other structures erected for the celebration.

During my first visit to Iran I was carefully shown about by the UN resident technical advisor. My assignment was quite limited and its objective was somewhat different from the type of assignment I usually undertook. I was to evaluate the progress of the organizational and training support which the UN had provided to the Iranian Geological Survey through the work of two geologists: Dr. J. Stocklin, a Swiss, and Dr. Gordon Williams, a New Zealander. Through the survey which these men had directed as UN experts, they had made an important contribution to the geological mapping of Iran.

The terms of service of these UN experts was about to expire, and the Iranian government had apparently decided that "monies spent making maps could be better spent finding mines." I put this statement in quotation marks because on my first visit I learned that all policy, and possibly authority, appeared to stem from highly placed individuals. These individuals were few in number and appeared to be older, trusted friends of the Shah who served entirely at his pleasure. Here it is essential to note that the Shah had complete constitutional authority to dissolve Iran's governing bodies. Those who controlled governmental affairs were themselves directly under the control of the Shah. Thus it is not surprising that the Shah appointed personal friends to the highest positions in Iran.

When I met with senior Iranian officials holding positions comparable to Canadian cabinet ministers, the meetings were usually in their homes. At such meetings no secretaries were present and no notes were taken. Recommendations concerning specific matters or ways in which particular problems might be handled were outlined orally. Careful attention appeared to be paid to the oral recommendations, but there was little discussion and no debate. After such meetings, I was usually told that I would be advised "in a couple of days" through the UN Resident Representative as to whether my recommendations had been approved or not.

At the time of my first visit to Iran, I was unaware that a dramatic event would soon attract international attention in mining circles and that that event would involve the UN mapping project which I was to assess, and the efforts of the Iranian government to regain a mining claim from a private owner and a giant international mining corporation. Although I sensed there was a problem, I could not then judge the extent of its impact.

Two years or so before my initial visit, the French government had offered the government of Iran the technical services of two field geologists. After this offer had been accepted and the geologists had arrived, they were assigned specific mapping responsibilities by the UN-appointed Geological Survey Director, Dr. J. Stocklin. On completion of their field work, the two French geologists properly presented their final report to Dr. Stocklin. For some reason, their report was promptly marked "Confidential" and filed in the survey office. Thus it was not published and its circulation, if any, is unknown.

In their report the two French geologists had described a small but very rich copper deposit they had visited which was in modest production and privately owned. What was of dramatic importance was that these geologists had identified and related this small deposit to a probably new, rich, and enormous "porphyry-type" copper deposit of possibly vast importance. They were naturally proud of their technical achievement. Since their work was not made known publicly, at least in Iran, they submitted, in due course, a version of their findings to an English-language European mining journal.

Publication of that report stimulated immediate interest and a British–South African mining group had quickly completed an arrangement to purchase the property from its Iranian owner. This led to quick intervention by the government of Iran, but not before the first foreign drilling indicated the tremendous worth of the deposit. It became known as the Sar-Chesmah, and many experts regard it as probably the largest and richest copper deposit in the entire Near East.

My second assignment in Iran in 1974 was less hurried and more satisfying to me than the first since I was not limited to a "yes" or "no" recommendation regarding a three-year-old program that had effectively run its course. This second mission presented an imaginative challenge that I could not resist. I was asked: "What could be achieved economically as far as minerals are concerned in the huge and totally underdeveloped desert area called the Dash-el-Lut, in eastern Iran bordering Afghanistan and Pakistan?"

On arrival in Teheran, it did not take long to program my organic computer with the limited technical data available. This done, I set out like a relaxed tourist to enjoy the sights, sounds, and splendour of the heartland of Iran – Teheran and its environs – as evidenced by its treasures of art in many forms, structures, tapestries, sculpture, exquisitely embellished manuscripts, and jewels.

I viewed the famous Crown Jewels. To my surprise I was not as impressed as I had expected to be. Ostentatious opulence repels me and this was such a case. Too much, in too small a space and garishly presented. The Tsarist Crown Jewels in the Hermitage in Leningrad or the British Crown Jewels in London were, I felt, more elegant historical displays.

But not all in Teheran was beautiful at that time. In the city suburbs there was much evidence of poverty and senior public officials everywhere complained voluntarily about inflation. At dusk, helicopters circled above the city and suburbs. "Why?" I asked.

"Crowd surveillance!" I was told. The Shah and his government were clearly troubled by evidence of unrest or by the congregation of public crowds.

After a day or two of relaxation, I addressed myself to the mission in hand. I was certain that the highly important and efficient state petroleum company should have at least some aerial geophysical information regarding the vast sand-covered Dash-el-Lut area. My enquiry to them revealed that they had performed some aerial work over that area. Their work, however, had indicated the presence of crystalline "basement rock" of no interest to oil and gas explorationists. Nonetheless, that is a general classification for rock types in which many minerals can occur. Thus I sought further details.

I learned that a year earlier two young geologists of the Iranian Survey had travelled by jeep across the Dash-el-Lut desert along the historic thirteenth-century "Silk Caravan Trail." I asked to meet them and asked, "What did you see when you crossed the desert?"

Their answer was direct and simple. "Not a thing but sand – terrible dust storms, sandstorms – just sand"

I persisted, "No evidence of rock outcrops or minerals?"

They replied: "No, not even in the samples of sand we brought back and examined. In one place we did find bits of slag."

"Slag!" I exclaimed. "You mean the glassy clinker from melted rock?"

"Yes, probably done by people in ancient times who passed along the Trail."

"Where?" I pressed.

"About half-way across," was the answer. And it was the answer I wished to hear. Slag is the refuse from smelting of metal from rock. The presence of slag meant metal or a mineral deposit nearby.

I promptly prepared a plan for an exploration program, and a recommendation for UN support, to study the area where the young Iranians had found evidence of "slag," and much of the adjoining desert as well. I left a copy of my proposal with the UN Resident Representative to pass on to the government, with the added recommendation that the UN manage the plan if so desired, and a copy with a senior government planning official. Three months or so after I had reported to the UN, and while I thought they were still considering my recommendation for the exploration program, a UN official put in front of me the summarized description of a completed drillhole showing high contents of copper, zinc, and gold.

I was not aware that any action had yet been taken in Iran nor that any drilling had been started, and I could not explain the origin of the important drilling results. My further enquiries revealed that my enthusiastic recommendation had prompted the Iranian Bureau of Mines not to wait for further UN assistance. With the help of the two young Iranian geologists I had "quizzed," officials of the bureau had located the site of the slag, and examined the terrain more carefully. A patch of rusted sand was discovered and below it ancient excavations in oxidized rock. The bureau had then rushed in a diamond-drill and the description of the first core had been sent to me, probably intended as a fraternal "thank you" from a very happy Iranian geologist. In the following three years, with the help of foreign contractors, a moderate-sized profitable mine was developed. A small section of the Marco Polo Trail as it crossed the Dash-el-Lut desert, began to "bloom" again.

My later missions to Iran were related to uranium exploration. The first of these was to evaluate a long and expensive aerial radiometric program conducted by the French government as a bilateral aid contribution. Its general conclusion was that Iran did not have sufficient domestic uranium to support a nuclear energy program. In principle I agreed with the French conclusion. But I felt their procedures and techniques had been too strongly biased toward identification of giant-sized "sandstone-type" deposits only. Their radiometric surveys had been conducted solely from the air, with consequent lower efficiency.

I felt that some modest-scale, ground-level, radiometric surveying should be conducted for small, yet probably rich, deposits before it was finally concluded that there was no uranium in Iran. Accordingly, I drafted a program to involve jeep-transported detection equipment. In my view, one season's work with perhaps four jeeps, at a total cost below $100,000, would suffice as an initial test. I indicated that I would recommend such a program for support by the UN.

The UN Resident Representative with whom I discussed my ideas was shocked and told me he would be embarrassed to suggest such a modest program to the Shah's planners. "After all," I was reminded, "the French program cost over $5 million."

I insisted and explained my exploration philosophy crisply: "In this business I start at a crawl. If I'm encouraged, I walk. If I'm more encouraged, I run. All before I jump!" I heard no more of that proposal for some time, and then I received a long distance telephone call from Teheran enquiring if I was available to serve the government of Iran as a private consultant to its nuclear agency, Urivan, regarding the search for uranium deposits in Iran. Assuming the call related to the large French program which I had earlier evaluated, I cautiously replied that I was available and was told they would contact me again.

The next telephone call came three months later, from an Iranian official in Houston, Texas. A young man with a bright, westernized voice said he was a senior aide to the director of Urivan and on his way to Canada to meet me. Subsequently, he called me from Denver, Colorado, and New York City before appearing in my Toronto office.

The Iranian nuclear agency, Urivan, had been directed, he said, by an order of the Shah, to set in motion, without delay, and with the advice of French, American, and Canadian experts, a program of aerial radiometric surveying of half of Iran's entire land mass. Fifty million dollars had been allocated for the project. Various senior

officers in Iran had recommended that I should advise their government, if I were agreeable, on "ground follow-up aspects" of all air-
borne indications. All this amazed me.

"Have you not seen the reports of the earlier $5-million French
program in which helicopters were used?" I asked.

"Sure!" he replied.

"And my evaluation of it for your government through the UN?"

"Sure!" he again replied

"And have you heard of the very modest program I proposed for
the UN follow-up of the French program for better 'ground-level'
efficiency?"

"Oh, sure!" he replied. "We gave some of your jeep work a trial
and it worked!" That's why I'm here; I have authority to arrange a
contract with you."

I spent that evening reviewing my files on my earlier missions to
Iran, and mulling over the new information I had received that day
to update my "organic computer." I fell asleep wondering what its
"printout" would offer the following morning.

When I arose in the morning the answer was: "Why not, but be
cautious." I agreed on a simple service contract. I was to be "on call"
to the Shah's Urivan agency for one month, each calendar quarter,
for one year. My initial responsibilities, I suggested, would be classroom and field training of young Iranian professionals in the technical
procedures of ground testing and evaluation of aerial radiometric
anomalies.

Our lecture and field program started well. But the foreign surveying contractors engaged by Urivan were slow in becoming organized and in producing the data with which the eager students and
I were to work. During 1977, the political and economic fabric of the
country began to disintegrate. That year, internal and external criticism of the Shah's regime mounted steadily. The dusk patrol of helicopter surveillance had given place to such surveillance on a constant
basis, wherever and whenever a crowd gathered – a marketplace,
bazaar, mosque, or car accident. Clearly the authorities were edgy.
I welcomed notice in mid-year that the final two months of my service
contract would be indefinitely postponed. The situation in Iran wors-
ened drastically in 1978 despite the Shah's claim in June of that year
that nobody could overthrow him.

By mid January 1979, following four months of rioting in Teheran
and other centres of Iran, the authority of the Shah had totally col-

lapsed through internal corruption, mass demonstrations, and the religious onslaughts of the Ayatollah Rouhollah Khomeini, whose stern opposition to the Shah was ultimately the key factor in the fall of the Iranian government. Khomeini had been jailed in 1963 and later exiled to Iraq. Expelled from Iraq in 1978 and allowed to enter France, he returned to Iran on February 1, 1979, to a welcome by a crowd of three million at the Teheran airport.

Eleven days later Khomeini finally defeated the Shah, who had fled to America on January 16. The crusader for Moslem fundamentalism had deposed the Shah, the most conspicuous symbol in the Near East of the "decadent" west and was able to utter the traditional Iranian phrase, "*Shah mat!*" From this phrase, meaning, "The Shah is dead," comes the word *checkmate*.

The Shah lived on for a short period, but what he stood for had been swept away in Iran's rising tide of political and religious fundamentalism, a fundamentalism that is spreading through much of the Moslem world. In countries in which the dominant religion is Islam, such as Afghanistan, Egypt, Iran, Lebanon, Pakistan, Somalia, and Turkey, I have noted this dramatic religious revival. It is apparent in public criticism of the conduct of governmental affairs and social conduct by Moslem ideologists, as: "See how western decadence is ruining us. We must return to the fundamental values of Mohammad." Political adversaries of those in power in such states did not hesitate to use clerical criticism for their own purposes.

In Europe and America, just as in the Islamic world, there is much criticism of both political and religious leaders whose actions have contributed to a widening lack of integrity and disregard of moral standards. This grave malaise in America had resulted in a mushrooming of revivalist or evangelical leaders and an astonishing growth in the number of their followers. The strong implication is that the conventional church, guardian of morality, has failed. Some of these church critics aspire to presidential power to save America from the moral ruin that apparently engulfs it. Yet, even in confused America, certain of these ideological crusaders have been guilty of the moral and financial corruption which they condemn. Increasing moral decadence in America cannot be denied.

As I review this moral turmoil from within many of the countries where it simmers, I have observed that the best leadership appears where and when a nation is served by two leaders; one, the statesman or political administrator, and the other, a spiritual or ideological counterpart. Prominent and successful models that come to mind are India during the Nehru-Ghandi era, and China during the Chou En Lai-Mao Tse Tung era.

But even with this model, there can be failure – usually when the jealousy for power corrupts the union of only two. Perhaps it is the stigma of the human race. The Old Testament perhaps chronicles its beginning, when, of the first two brothers created upon Earth, one saw cause to kill the other.

In regard to Iran, the turmoil is not yet ended. There may well have been a period of spiritual purification through Muslim eyes but my "best model" for total leadership success requires that there be a counterpart to the ideological power of the Ayatollah – that of a practical statesman.

With the Soviets in Afghanistan

From Iran I moved on to Afghanistan, where the issue of Muslim fundamentalism was also evident but only then as a flicker – it would not burst into flame for another decade.

I went to Afghanistan in 1973 to assist in the development of the mineral resources of that land-locked country, the greater portion of which lies at heights of between 2,000 and 10,000 feet above sea level. Given its ruggedness, it is not surprising that much of the Afghan population is nomadic and that these insular and fiercely independent bands are chronically opposed to government officials, who come primarily from the educated classes living in the capital, Kabul, and the other leading cities of Kandahar, Herat, and Mazar-i-Sharif.

Afghanistan is divided into three distinct geographic regions by the Hindu Kush and its subsidiary ranges. There is a northern region of plains and relatively fertile foothills sloping toward the Amu Darya River which forms the national boundary with a considerable portion of the Soviet Union. Pakistan borders Afghanistan to the south and east as Iran does on the west. Southern Afghanistan is a region of high plateaux with a sandy desert in the south-east. Between the northern and southern regions is the central region with its lofty mountains and deep, narrow valleys.

Such narrow valleys, which serve as spectacular passes through the red-rock mountains of Afghanistan, were used as early invasion routes into and through the country and, later, as caravan trails over which conquerors carried the riches of India to Europe. Darius, Alexander, and Genghis Khan used such routes as did Marco Polo. Another more southerly route, now favoured as a communication and transportation corridor, follows the Kabul River, a tributary of the Indus, and connects Kabul with Peshawar in the north-west frontier region of Pakistan.

This southern route was opened for vehicular and rail traffic by the construction of a tunnel beneath a mountain ridge known as the Khyber Pass. The area has become a notable modern tourist attraction because it is one of the rare points where one can meet and barter with the mountain nomads at minimum risk. Obtainable there are beautifully hand-crafted firearms, made entirely by mountain craftsmen using primitive materials and tools, scrap steel, bellows, and charcoal fire, as they have done for centuries.

When I worked in Afghanistan, my base was in Kabul, a city of contrasts. Like most of the country, the capital city is a rocky place in the midst of mountains. Its modern landmark when I was there was a fully equipped Hilton Hotel which commanded a remarkable view in all directions. From it there radiated a few roads, some blacktop but mainly cobblestone, over which all manner of carts, wagons, and some automobiles passed or bumped. On the street there were also pack mules and many pedestrians in all manner of dress. Western businessmen travelled by rare car or taxi.

Some shops were quite modern by western standards, others, we would regard as "junk shops." As a prospector, I, of course, favoured the latter. In one of them I found a fine piece of lapis lazuli, highly valued for its gold-speckled, deep blue colour. To the shopkeeper, it was just another nicotine-covered ashtray, but it responded to some discreet scratching on my part to show fine gemstone. To repay the merchant and mollify my conscience I also bought from him the small brass saucer that he insisted was a better ashtray!

From Kabul I travelled with a lone companion-interpreter, north, south, and east along the famous Khyber Pass to the Pakistan border. Near Kabul there had been some limited mining activity and in the Khyber Pass area some copper, gold, and, more recently, chrome had been produced. The most notable mineral product in both ancient and modern times is the semi-precious lapis lazuli, found in Badakhshan in north-eastern Afghanistan. These historic deposits were visited by Marco Polo in the late thirteenth century.

Afghanistan served as a buffer zone between the interests of the

Russian Tsarist Empire and the British colonies of India and Pakistan for over a century. In 1873, British authorities obtained from the Tsarist government an undertaking that Afghanistan was not within the sphere of Russian influence and that the Amu Darya River, then known as the Oxus, would be the northern boundary of Afghanistan. However, argument on this subject continued until 1884 when it was agreed that a joint commission of British and Russian officers would formally demarcate the northern boundary.

In 1907, an Anglo-Russian agreement was finally reached. Britain certified that it had no intention of altering the internal political status of Afghanistan, and Tsarist Russia confirmed that Afghanistan was beyond its sphere of influence. In this period the interest of Great Britain was to protect its colonial possessions in India and Pakistan from Tsarist encroachment. Later, after the Second World War, the British interest in protecting its historic arrangement was succeeded by the determination of some western countries, led by the United States, to contain "Soviet influence." Afghanistan was inevitably caught up in this new phase of the struggle between the two great ideological-economic superpowers.

In the mid 1960s, the King of Afghanistan concluded that his Kingdom should be transformed from an autocracy into a democratic state. He removed the royal family from politics but failed to make the elected parliament effective owing to the jealousy and independent nature of the nomadic tribal leaders. In 1973, Muhammad Daoud Khan, a cousin of the retired King and former prime minister, assumed control, announced that Afghanistan was a republic and that he was now president. Daoud Khan had friendly relationships with the Soviet Union and had sought their assistance at every level of national development.

Evidently the Soviets had responded with dispatch and efficiency. By the time I was there in 1973 they had established major educational facilities, including polytechnical institutions with large numbers of students studying engineering and technical subjects. They built hospitals and provided medical training. Soviet administrators were appointed in every department of government to train Afghan nationals.

The Soviet contribution toward all forms of education was striking. It appeared to me to be devoid of obvious ideological doctrine. I was fully aware, of course, that Soviet teachers, engineers, and technicians were the Russian counterparts, in Afghanistan and elsewhere, of the priests and missionaries who accompanied or followed the explorers, the conquistadors, and political masters in earlier colonial eras. The Afghani professionals with whom I met and worked felt considerable pride in their technical upgrading, although some expressed resentment at having to take orders from an "intruder." Not all educational assistance was provided on-site in Afghanistan. The more intelligent Afghani men and women were offered higher training in the Soviet Union. Those few with whom I discussed this, and who had experienced foreign training, viewed it as a great privilege.

By the time of my mission in Afghanistan, the Soviets had undertaken and completed several major infra-structural improvements. Among these were airports and a great wide expressway extending the entire distance from the northern to the southern edge of Afghanistan and its borders with Pakistan via Kandahar. The only obvious signs of Soviet armament that I saw throughout that country were a couple of compounds filled with camouflage-painted tanks beside this expressway. No military personnel were in view when I was there.

The Soviets had explored aggressively for hydrocarbons and minerals in certain parts of Afghanistan. Discoveries had been made and production was commenced from large natural gas reserves on the Afghani slope of the Amu River. Pipelines conveyed the gas into the Soviet Union and to a northern Afghani centre where, I was told, they were developing electrical energy and a urea and petrochemical complex for the Afghani government. The Soviets had been less successful in their mineral search, however, despite having rediscovered an ancient mining area which may have been worked earlier for its meagre content of gold.

This ancient mining site had been identified through soil geochemistry. At the time I visited it, it had been trenched and considerable diamond-drilling had been completed on it. They were about to mine and bulk-sample a portion of the deposit, which appeared to be large, prior to making recovery tests for copper and gold. I was favourably impressed with the exploratory program conducted by the Soviets to that point.

In addition to this copper-gold deposit, the Soviets had done some additional work in an area of small but rich pods of chrome-ore. They had also worked in widely scattered areas where limestone, gypsum, and talc were known to occur. I was taken by Soviet guides, accompanied by Afghani geologists, to see several of these deposits. All of these were of local importance but little more.

These side trips took the form of two- or three-day excursions and were invariably in the hill country which, at the time of my visit, was already covered with early patches of snow and ice. Several times I stayed in the crude bush-shacks of the Soviet geologists and a few Afghani prospectors. Theirs was as hard a life as I had ever experienced. Up at dawn, bathing in the icy water of a nearby creek, heavy meals and trudging the hills and valleys throughout the day exhausted the hardiest of men by nightfall. I marvelled at the dedication of the Afghani and Soviet men with whom I worked and wondered about the source of their motivation. In Canada, mine had been clear – initially at least – to achieve technical distinction and financial security.

Except for a rifle slung over the shoulder of an occasional policeman in the city of Kabul, it was only in such bush-camps that I saw any firearms. I was told they were used for game-hunting or for protection from aggressive hill tribesmen. Practically all the nomadic "hill-people" carried firearms, and woe betide any low-flying helicopter, which seemed to be their favourite "game." During the early 1970s, my UN assignments in Iran and Pakistan took me to areas bordering on Afghanistan. While I was in Baluchistan, the westernmost province of Pakistan, I wished to examine the Saindak area of ancient diggings. Thus I suggested to my Pakistani colleague that we employ an air force helicopter to take us there. He told me that taking a helicopter there would be too dangerous because of ground fire from the Baluchistani hill-men. Similarly, in the Dera Ghazi Khan area of Pakistan, near the Afghan border, ground fire from the hill-people was encountered by an aircraft chartered by the UN. Thus I carried out my work in Afghanistan and its borders on the ground and not in the air.

When I first went to Afghanistan, I had been introduced by the UN Resident Representative to the Afghani deputy-director of his country's Geological Survey. I asked if I might visit his offices and the field-mapping department. He spoke fluent English, and, with a humorous twinkle in his eyes, said, "Yes, we will go to the mapping section, but first, I will take you to my leader." I was introduced to a Soviet colonel, a large, burly, outgoing person who, despite his military rank, wore no uniform, as was the case with all Soviet advisers I met.

The Soviet officer, who was the nominal director of the Afghanistan Geological Survey, appeared puzzled, initially, on learning of my role and presence in Afghanistan. But he readily promised his total co-operation and lived up to that promise. A graduate in geological sciences from the University of Leningrad, who was obviously enjoying his two-year assignment in Afghanistan, he spoke English fluently and conducted himself like an enthusiastic professor before a serious student. Unrolling large manuscript maps, he pointed out the substantial Soviet achievement of completely remapping the geology of Afghanistan. Several of the large sheets, he said, were being printed in modern printing facilities which the Soviets had installed in the Kabul geological department.

At several of my later meetings the director was keenly interested in my evaluation of the various deposits I had visited. He concurred with most of my conclusions and recommendations and appeared pleased with my suggestion that I recommend to the UN that they should provide two industrial mineral specialists to be attached to the Geological Survey for one year. One was to make a national inventory of such deposits and the other to advise on the broader national utilization of such minerals. Then the director revealed to me his "favourite development project" for Afghanistan.

It was totally unrelated to anything I had seen or enquired about earlier, save for vague references to gold production in ancient times. He wished to discuss, in the light of the current "economics of gold," the potential of the alluvial gold of the Amu River within the river itself and drainage slopes into it, including the Afghani slope. I enquired about what he knew of the present gold content of that vast drainage system. He presented me with a two-inch-thick pile of folded maps, saying, "These are our sampling and assay plans for the Afghani side. Study them in our library here if you wish!" I did so and was favourably impressed.

Before parting company with the director and deputy-director I suggested they undertake some detailed exploration in the southwesterly corner of Afghanistan, close to both the Baluchistan border and the Iranian border of the Dash-el-Lut desert. Earlier I had assisted in identifying copper deposits in both of these areas, the one in Iran being of appreciable importance. "But we cannot!" protested the Soviet director. "Both those borders are ill-defined. Our presence near them could provoke an incident."

My mission in Afghanistan was unique in that there I was largely a UN observer of Soviet bilateral aid. I had seen in other countries (two in Africa, in Burma, in India, and over-flying Egypt) the end results of such aid, but only in Afghanistan and Cuba did I see them actively involved in the technical assistance process. In Somalia I served in an advisory role to Soviet professionals recruited and directed by the UN. I grew to admire these men as technical professionals, particularly because of their ruggedness and resourcefulness. I view them, in practical terms, as not unlike Canadians, Scandinavians, or Australians. As yet I have not met an ideological fanatic among them.

Soviet bilateral or "foreign" aid, unlike most of the aid provided by western countries, is rarely a self-help or charitable activity. Usually it involves "hard-nosed" barter. India may receive Soviet aid for the development of iron and manganese mines and the erection of a steel mill, but she must provide equal value to the Soviet Union in manufactured railway cars, steel rail, and plate. Cuba may receive engines, oil, and manufactured goods but in return must ship sugar and nickel to Russia. Afghanistan may receive industrial goods but only for natural gas, animal hides, and other items useful to the Soviet Union.

On the basis of considerable personal observation of various forms of "foreign aid" in operation I have come to the conclusion that the barter pattern is immeasurably better, in every respect, for third-world countries, than the monetary loans or charity-philosophy of the western world. The barter system requires collective discipline on the part of all concerned. Barter arrangements can contribute to the development of those qualities of co-operation and self-determination which are essential in both human and national development.

My views concerning barter have been shaped, naturally, by my own experience. I have found that a clear vision of one's objective, a high level of personal discipline and steady ongoing work, either physical or intellectual or a combination of both, are all required if one is to achieve something of enduring value in both the short- and long-term dimensions of one's life.

In this and the preceding chapter I have endeavoured to provide a survey of some aspects of the fascinating, and for me highly satisfying, work in which I engaged on behalf of the United Nations. Much more could be written about that period and my other wide-ranging involvements over a very full life. Yet, increasingly, friends and acquaintances pose me the question: "You seem to have been everywhere and seen everything. What are your reflections on it all?"

Regretfully I must confess to a feeling of cynicism and despair for the human race as a whole.

Each fragment (country or nation) takes fierce and often vicious pride in the ideological rightness of its fragment. The fragments are and have forever been engaged in endless and often fatal struggle to convert or destroy other fragments that reject subjugation.

In most countries (or fragments), as material development and individual freedom increase, moral and cultural standards decrease apace, both in internal and external terms.

As individual freedoms increase, physical and material rivalry becomes increasingly aggressive and with decreasing morality this degenerates into human violence, internally, toward other members of the fragment, and externally, toward those of other fragments. Lowered moral standards and high technology can culminate in a form of non-personal aggression that leads to the mass killing of others.

The paramount human tragedy is that the victims of such inhuman acts are increasingly non-involved civilians and that the act itself is invariably justified as the moral defence of some ideological or spiritual entity that has, commonly for centuries, served as a model for universal morality and peace among all men.

A second frightening sphere of human self-destruction is increasingly apparent, particularly in the more highly developed societies. It is the wanton destruction and poisoning of the environment, both regionally and globally. It is motivated in most instances by human greed, most marked in the industrial and consumer sectors of society.

This human suicidal phenomenon has already in the past century significantly despoiled our waters and atmosphere; the two major physio-chemical contributors toward the origin and evolution of all organic life upon our planet. To an abstract biologist Man could more properly be viewed as a wanton tramp than the noblest of beasts upon the planet Earth.

XVII
Envoy

To a considerable extent, my life has been a journey of discovery. Some of the discoveries were exciting and joyful; others were disturbing and sombre. In the foregoing chapters I have sought to describe some of these discoveries, what led up to them, and what I learned from them.

Most (but not all) of my mineral discoveries were products of my innate curiosity and persistence. All of the primary discoveries in which I have been involved, however, were shared with one or more persons, and all these people have contributed in significant ways to the richness of my journey through life.

I have always had a drive to excel in all my undertakings. This soon became a self-propelling force in my life and led to my determination to succeed in areas where others thought success was not possible and occasionally in fields where no one else had sought to be successful. It was a combination of this emphasis on excellence (received, I believe, from my mother) and persistence (received from my father) that made me ultimately successful in developing uranium mines in Ontario and the Northwest Territories, copper and gold mines in Manitoba, and a copper and cobalt mine in Ontario, and that allowed me to complete successfully many other projects in several countries in my work for the United Nations Technical Assistance program.

Thus as I look back over my lifetime, I am increasingly aware of the rich – though non-material – inheritance left to me by my parents. What they left me, I could never have acquired with money. Besides my life they gave me an enduring appreciation for high standards in all areas of human activity and a realization of the need for persistence in adhering to and achieving such standards. My parents, particularly my mother, exerted upon me formative and lasting influences which have benefited me throughout my life.

My Father, My Mother, and My Brother

Midway through the First World War, my father, in company with his fellow volunteers of the 10th Company of the 147th Regiment, found themselves leaving Vancouver on their way to the war in France. His departure left my mother with complete responsibility for her little family of two sons. My mother was a most extraordinary person. Though tiny and fragile in appearance, and of delicate health, she was strikingly elegant in manner and speech, with the fierce energy, courage, and the regal soul of a lioness. My brother and I were her two cubs, and she was determined that some day, I, as the elder son, would be the leader of the pride! Although, lively, sturdy boys that we were, we doubtless tried our mother's patience and strength, she kept us in line, not by molly-coddling, persuasion, or parental bribery, but by her constant and fierce will and by challenging us to be the best.

Our father returned to us badly wounded and in need of ongoing medical care. Nonetheless, determined to ensure that we would have a good life together, he worked on the cooking staff of Resthaven Military Hospital in Sidney, near Victoria. Until he died, in late May 1918, our father and mother persistently fought adversity on our behalf. While my memories of my father's funeral are still vivid, my recollections of him while he lived are limited. It seems quite clear, however, that I inherited from him my curiosity, my sense of adventure, and my capacity to pursue an objective tenaciously.

When father died, I was only six and a half years of age. He had accompanied me only a short distance along my journey through life, but that was a crucially important formative distance. Equally as important were the many things I learned through his death and the responsibilities I had to assume because of it. Before I had reached my teens I had realized that responsibility for myself, my mother, and my brother rested with me. I knew that to care for my mother and to realize her ambitions for me I had to continue my education and to earn money at the same time.

My brother, Gerald (whom I always called Tibby, a nickname derived from my childish efforts to pronounce the French word *bébé*) was not particularly interested in education. He left school as early as he could and apprenticed as a chef in an exclusive businessmen's club in Victoria. After a couple of years there he took a job as a cook on a tramp steamer plying the world's oceans. We rarely heard from him during his years at sea. In England he met and married an English nurse. When the Second World War began, Tibby, like our father in the First World War, promptly enlisted.

In the course of his duties as a courier for British General Staff officers in southeast Asia, Tibby rode his motorcycle over a land mine. He was hospitalized and later flown back to his wife and young daughter in England. He never fully recovered from his head injury and suffered from dizzy spells, headaches, and insomnia.

Tibby and his family moved to Vancouver, where he attempted to develop a business of his own, but his illness became more pronounced. Although he underwent frequent medical examinations by various specialists, none seemed able to diagnose the source of his problems. Finally, as a last resource, exploratory surgery of the brain was performed. It was found that Tibby was suffering from a malignant tumour of the brain. The most competent medical help was secured for him but on July 5, 1958, at the relatively young age of forty-five, my brother Tibby died.

Tibby's widow and daughter returned to England. I have kept in touch with Tibby's family over the years and know that his daughter Yvette still cherishes memories of her life in Vancouver and of her grandmother, Marthe.

Following Tibby's death I tried without success to persuade my mother to join my family and me in eastern Canada. But she was independent and self-reliant and she elected to remain in Vancouver, living alone in the rambling house I had secured for her and Tibby and his family. She was surrounded and assisted by a legion of friends, from local merchants and neighbours to the policemen and firemen who worked in her neighbourhood. They did not wait for emergencies to arise before coming to see her, but frequently dropped by for a cup of tea and a chat, or sometimes for advice.

When she was about eighty years of age my mother required minor surgery. Afterwards she went to convalesce in a fine nursing home in a Vancouver suburb where she was given special care and attention. She became deeply attached to those attending to her needs and they became attached to her. Thus she decided to remain in that home, which she considered to be her hotel, for the remaining years of her life. I visited her there almost monthly.

Toward the end of her life she ceased to speak English and her other acquired languages and spoke only in French, her mother tongue. When she died on March 26, 1972, in her eighty-eighth year, several of the nurses who had cared so lovingly for her had become fluent in French through her tutoring.

My mother had always spoken fondly of France and particularly of her native Normandy. To her mind the beauty and charm of her homeland were unsurpassed by any other nation. As soon as my professional success and financial means allowed, I suggested to her that we visit the land of her birth together. To my surprise and sorrow, she reacted with nervous apprehension. Two world wars had intervened since she and my father had left France. Her home town, Falaise, had been ravaged and the Renault family had become widely scattered. Many of my mother's contemporaries had died and what little correspondence continued was with relatives she did not know well. My mother chose, perhaps wisely, never to return to France, not even for a visit. Her beautiful memories of her homeland went with her, unbroken, to her grave.

Mary, My Wife and Lifetime Supporter and Partner

Among the fortunate events in my life none ranks higher than my meeting with Mary Toine Torvinen. A woman of considerable spiritual and physical beauty, Mary was a sturdy, blue-eyed blonde, calm, steady, and patient, almost the total opposite of my frail, black-haired, highly expressionable, brown-eyed mother. Mary had been born in Finland and brought to Canada as a child by her prairie homesteading parents before the First World War.

This girl who grew up on an Alberta farm and later taught in a one-room schoolhouse was the ideal wife for the physically restless, ambitious, and independent prospector and geologist I became. While she always trusted my judgement, Mary remained a remarkably independent person. Typically Nordic, she excelled at and found much happiness in all forms of handicrafts and art, particularly pottery and weaving, and in all aspects of farming. During my many absences, Mary kept busy in these activities and with various charitable agencies. There was wide scope for her and her friends to enjoy these pursuits at our winter home near Ocho Rios in Jamaica and at our farm near Kettleby, Ontario.

Mary was not fond of traveling but did indulge in a few trips to spend time with me in South and Central American outposts of the UN. We also travelled together to the Soviet Union and, with our daughter Marion and later our grandchildren Marea and David, over much of Europe and the Mediterranean countries and to Morocco.

I could not have succeeded professionally and financially to the extent I did without Mary and her quiet counsel and encouragement. She was the perfect partner, caring for and sustaining my domestic and social life superlatively. Her ability and independence freed me to follow the will-o'-the-wisp path of a carefree explorationist, ultimately bringing us financial benefits far beyond our family's needs and enabling us to share our good fortune with others.

Mary passed away peacefully in her sleep when we were on holiday together in December 1977, just two days after our fortieth wedding anniversary, ending a two-year period of cardiac problems. Three others of her immediate family had pre-deceased her from the same scourge. All of them had died during the month of December.

My Teachers

Among partners of considerable influence during my formative years were teachers who stimulated and encouraged me. The first of these must remain nameless since their contact with me was so long ago that their names have slipped my memory. I recall, however, in the third grade, being told to "do anything artistic" as homework. This challenge charged me with enthusiasm. As I made my way home, I gathered several small, dried-out shrub branches and various scraps of tin foil and coloured paper from the roadside. At home, I announced to my mother that I would make artificial flowers. She added encouragement, a spool of thread, a handful of coloured cotton scraps, and a pair of scissors to my supplies and left me on my own.

The next day my teacher was so delighted that I was promptly paraded before half a dozen other classes clutching my artificial flowers. My mother's invocation to "be the best" had paid off, without much effort or pain to me and at no cost save for patience and imagination.

A year later I scored again with an essay entitled "From Tadpole to Frog," which was so highly regarded that it was read by the vice-principal before the entire student body at the morning assembly, following the singing of "God Save the King." I had "arrived" – in my own mind at least – as a literary genius.

Later, in a senior grade at Boy's Central School in Victoria, I faced an Amazon of a woman who stood, arms akimbo, glaring at all twenty-five of us, and vowed she was going to teach us English – spelling, grammar, and punctuation. This veritable tyrant, through her talent and the brute force of her personality, lifted for us the lid of Pandora's box, exposing us to the awesome power of words. Her classes regularly produced some of the champion spellers of the province. I was not one of those but the power of a broad vocabulary became imprinted upon my mind thanks to her. Some of my favourite "reading" at the time consisted of thumbing at random through a pocket dictionary, an exercise I enjoy to this day, now in three languages.

Although Ira Dilworth, the principal of Victoria High School, taught no class that I took during my attendance there, we became acquainted through my unorthodox extracurricular activities. With the reluctant assistance of my brother and another class-mate, I became the "Beanie King" of Victoria's schools, sewing, on my mother's treadle machine, scores of felt beanie caps in assorted school colours to sell to students. This commercial venture by a student called for examination by the principal, following which inquiry it was permitted to continue.

Later, my friend Ken McKenzie and I set up a "used text-book shop," offering such fierce competition to the city book shops that they complained to Principal Dilworth. Again, I was called before him. I was my family's provider, I explained, and again Ira Dilworth understood. Principal Dilworth's tact and sympathetic understanding in regard to my problems were great, and on matriculation I was one of four students recommended by him for interviews by bank representatives seeking junior people for training. Although I declined this opportunity I was highly encouraged by his confidence in me.

Walter Gage is high on my list of teachers who provided major inspiration to me. His brilliance as a teacher, his charm and wit and friendship, were motivating factors behind my decision to undertake a university education two or three years after my matriculation, even though I was almost penniless in the midst of the Great Depression. Later, at the University of British Columbia in Vancouver, I was inspired and encouraged to continue by Professors M. Y. Williams, Harry V. Warren, and Henry Gunning among others.

After my formal education was largely completed, I faced the competitive world of the private sector. At this time I was lucky enough to receive counsel, direct assistance in various forms, and other help in deciding on the right course for my life from several extraordinary people. Among these "Trail Partners" was Dr. Howard James, in turn an employer, counsellor, and friend for forty-four years, until his death in 1979. No one could have been a better friend than Howard James was to me.

Moolah Joe

Soon after the end of the Second World War, Mary, Marion, and I moved from British Columbia to Ontario and Joe Hirshhorn began to exert an influence on our lives. The time I worked for him, a short but dynamic six years, had the brilliance of a shooting star, and was followed by nearly a quarter of a century of continuing friendship. Joe died on August 31, 1981.

Joe had outstanding courage as an entrepreneur. He wasn't afraid to risk large amounts of money in new mining ventures, but he usually analysed a project thoroughly before he placed his money on the line. On at least one occasion I recall, Joe's life was on the line as well.

Joe had had a telephone altercation with a particular stockbroker which had degenerated into a shouting match that ended with the broker's declaration that he was coming over to kill Joe. Joe immediately told me of the conversation and of what might happen, and I had all the doors of the office locked. Nonetheless, by some means the irate broker got in and made his way to Joe's office. Imagine my horror to hear this apoplectic man shout: "I'm going to get you, you little Jew!" Joe stood his ground, grabbing a small piece of stone sculpture from his desk for defence. The assailant, a much larger man, approached with clenched fist upraised. Suddenly his legs gave way. He slumped to the floor, having suffered a seizure in the nick of time.

Although the fast pace of the financial world seems occasionally to give rise to encounters such as that one, there was another side – the friendships we developed were enduring ones. My work with Joe Hirshhorn gave me my friendships with Charles Davidson, Oscar Weiss, and Val Duncan. Each of the three, in their own distinctive way, contributed greatly to the good fortune which I have enjoyed.

More Recent Years

Partners in my post-Hirshhorn endeavours and my United Nations' work from 1962 to 1980 were many, but those of whom I think first are Director Roberto Arce, John Carman, Wilhelm Groenveldt-

Meijer, James (Hamish) Brown, and Joseph Barnea. They were all senior staff members and colleagues in the various Technical Assistance agencies in which I served. As senior officials they put my program recommendations into protocol-acceptable form and followed with equal interest the "winners" and the "losers" that emerged. And, on average, we scored very well together.

When I returned to private-sector consulting, principally in Canada, I was fortunately able to attract some of the best of young professionals in my field of service. They responded brilliantly to the responsibilities and authority that I loaded upon them. One of my greatest continuing pleasures is to look around and note how many have become leaders in their respective fields of specialization. A roll-call of past protégés and colleagues now has its sad notes. Three of my most stalwart field lieutenants, Harry Buckles, Donald James (son of Dr. Howard James), and George Checklin died while still in their professional prime.

There have been some whose lives have been devoted to educational and related cultural activities who have broadened my perspective on life through their encouragement of my participation in their activities. Joe Hirshhorn, to use his expression, "needled" me into prospecting in the world of art, an activity which has become a joy and pleasure to me. Dr. Chick Hendry, long-time head of the University of Toronto's School of Social Work, and Dr. Roby Kidd, one of Canada's foremost adult educators, became fast friends of mine. Together we three tried hard, with uncertain success, to bridge the worlds of the social and technical scientists.

Howard James, Walter Gage, Herbert Fiddes, and Alex Sutherland joined with me for over twenty years in various low-profile character-development programs based in British Columbia. These included financial assistance for qualified and ambitious students without sufficient money to proceed through university; the rehabilitation, including education and employment, of juvenile delinquents; and even assisting struggling authors toward publication of their work. Together, we enjoyed considerable success in our efforts.

Ed Parker introduced me to Ryerson Institute of Technology in its infancy, and I served on its board of governors until my work with the United Nations limited the time available for my effective participation. Given my early connection with Elliot Lake, I had an obligation, I felt, to accept an invitation to assist in the work of the

Elliot Lake Centre of Continuing Education, initiated by Prime Minister Lester Pearson and Ontario Premier John Robarts. In the work of the Elliot Lake Centre I became associated with a considerable number of public-spirited Canadians, including Pauline McGibbon, who later became Lieutenant-Governor of Ontario, Joe Morris, a leader in the Canadian Labour Movement, Herman Geiger Torel, of the Canadian Opera Company, and Norman MacLeod Rogers, a Toronto lawyer who was for many years a leading member of the Board of Trustees of Queen's University.

With three other members of the board of the Elliot Lake Centre – Captain William Kidd, who had retired from the Royal Canadian Navy to become the Executive Director of the Centre; Arnold Edinborough, whose name is synonymous with business and the arts in Canada; and Dr. McCormack Smyth, Dean of Atkinson College, York University – I shared in the founding of the Canadian Institute for Radiation Safety, now widely known by its acronym, CAIRS. This institute is dedicated to the search for and the development and implemenation of practical means for the monitoring and protection of those exposed to high radiation levels in their workplaces.

The Staff that Supported Me

I could never have carried on my professional and voluntary activities without the practical support of personal secretaries who worked so tirelessly for me. During more than forty years as a professional geologist I have had only four full-time secretaries. When I consider all they did for me, I can only adapt Sir Winston Churchill's oft-repeated tribute, "Never has so much been done so well by so few." Thelma McDougall tended to me during the pre-Hirshhorn period; Mary Kumomoto worked for me while I was in Joe's employ; and Charlotte Henning (later Charlotte Wolf) served me well and faithfully for almost twenty-five years after that, until 1984. In recent years, Daphne Shandley has attended to my secretarial needs efficiently and cheerfully.

In the early years of my United Nations' service, when I was abroad for so much of the time yet continued to provide technical consulting services for certain clients, I relied upon an excellent administrative manager, James (Duke) Hague. Later, when I became involved in realty development, Joanna P. Stewart managed my affairs effectively for me. All of these fine people helped me immeasurably and I record here my continuing appreciation to them.

My Immediate Family

Life is much lonelier without my wife Mary, but it goes on through our daughter Marion and our two grandchildren, Marea and David. Their future is of deep and continuing interest to me.

Marion has many of the finest characteristics of her grandmother, Marthe, and the practical qualities of her mother. Like her grandmother, Marion has strong emotional roots in France, having completed her education there and having lived there for considerable periods of time.

Both grandchildren are in the early stages of their own professional lives, Marea in the field of decorative arts in France, and David currently considering several possibilities. They share with other intelligent and sensitive young people of this time in the uncertainties produced by the mixed signals received from the hyper-sophisticated society in which they are immersed. I have yet to thoroughly introduce them to the liberating world I know and love best; the sadly diminishing wilderness trails of many countries where nature exerts her own harmony.

Reflections and Appreciations

During the first twenty-five years of my life, I struggled constantly against adversity and extremely limited financial resources, for which, in retrospect, I have no regrets. Economic and social restraints imposed upon me from my earliest years forced me to develop the imagination, ingenuity, resourcefulness, and self-reliance with which heredity and my environment had endowed me. My status as the oldest male of the household required that I develop independence and self-confidence. The cheerfulness, optimism, and human sensitivity which seem to have been with me ever since birth have enabled me to proceed gratefully through life and have stimulated me to share my own good fortune with others. As I grew to maturity, however, I became profoundly concerned by the increasing brutality of the age.

While I was completing my undergraduate studies at UBC the tragic destruction of human life was beginning in Ethiopia and spreading to Spain and other countries in Europe. A pseudo-prosperity born of war preparations appeared to modify the social and economic depression. The Second World War erupted, a war between combatants all of whose roots lay in organized Christianity, all of whom were Caucasian, and all of which were, initially, Western democracies allegedly based on individual freedom. The last dreadful chapter of that war was written when the world's first nuclear bombs were dropped. When the carnage was over some 30 million lives were lost, probably 75 per cent of them innocent noncombatants.

I was shocked and saddened by these immensely tragic and rapidly occurring events. My carefully considered and committed moral and social standards and bases of trust were jolted askew. I trace much of my actions to help the disadvantaged of the world to my feelings at that time.

My leanings towards the scientific world of chemistry and geology brought me closer to the world of "things" rather than that of "people." I fell in love with the wonders of the wilderness, in particular with the natural phenomena of rocks and their uses. I "read the rocks" as others enjoy a good library. The rocks and the fossils they contain tell me the history of our planet over three billion years of time. They tell me of the organic evolution of all life upon the Earth through several great cycles.

Yet the world of people also fascinates, concerns, and often troubles me. I am a highly privileged person. My work has put me in contact with the "near-leadership" of diverse ideologies of many countries in all stages of socio-economic development and of every political structure. My life has thus been considerably enriched and I have been afforded opportunities to participate in "quiet diplomacy" in many ways, all to the end, I would like to believe, of better international understanding and therefore world peace.

Affluence and its many distractions, such as we enjoy in North America, promote preoccupation with frivolities, polemics, and bland indifference to the "real world" of poverty, injustice, and hopelessness. Our governments show a tendency to become intoxicated with – and to misuse – military power.

To be taught and to teach in the field of international relations and world peace, I have served as an organizer, officer, resource person, or participant with many groups or institutions. Primary among these have been the International Pugwash Conferences and the European East-West Round Table. My work in the Canadian Peace Research Institute and my association with its founder Dr. Norman Alcock brought me in touch with widening challenges. The Albert Einstein Peace Foundation, an American outgrowth of the Pugwash Conferences, is one of the agencies which gives me hope for the future.

I am well past my allotted three score and ten years. Ahead of me lie the "Final Mile," the "Last Portage," the "Great Divide," or in classier modern phrases, the "Sunset" or "Golden Years." I look toward these way-signs with no fear, sorrow, or regret. My principal emotion, as it has been all my life, is fascinated curiosity.

Life is an unclear and perilous course at best. During my extensive travels around this planet I have survived many grave risks. Probably there were other dangers, entirely unknown to me, also lurking in my path, that were discreetly dispatched by my helpers and guides. I am forever grateful to those who have made my way safe. But I have never felt it necessary to carry a firearm. I marvel at my own ability to dispose of dangers with my bare hands when I remember being charged by a savage beast and attacked by a criminal armed with a revolver.

But survival is not alone an adequate foundation for pride or satisfaction, and nor are the material rewards which surround me. My greatest satisfaction is the awareness that I have lived up to the hopes and expectations of those to whom I owe so much: my mother Marthe and my wife Mary, my teachers, co-workers, and a legion of loyal friends throughout the world. Some are with me now only in spirit, but all have important places in my life.

Evidence of esteem closer to home also provides me with great satisfaction. I have received several honorary doctorates from across Canada; recognition from our national and provincial governments and professional honours and medals from scientific and technical institutions. And finally, I occasionally receive primary school essays from youngsters who view some event from my past as an enviable model; this must rank as a reward far greater than anything material.

Although I am in good health, this miraculous complex chemical organism which is my human body increasingly shows signs of wear and tear. More significantly, those blissful built-in tranquilizers that mark the approaching end – loss of hearing, sight, and memory – are making inroads. I am withdrawing, with as much grace as possible, from the business world and from my professional sphere to luxuriate as a contemplative philosopher.

Index

Bennett,
  William J. — 189
Benson, Robert — 249
Bernischke,
  (geologist) — 90-91
Berton, Pierre — 179
Bethlehem Copper
  Mine, B.C. — 87, 181, 183
Bethune, Dr.
  Norman — 364
Bichan, Dr. James — 272
Bicroft Mine — 232
Big Z — 171, 195-249, 251, 253, 255, 267
Bird, (prospector) — 74-75
Bischoff, Carl T. — 177
"Black Angus"
  (prospector) — 84-86
Blahey, Ed — 254
Blind River, Ont. — 62, 163, 170, 181, 183, 189, 193, 196-99, 207, 209, 214, 223-24, 227, 234, 246, 251, 262, 313
Bloom,
  (prospector) — 74-75
Bonanza Creek — 125
Bones, Olie — 177
Bouck, Bill — 163, 189, 193, 197, 205, 210, 212, 215, 227-29, 233, 236, 241, 248-49, 267-68
Boulding, Dr.
  Kenneth E. — 333
Bower,
  Margaret E. — 311
Box Mine — 117
Boylen, Jim — 136
Boy's Central
  School — 23, 33, 473
Boy's Naval
  Brigade — 21
Bralorne Mining
  Company — 44, 46-47, 49, 55, 56, 301-302, 304, 318, 367

Brantford, Ont. — 166
Breton, Aimé — 169-71, 199-204
*Bridge River
  Lillooet News* — 53
Bridge River
  Valley, B.C. — 30, 44, 47-56, 81, 93, 111-12, 169, 275, 298, 300-302, 304, 305
Britnania Mining
  & Smelting — 305-10
Brown, Percy
  Lorne — 252, 263
Brown, Hamish — 393, 395-97, 441-43, 476
Bryce, Robert — 162-63, 209
Buckles Mine — 209, 235, 242-43
Buckles, R.H. — 174, 181, 188, 189, 207, 212-13, 215, 218, 242-43, 252-53, 476
Buckles, Ruth — 215
Buffam, Dr.
  B.S.W. — 134
Bull, Ernest — 303
Burke, Joe — 237-38
Burns Bros. and
  Denton — 242-43, 249
Burns, Charles — 242
Burns Lake, B.C. — 112, 116, 185
Byrne, J.J. — 136

C
Cadwallader Gold
  Belt — 47, 297
California Institute
  of Technology — 40
Campbell, Bob — 168
Camray Deposit — 168-69, 232
*Canadian Deposits
  of Uranium &
  Thorium* — 200
*Canadian Geo-
  graphic Journal* — 179
Canadian Institute
  of International
  Affairs — 367

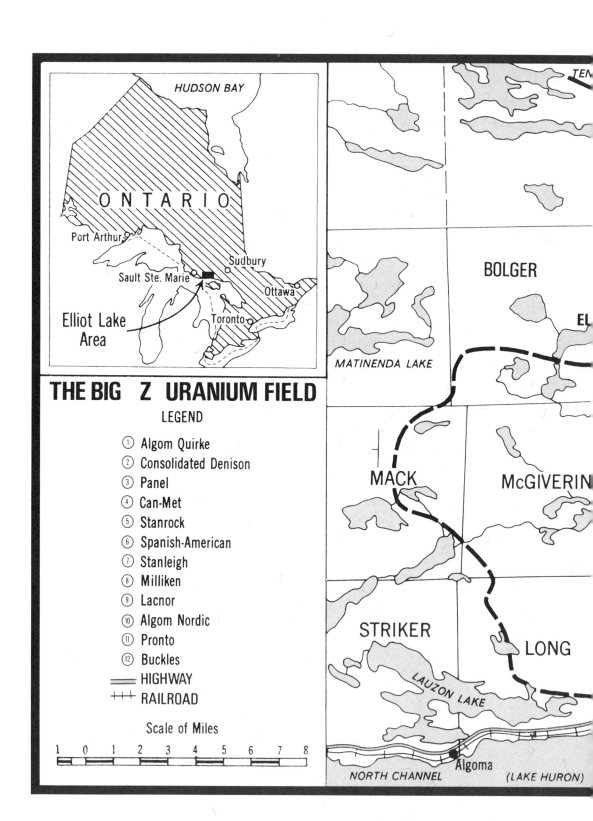

HUDSON BAY

O N T A R I O

Port Arthur

Sudbury

Sault Ste. Marie

Ottawa

Elliot Lake
Area

Toronto

THE BIG Z URANIUM FIELD

LEGEND

① Algom Quirke
② Consolidated Denison
③ Panel
④ Can-Met
⑤ Stanrock
⑥ Spanish-American
⑦ Stanleigh
⑧ Milliken
⑨ Lacnor
⑩ Algom Nordic
⑪ Pronto
⑫ Buckles
═══ HIGHWAY
+++ RAILROAD

Scale of Miles

1 0 1 2 3 4 5 6 7 8

TEN

BOLGER

EL

MATINENDA LAKE

MACK

McGIVERIN

STRIKER

LONG

LAUZON LAKE

Algoma

NORTH CHANNEL   (LAKE HURON)